THE PSYCHOLOGY OF SUSTAINABILITY

COPYRIGHTED MATERIAL — DO NOT DUPLICATE, DISTRIBUTE, OR POST

THE PSYCHOLOGY OF SUSTAINABILITY

UNDERSTANDING THE RELATIONSHIP BETWEEN SELF AND EARTH

First Edition

Edited by Ron L. Chandler

University of Florida

COPYRIGHTED MATERIAL — DO NOT DUPLICATE, DISTRIBUTE, OR POST

Bassim Hamadeh, CEO and Publisher
Mazin Hassan, Acquisitions Editor
Amy Smith, Project Editor
Jackie Bignotti, Production Artist
Stephanie Kohl, Licensing Coordinator
Natalie Piccotti, Director of Marketing
Kassie Graves, Vice President of Editorial
Jamie Giganti, Director of Academic Publishing

Printed in the United States of America.

COPYRIGHTED MATERIAL — DO NOT DUPLICATE, DISTRIBUTE, OR POST

CONTENTS

CHAPTER 1

Introduction to the Psychology of Sustainability and Understanding Our Self-Earth Relationship

Any solution to a sustainability problem that does not first address factors negatively affecting human dignity will ultimately not be sustainable.

In the following chapters you will discover what decades of psychological investigation have revealed about why we behave toward each other and Earth as we do. You will likely be surprised to learn that common explanations for our destructive behavior, such as avarice, hegemony, and fundamentalism, are symptoms not causes. Put another way, avarice, for example, is not *why* we are destroying each other and Earth; it is *how* we are doing so.

Most of you know or will not be surprised to hear that there is a strong relationship between how we think, feel, and act toward ourselves, and how we think, feel, and act toward others, and that this relationship has a direct effect on our experience of dignity. You might, however, be surprised to hear that there appears to be a connection between how or to what extent we experience dignity with how we perceive our responsibility to act sustainably, and whether or not we actually do.

The quote at the top of this page is the first tenet of the psychology of sustainability. With this tenet in mind, and as you read the feature article for this chapter *From Epicurus to Maslow: Happiness Then and Now and the Place of the Human Being in Social Theory*, as well as following chapters and feature articles, consider that the spectra of all life experiences are inextricably linked and interdependent continua that constitute the essence of human ecology. Through discounting of individual and societal need to experience dignity we have failed to attend thoughtfully to the health of our human ecology. A product of this neglect is the state of our life support system: Earth. All is not lost though. If we consider that "the future is nothing more or less than a decision today" (fourth tenet of the psychology of sustainability), and, informed by the psychology of sustainability and with improvement of human dignity at the heart of our intention to effect resilient sustainability solutions, we will find that the current situation is our greatest opportunity.

Seven Tenets of the Psychology of Sustainability

Any solution to a sustainability problem that does not first address factors negatively affecting human dignity will ultimately not be sustainable.

Every sustainability problem is first a social problem and therefore a psychological problem.

Thinking creates emotion; emotion creates behavior.

The future is nothing more or less than a decision today.

The effective agent for sustainability is first her or his own fear master.

At the heart of all human behavior (the worst, the best, and all points between) is the unconscious or conscious experience of personal mortality.

Any service to the common good attends to the comprehensive problem and is a portal to our greatest opportunity.

READING 1

From Epicurus to Maslow

Happiness Then and Now and the Place of the *Human Being* in Social Theory

Gerald Gutenshwager

Πάντων χρημάτων μέτρον άνθρωπος Πρωταγόρας
The human being is the measure of all things

—*Protagoras*

Abstract

Protagoras said, "The human being is the measure of all things". This implies, among other things, that language, science and religion are human inventions, as are economics, money, efficiency, race, conflict, etc. As symbol-using animals, we have created these concepts to serve our purposes. But as our societies have increased in size and our concepts have become more abstract, there is a danger that we will forget our authorship and reify these symbols. This inhibits change in the way we name things, so we are always in danger of misunderstanding the reality we are describing. We seem to be at such a stage now as we employ 18th and 19th century theories to describe and, more importantly, create 21st century reality. One such idea has to do with human needs. Influenced by the abstract (economic) concepts we use, we have lost our sense of what we truly need. Epicurus and Maslow may help to review and reassess those concepts. Epicurus, by suggesting that our material needs are quite simple but that emotional and spiritual need satisfaction requires a small scale loving community, free from fear, and Maslow, by suggesting that our emotional development is

Gerald Gutenschwager, "From Epicurus to Maslow: Happiness Then and Now and the Place of the Human Being in Social Theory," *Cadmus*, vol. 1, no. 6, pp. 66-90.

COPYRIGHTED MATERIAL — DO NOT DUPLICATE, DISTRIBUTE, OR POST

age-related, which, besides therapy, may help in suggesting revisions in socioeconomic theory that would ensure the social conditions that would allow this development to take place successfully.

1. Three Challenges Facing Humanity Today

Humanity is faced with three major and interrelated challenges in the 21st century, all of which are derived in part from outdated assumptions, or metaphysical beliefs, as E.F. Schumacher called them in 1973 in his classic book, *Small is Beautiful*.[1] These are assumptions about nature, and about human beings and their societies that we have inherited from the past. They are found embedded especially in current mainstream economics, the (self designated) 'queen' of the social sciences, and continue to have effect because of an indifference to the message of Heraclitus that, "We cannot enter the same river twice", often rendered as, "τα πάντα ρει"–"all things change (flow)", a metaphor expressing, among other things, the idea that we are always in danger of applying obsolete ideas to new circumstances.

The challenges of the 21st century, themselves, are economic, environmental and in particular, philosophical (psychological). Mainstream economists derive their assumptions about the economic system, about nature and about humans from the beliefs and conditions that were prevalent in the 18th and 19th centuries. More specifically, these assumptions were designed to liberate humans from the religious dogma that constrained the freedom of thought and behavior at that time. In the place of an (angry) God, they substituted, on the one hand, a reductionist and mechanistic interpretation of Newtonian physics, which assumed that the universe was like a giant autonomous clockwork, such that if we reduced it to its smallest parts and understood the initial conditions and causal relationships between those parts we could "reconstruct" that universe or parts of it to our own advantage through engineering. This Newtonian framework could then, according to economists and other positivist social scientists, be carried over onto society so that it too could be "reconstructed" through *social* engineering, with the difficult question of *who* was to do the engineering usually left vague, if not completely unanswered. In any case, for the scientist, it was not to be God or any of his earthly representatives who would conduct any part of this cosmic 'orchestra'.

On the other hand, this assumption was accompanied by the necessary Cartesian belief in the separation of the mind and body, this having to do especially with the relationship between the "objective", "value-free" scientist, and the social and/or natural reality under study. It was seen as necessary that scientists and engineers be untainted by religious or other dogma and *apart* from the reality under study, though their discoveries might allow them to seek to control it by exploiting its basic laws. Humanists and humanistic social scientists, while seeking objectivity, have never believed themselves to be *apart from* the reality they were studying, and now quantum physics believes that this is not even true for those studying the elements of nature, particularly at the sub-atomic level, and probably at larger levels as well.[2] In other words, in the quantum world scientists and engineers are now seen as a *critical* part of the physical reality they study, with their thoughts and actions potentially altering that reality. How much more would this be true for social scientists, especially economists, who are advising governments and businesses all over the world?!

At the same time, the 18th-19th century economic theorists were living in a smaller scale society and the relatively under-exploited nature that existed at that time. Their assumptions were thus based upon different kinds of human relationships and a different kind of environment. And furthermore as we question the extreme Cartesian belief, as stated above, we may now suppose that the effects of those assumptions (and the resulting theories), themselves, have contributed to a change in that reality, making it something quite different in the 21st century! Thus, those assumptions may have been useful then but are clearly less supportable today. So from Protagoras' wise saying that "Humans are the measure of all things", we arrive at the 18th and 19th centuries and beyond to the assumption that, "Money (or Newtonian science) is the measure of all things", and *in the process have pretty much lost all idea of the human measure.*

In other words, matching the well-known structural crises of the economy and the environment, there is also a philosophical crisis related to how we think about and conceptualize these crises, for, indeed, 'the body and the mind', as well as all things in the universe, are now seen by quantum physics to be connected. This philosophical crisis ranges from how to address the rather limited epistemological axioms of positive science, especially in the social world, to questions about how we are now to understand ourselves collectively, and how we are to set and evaluate goals for a future that would be free from these structural crises. Specifically, what are human needs, and how can they be satisfied? How can we best organize society and establish systems of social control to meet these needs? How do we establish moral values for behavior? In what sort of social environment can we begin to answer these questions? etc.

2. The Economic Crisis

Looking first at a key assumption of mainstream economic theory, it has been obvious for many years now that, among other things, the so-called 'free' market system composed of isolated decision-makers cannot (automatically) solve the imbalance between production and consumption. Nor could it ever; 17th and 18th century economic theorists, working within a deterministic Newtonian framework, couldn't have appreciated this. Looking beyond economics, we might find quite a number of different understandings of such an assumption. For example, in physics it would appear that the idea of a system composed only of *isolated* elements would be something close to entropy (or the end state of our solar system some billions of years from now). In literary history the outstanding example we could find of the detached decision-maker, aside from the occasional hermit, would be that of Homer's one-eyed Cyclops, a primitive creature who lives in a cave isolated from all other creatures and with no sense of the meaning of community, laws or society. As for the biologist, who works with *living systems,* such an anarchic situation would likely signal a spontaneous evolutionary move to create greater order, as a logical response to such a state of crude disarray.[3]

Indeed, in an economic system, a truly free market would be anathema to most businessmen, and they would likely seek to establish order by reducing the number of independent decision units through merger and takeover, which is exactly what has happened historically. Thus, in today's reality the term 'free market' has come to be used throughout the world as a cover for this actual process of consolidation, where larger economic units move in to take over smaller ones, particularly in less developed economies. To what extent economists themselves are aware of this deception is hard to tell, given that they are working within a 19th century idealist (mathematical) framework that 'proves' that such a market system is 'efficient' in this respect.

At the same time, larger production units can take advantage of economies of scale, while also exerting greater control over the conditions of the market. One long-term result of this has been a chronic tendency to overproduction in the industrial countries (the system produces more goods than consumers can consume, especially with the income available to them). As a consequence of this trend there has been a tremendous effort by capital, for over a century now, to interfere with the free market by stimulating an increase in consumption through any means possible, i.e., through advertising, marketing, loans, credit cards, and even architecture and art, etc. rather than reduce its profitable production.[4,5] One by-product of this effort was and is to distort the psychology of people, especially young people, with the idea that only wealth and the consumption of goods could define the successful (and happy) human being. I need to stress that this portrait of success is the product of a ***colossal human effort*** by powerful commercial, industrial and financial interests, with considerable help from psychologists and artists, and ***not*** some inevitable 'natural' evolution of the social system, as is assumed in the mechanistic ontology of economic thinking.

The thought that a better distribution of wealth would give even a partial solution to this problem inspired Henry Ford (only briefly) in the 1920s. Economists and political leaders were also inspired (though not ultimately persuaded[6]) by this thought during the application of Keynesian theory in the decades from 1930 to 1970 in America, and in a more substantial form in the welfare states of Europe. However, with the rise of monopoly capitalism and its 'globalization' over the course of the 20th century, along with its new (old) ideology, neo-liberalism where privatization and the market are sacred, this option is no longer considered 'fashionable'.

Another (unfortunate) result of the inability of the market to maintain a balance between production and consumption has been the shifting of capital from production (the real economy) to the financial sector (banks, stock markets, and other forms of gambling) for speculative investments, in spite of the increased risk associated with such investments. This form of investment is also accompanied by a certain mentality, that of the gambler, who is totally unaware and unconcerned with the broader human and social effects of his activity. To quote Marx, who is describing a similar situation in 19th century France:[7]

> [They] ...get rich not by production, but by pocketing the already available wealth of others. In particular there broke out, at the top of bourgeois society, an unbridled display of unhealthy and dissolute appetites, which clashed every moment with the bourgeois laws themselves, wherein the wealth having its source in gambling naturally seeks its satisfaction, where pleasure becomes crapuleux (debauched), where gold, dirt and blood flow together. The finance aristocracy is nothing but the resurrection of the lumpen proletariat at the top of bourgeois society.

"Every time a speculative bubble bursts, the absurd 'logic' of the basic assumptions of neo-classical economics and of capitalism becomes more obvious, and a more rational organization of the economic system with a more equitable distribution of wealth, more necessary."

These capitalists are even more morally indifferent than the industrial capitalists, who must at least be somewhat concerned with their labor force, to say nothing of their customers. Given this casino atmosphere, the more profitable these investments are, even if only temporarily, the greater is the imbalance of wealth that is created, which tends to exacerbate the problem of under-consumption—overproduction, etc. As a result of this mentality, we also see a chronic tendency towards an over accumulation of capital among the wealthy. The system becomes even more unstable, as profit is increasingly based on lending (i.e., for consumption and not for productive investment) and on fly-by-night speculation. Every time a speculative bubble bursts, as we see all too frequently, the absurd 'logic' of the basic assumptions of neo-classical economics and of capitalism becomes more obvious, and a more rational organization of the economic system with a more equitable distribution of wealth, more necessary.

3. The Environmental Crisis

The environmental crisis, in the meantime, is much more serious than the economic crisis, which can in time be reversed, whereas the changes that are occurring in nature are likely to become increasingly irreversible.[8] Capital and the neoclassical/neoliberal approach for the most part ignore this crisis, believing, it seems, that, "Après moi le deluge" (after me the deluge), or, in another version, that science and technology will in time solve all such problems. It should be emphasized that most economic theories of the 18th and 19th centuries saw nature as an open system, which one could exploit *ad infinitum,* such that it enters economic calculations as *income* and not as *capital.* And this assumption still characterizes capitalism, but also, unfortunately, to a large degree, 'socialist' systems, insofar as they are also directed to infinite growth, with the same deleterious effects on the environment. Today, more and more people are coming to understand the limitations of this assumption, except, unfortunately, for most corporate executives and mainstream economists, whose ideology inhibits them from acknowledging the problem. As for politicians, journalists and many scientists, we hear them repeating the 'mantra' of growth, as if this had nothing to do with the environmental crisis. Part of this mentality is the belief (and desire) that we could solve the problem of inequality only through growth, rather than through a radical change in the socio-economic structure.

Here we are reminded of the Greek myth of Erysichthon. In his insatiable desire for power and control (not unlike that of today's bankers, technocratic planners and politicians), he was willing to sacrifice nature, represented in the myth by his cutting down of the forests, including the sacred tree of Demeter, the goddess of the harvest or more literally, "Mother Earth". As punishment he was cursed with a hunger so ravenous that he ate everything in sight ... until he finally ended up eating his own flesh! We can only hope that today's corporate and political leaders, and economic theorists will realize their folly before they have consumed everything in sight, they, themselves included.

But to solve the global environmental problem would require some sort of full and genuine democratic socio-political cooperation, something that has only been rarely seen in humans except among hunters and gatherers. The moral emphasis on 'possessive individualism', which we have also inherited from the 18th–19th century, along with its predatory competitiveness, does not serve us well with respect to this question.[9] Also, the over accumulation of capital and the ever greater emphasis on large scale corporations, technology and financial entities that follow from this, do not allow much freedom for more creative and flexible thoughts and actions in the dialectic between humans and nature. Nature, however, has limits beyond which Homo sapiens cannot survive; one can only hope that we will recognize this critical problem before it is too late.

Meanwhile, there are, of course, many, including economists, who are concerned with environmental problems and who offer thoughts on solutions and strategies for the future.[10,11] The most important thing to realize is that it is absolutely necessary to reorient most of the assumptions about political-economic systems, about society and nature that we have inherited from the recent past when capitalist-directed science and technology flourished unabated.

"Social theories based on a mechanistic Newtonian-Cartesian science and those that ignore human consciousness and intention, do great harm in their application to society."

4. The Philosophical Challenge

The first philosophical assumption that we must question is that nature and society are the same. We need to understand that social theories based on a mechanistic Newtonian-Cartesian science and those that ignore human consciousness and intention, *do great harm in their application to society.* Without humanity and ethics, both missing in natural science, these theories and the mindset that accompanies them tend towards a fully controlled 'brave new' technocratic society. This leads to increasing despair and nihilism in humans where the only 'freedom' is to be found in the phantasmagorical reality of television, on the one hand, and consumerism, on the other.[12, 13] The future, if we are to survive, must be built upon love and cooperation, on equality, on respect for nature, and on a substantial reduction in the demand for material goods, especially those that consume large amounts of energy to produce.[14] This implies a qualitative shift towards a balance between the physical and the spiritual needs of humans, which in turn will require a significant change in the education of the young and old alike, so that we can learn to live as self-determined people and not as slaves to advertising and technocracy.

"Economics would like to see itself as a natural science (physics, preferably) being applied to society, and thereby assume that human consciousness and intention play no role in the events that are observed and measured in the social context."

It is worth reflecting here on a statement by Robert Kuttner, co-editor of the magazine *American Prospect,* as referred to in an article by Eamon Javers and Jim VandeHei,[15] in support of the massive amounts of *public* money that must be given to the plutocrats in order to "solve" the financial crisis in America and Europe *that they themselves have created.* "This," says Kuttner, "is not about ethics, it is about economics". So if you believe Kuttner, economics is without ethics, is amoral, with the result that while economics can distinguish between rational and irrational, *it cannot distinguish between moral and immoral!* (This is quite apart from the thoughts and actions of any specific economists; it is simply that they must find moral inspiration outside of their science, if they are interested).

"Human societies are based upon consciousness."

Following Democritus, however, this moral indifference requires an explanation, and there appear to be several reasons. First of all, economics would like to see itself as a natural science (physics, preferably) being applied to society, and thereby assume that human consciousness and intention play no role in the events that are observed and measured in the social context. Actually, this is only partially true, because economics does assign consciousness and intention in the form of the "economic man", a caricature of the human in the form of a 'robotic' rational man who thinks and acts in total isolation from his fellow human beings. Thus, moral concerns would play no role in such a construction.

Secondly, in a related way, as a natural science, economics is obliged to be 'value free', in part a residue from the (still) unresolved conflict between the spiritual and the material, in this case between science and religion.[16] That greed, envy and fear, as mentioned below, are implied moral values in this construction is left unexamined for obvious reasons.

Third, when Keynes (and Roosevelt) threatened the orthodoxy of mainstream economics in the 1930s, with a macroeconomic theory not built up from reductionist individualism, there was a small crisis in the science of economics. There was also a political crisis of sorts, as the moneyed classes rallied to cut back on the New Deal after the elections of 1936, thus sending unemployment shooting back up again. World War II interrupted and temporarily resolved this crisis by creating a military Keynesianism, which continues until today in much of the capitalist world.

Meanwhile, the McCarthy witch-hunt of the 1950s in the United States sent academics scurrying for cover. That is, any suggestion of government interference in the economy, as recommended by Keynes and carried out by Roosevelt, might be construed as 'creeping socialism'. Most economists gladly (or reluctantly, as the case might have been) returned to the micro-economics based orthodoxy, and protected themselves with a wall of (mathematical) abstractions, often with little relation to reality, in order to prove their value-free 'innocence', a tendency that had earlier caused Keynes to say that:

> Too large a portion of recent 'mathematical' economics are mere concoctions, as imprecise as the initial assumptions they rest on, which allow the author to lose sight of the complexities and interdependencies of the real world in a maze of pretentious and unhelpful symbols.[17, 18]

However, human societies *are* based upon consciousness. The human mind contains logical, emotional and moral dimensions, and human actions that produce the social structure are always guided by these three parameters. Therefore, when Marshall celebrated the separation of economics from moral philosophy in London at the end of the 19th century, he heralded the growing irrelevance of economics to human society, *except,* of course, to the extent that its theories (and ideology) are continuously *imposed* upon society through education and behavioral programs and policies. But, insofar as this is true, economics itself, becomes a part of the *social construction* of reality, and is no longer only theorizing about it.

In the final analysis, Marshall also heralded the likely disintegration of the capitalist system, if not human society, itself, as we now observe the degradation of nature that has followed. Unfortunately, it seems that most mainstream economists and businessmen then, as now, have not been able to appreciate that *no society could long survive without emotions and ethics.* This is what Plato meant with his saying that, "All science without justice and the other virtues must be seen as mere cunning and not wisdom". But that was at a time when science was still a branch of philosophy, unlike today when philosophy is considered by many scientists and engineers to be, at best, an interesting pastime.

Thus, a key philosophical challenge is to bring virtue or moral philosophy back into science. Not that science, especially economics, does not contain a moral and emotional framework; simply it is not very obvious, or discussed very much, given its claim to a 'value-free' status. Thus, this third challenge, which is closely related to that framework and, ultimately to the other two crises, is to define the place or role of the human being (including the scientist) in the socio-economic system. For the positive sciences, which have largely replaced religion and philosophy in social thought, the human being is little more than a cog in the Newtonian mechanistic world. In this world there is no place for emotion and ethics, two of the major non-material dimensions of human existence.

For economics this is especially important, since there are, indeed, emotional and moral dimensions implicit in economic theory. Here we refer to *greed and envy,* along with the necessary *fear* (of others) that accompanies such a value system as a means of social control. In this value system the mind must be focused on *cunning,* which, in this world view, is the only ability that humans need to be concerned about in life, a life that for mainstream economics, especially, is pretty much like a game of 'poker.' Thus the wiliest will be the most successful in life, and will represent the 'ideal man' in this philosophy, despite the degraded position assigned to him by Plato.

If economics, and science generally, did not play any significant role in society, this characterization of humans would simply be sad. But economics, and the 18th–19th century liberal 'philosophy' of the merchants, bankers and industrialists that still accompanies it, along with modern technology, largely determine our lives today. They restrict our daily lives to an inordinate degree, especially if we are unable to understand how crucial is their influence on our thoughts, both practically and theoretically.

This leads to the question about what should be, ultimately, the role of the human being in a more philosophical social vision. If Protagoras was right in believing that neither science nor religion but *the human being* should be the measure of all things, then how should we define humans and their needs? How should we define human happiness, especially if we believe that this is the ultimate goal of science? We should be able to improve on the strictly limited (and fabricated) *Social Darwinist* definition of humans that we have inherited from science, economic theory and political ideology of the recent past and, more specifically, the interpretation of this 'tradition' that characterizes contemporary socio-economic doctrine. And, finally, could a deeper understanding of humans help in the solution to the other two crises that bedevil us so much today?

5. Happiness Then and Now

Two hundred years ago only a few people possessed the wealth and luxury that are now associated with modern living—whereas today ...? Of course, there is a substantial middle class in the developed countries that enjoys the material benefits of modern society, a class, which unfortunately is dwindling under the influence of the 'New World Order'. This is true even in the U.S. where the median family income has not increased at all for more than thirty years, and has not actually declined because there are so many more women working now.[19] But beyond this there is a worldwide alienation in this middle class that is not consistent with the material wealth and amenities that they enjoy. (On the other hand, does anyone truly believe that the very wealthy are happy, in spite of the persistent advertising about the 'rich and the famous' we see in the media?)

So, one must ask, with all the economic development and the evolution of science and technology in the last 200 years, what are we now able to offer to modern humans? First, throughout the whole world more than half of humanity has witnessed from very little to almost no improvement in their material lives during that time. Clearly, many people benefit from the wonders of medicine, and a minority enjoys progress in the use of energy, communications and transportation, and general comfort in everyday life. But is this minority happier now, even with these improvements and amenities? Perpetual war, crime and other sociopathic indices, e.g., divorce, drug abuse (including caffeine, nicotine and alcohol), prostitution and pornography, as well as bribes, kickbacks, patronage, fraud, theft, etc., which are common phenomena at every level of life today, altogether reflect a general collapse of the moral structure in today's society. These findings would cause one to suppose that, no, today's humans are not happier, despite the apparent progress in science and technology. And research that addresses directly the phenomenon of happiness draws the same conclusion.[20]

We have no measurements of happiness from 200 years ago, although certainly there was much misery associated with the poverty that characterized the lives of most. Today's worldwide poverty, meanwhile, still deprives many people of the basic needs for adequate food, clothing and shelter, and more than that there is still a general lack of some sort of security in life and the assurance that the few things that people have will not be taken away in one fashion or another, at any time that suits the ideological demands of the system—as we see in the recurrent financial crises that mark the history of the modern capitalist world. Of course this deprivation could lead to forms of sociopathic behavior then as now. But shouldn't we have solved these problems by now? In any case, shouldn't everyone be happier now? *Wasn't this the promise of science and technology and free market capitalism in the 19*th *century?*

6. Economic Theory and Happiness

In a sense, poverty and insecurity should have been eclipsed long ago; because, for nearly a century now *we have a production capacity that could satisfy most of the basic material needs of all people.* However, by the time we arrived at such a capacity both the politico-economic system and economic theory had become trapped in a severely limited perception of society and of human needs, as propagated by certain 18th-19th century philosophers and theoreticians. The result has been that 20th century corporate leaders have been 'obliged' to create (artificial) needs to fit this concept and this system of theory and practice. That is, the misery caused by poverty is an anachronism that requires an explanation, one, oddly enough, which is not far from the explanation for the unhappiness of the privileged few.

We start this explanation with a quote from Isaiah Berlin:[21]

> The history of thought and culture is, as Hegel showed with great brilliance, a changing pattern of great liberating ideas, which inevitably turn into suffocating straitjackets, and so stimulate their own destruction by new emancipating, and at the same time enslaving conceptions.

We recognize here the basic dialectical insight of Heraclitus, as mentioned above, which Hegel and others have used to analyze the philosophical and socioeconomic systems of their time and ours. This dialectic refers here to the relationship between thought and behavior, between consciousness and being, between subjective and objective reality and even between conjectures and refutations, as Popper would have it. Kuhn has interpreted straitjackets as 'anomalies' that would lead to scientific revolutions, whereas Marx interpreted them as basic systemic contradictions that would provide clues for the next phase of human history.[22] Thus, Marx, for example, began with an analysis of the subjective reality, i.e., the reality of ideas and thoughts, or the consciousness, that inspired the capitalist system at that time. This was a consciousness that made private ownership of the means of production sacred, that made workers selling themselves or their labor to those owners in order to survive seem natural, a consciousness that believed that everything, i.e., labor, nature, education, indeed, all of society, could be reduced to engineering, etc. Within a short period of time this consciousness resulted in the inescapable alienation of people, alienation from the products of their labor, from their communities, and from each other. Furthermore, the ideas that promoted this alienation, could, according to Alan Macfarlane, have begun as early as the 14th century in England.[23]

Marx, however, did not start with Hegel, but with Epicurus. His doctoral dissertation was an analysis of the argument between Epicurus and Democritus about whether society is deterministic in the same sense as nature, that is, if there are any mechanisms that allow the prediction and control of society in the same way that current Newtonian/Cartesian science and technology seek to control nature. His conclusion was that the humanist Epicurus was right, that there are *no* deterministic social mechanisms, and from there came his respect for the dialectic and for the human participation in the construction of social reality. He was quite modest in his expressions about what exactly would be the next (socialist) phase of humanity, despite the 'certainty' that some of his followers showed in later writings, as they sought not to exclude themselves entirely from the deterministic ethos of the age.

With these considerations we can clarify some of the basic problems of western society today. Capitalism has liberated the enormous human resources that were hidden beneath the various forms of despotism that lasted for 2000 years following the end of ancient Greek civilization. This liberation occurred in quite a 'natural' way as a result of the increase in commerce in the Mediterranean, aided in turn by the Renaissance that uncovered manuscripts preserved by the Arabs which revealed ancient Greek science and philosophy. The growth of commerce prompted the creation of industry and technology, which in turn contributed to an increase in the production of goods and the further development of trade, by now on an international scale.[24]

> *"Capitalism and mainstream economic theory and even liberal ideas about democracy are trapped in the 'straitjacket' of thought from the 19th century."*

The industrialization and urbanization that followed created a huge productive capacity, dependent, however, on a political-economic system based on the so-called free market and on an economic theory that rationalized it by focusing exclusively on production and investment for profit. (This emphasis on endless material production was true even in the communist Soviet Union).[25] Unfortunately, however, it ignores any human needs beyond those related to money, profit seeking and its mathematical theorization. Thus, if a need can be combined with a financial return, the system will offer an appropriate product or service; if not, it will simply not be met, at least not within the dominant politico-economic system. In theory and practice this system allows, though only grudgingly, a public sector to provide the necessary social and physical infrastructure to satisfy significant unmet needs, especially if their satisfaction would improve the productivity of the system in general. But again this is allowed only if it does not compete with the private sector. It is important to emphasize in this respect that with neo-liberalism in recent years the private sector has expanded enormously, while the public sector is increasingly being used as a conduit to channel public funds into the private sector, usually for excessively profitable activities.[26]

When the system arrived in the late 19th century with a production capacity that could soon have satisfied the basic material needs of everyone, especially in the industrialized countries, and over time throughout the rest of the world, it did not follow the logical development of doing so because it was not 'profitable'. All of the subsequent evolution of capitalism and of mainstream economic theory since then has been characterized by this outdated 'logic'. Thus, in the less developed countries of the Third World colonial capital has sought cheap raw materials and cheap labor, and subsequently, to the extent possible, new markets (consisting mostly of the privileged few), which on the whole aids more in the underdevelopment and the continued deprivation of basic needs in these countries.[27] We must exclude, of course, certain countries of Asia, particularly China, which have to a large degree freed themselves from this colonial syndrome and where now the local ruling class, itself, has taken on the 'onerous' task of exploiting its own people in the name of 'development'.

During the same period, in the industrialized countries themselves corporations have learned to manipulate consumers' emotional and moral needs to increase consumption, so as to not reduce the production that was the source of their profit. In a sense it might have been more logical to increase the income of workers so that they could consume the increased production, but this would have reduced profits. Caught in this contradiction, they have turned, on the one hand, to new forms of organization and technology to reduce production costs, ignoring the psychological and physical toll on employees and workers, as immortalized in Charlie Chaplin's

'Modern Times', and on the other, to advertising, credit, etc., as already mentioned, to increase the consumption of goods, including often those that are largely unnecessary, providing they yielded a profit. Meanwhile, the evolution of a technology that displaces workers further reduces purchasing power in the market. The combination of all these choices has contributed eventually to the current global socio-economic crisis.

The scientific, artistic and emotional manipulation of workers and consumers has reached a very sophisticated level today, forcing them to engage in a frantic but meaningless 'rat race', in which they work harder and longer hours to earn more money to buy goods they think they need, without a thought given to how these needs were created in the first place. Capitalism and mainstream economic theory and even liberal ideas about democracy are trapped in the 'straitjacket' of thought from the 19th century, and are unable to help the workers, citizens and consumers to free themselves from this impasse.[28, 29]

7. 'New' Perceptions of Happiness

We know that in large social systems there are many unintended consequences of people's actions: we think we're doing one thing but it turns out that the effects are not what we expected. The feedback loops in large systems are very slow moving and often interpreted in terms of outdated conceptions, so that reality usually runs ahead of thought. Thus, it has taken until now for more and more people to understand that the 'liberating' theories and ideologies of the 19th century do not fit the realities of the 21st. There is now an effort to bring science closer to real people and real needs. There are thousands of students and professors of economics who are looking for new, more humane 'reality based' economic theories, reflecting today's circumstances.[30, 31, 32] (See also www.paecon.net)

At the same time, in the larger industrial society there are millions of people seeking to satisfy non-material needs by fleeing the modern sector and the frenzied competition that characterizes it, living with smaller cars and simpler houses and consumer goods. They are seeking to reduce environmental pollution by using more 'friendly' technologies, and to eat fewer processed foods containing toxins from pesticides, fertilizers, etc., and generally to avoid the pressures for the 'good life' promoted by the media. In other words, they are seeking to create on a smaller scale a more moral and emotionally satisfying socioeconomic system to replace the large scale one that has now become so immoral and so irrational.[33, 34, 35] This is not, of course, to suggest in any way that the poverty-stricken people in the Third World should be denied access to those basic material goods and services that are so lacking there, to a large degree proportional to their over abundance in the First World.

It is not the first time, however, that people have realized that their society could not allow the fulfilment of important non-material human needs. Here we must mention one of the earliest and most important of such people, Epicurus, who left the city, not to avoid consumerism, but to find the essence of human life. Although the school of Epicurus lasted much longer than all the schools of the other philosophers, his thoughts have been distorted and his concepts perverted more than those of any other philosopher. Why? Because Epicurus tried to free humans from every sort of unessential physical and psychological need that might derive from the socio-political system. This has not made him popular in any system of power, anywhere, ever.

This is because people in positions of power are always looking to devise emotional and ethical justifications to legitimize their power. The Greek word for (political) power is 'εξουσία', which means literally 'outside the essence'. Insofar as the powerful are usually 'outside the essence' they seek those justifications outside the realm of the human and outside the essence of society, that is, in the realm of the metaphysical and in mechanisms beyond the human. When Nietzsche said, "God is dead", he meant that the metaphysical symbolic system of religion had lost its grip on humans because it had been replaced by science. Now unfortunately, following the idea of the dialectic, science, or at least the language of science, is increasingly used for similar symbolic purposes (of 'mystification'). Thus, for many people, including almost all businessmen, and the politicians who support them, as well as many economists, *economic theory and science generally play to a significant degree the social role of a metaphysical symbolic universe that legitimizes the power of the existing status quo.*[36]

Meanwhile, there are many contemporary people, who, like Epicurus understand that modern society pushes one beyond and outside the essential, and that society, therefore, needs to be redefined. Such an effort requires reflection, time and quiet, something not to be found in the city. Hence, the movements mentioned above, which have different names: 'cultural creatives', 'postmodern', ecovillagers, transition towns, 'harmonization movement', even Epicureans, etc.[37, 38, 39, 40, 41]

8. The Philosophy of Epicurus

How could Epicurus assist current Epicureans? What was the philosophy of Epicurus?[42] A basic presupposition of Epicurus was that happiness begins at the level of human beings, and that they should be happy here and now (and not after death, for example). To be happy, one should avoid physical pain and mental distress (what today we call stress). But, according to Epicurus, one should seek to avoid physical pain and mental distress *through reason and logic and not through gluttony and greed.* That is, what all the agitated critics of Epicurus have done for two millennia now is to distort the meaning of 'ηδονή' (hedonism) and to slander him by giving a totally opposite meaning to the word, all based on a big lie. *For Epicurus any pleasure of a given moment that would bring unhappiness to the next, either to one's self or to others, should be rejected.* Thus, his true maxim was frugality, simplicity in food, in drink, in housing, in clothing and sex, i.e., 'μέτρον άριστον' (measure in all things), *not* the current tendency to overeating and dieting, drug abuse and detoxification, overconsumption and over indebtedness, etc.

There is modern scientific evidence to support this philosophy. For drug dependence there is no need for discussion. As far as overeating is concerned, experiments with animals have shown that less food contributes to health and longevity. There was an impressive study of American Navy pilots who were imprisoned in North Vietnam (where they ate only rice and vegetables) compared with their fellow non-imprisoned pilots, which showed that in a whole range of body systems the prisoners were healthier than their colleagues who ate the usual meals of the American people![43]

Epicurus believed that to avoid psychological stress, the most important thing was to avoid fear. He believed that all psychological stress begins with fear, and furthermore, along with Aristotle, that fear is the chief weapon of power. Epicurus believed that fear is rooted in the fear of death, so he tried first of all to relieve people of this primal fear. It was also for this reason that his philosophy was in continuous conflict with western religions over the centuries that followed. He did not believe—as was also true of Thomas Paine[44] and other deists in the 18th century—in gods that would meddle in human affairs (supporting one or the other side in wars, sporting events, etc.), either before or after death. He believed that if such were true, gods would be human and not divine, thus disarming the power of all the religions that threaten humans with punishment through exile, excommunication, hell, or whatever. The same is true for all forms of power that use fear to control their subjects. Indeed, the more a system depends upon fear to govern, including fear of the enemy, of terrorism, of crime, of torture and execution, and in general fear of the 'bogeyman', the further away it is from democracy, whatever label is used to define that system. Thus, Epicurus entreated his students to avoid the fear of God, the fear of authority and the fear of death, fears often generated by ritualistic and sociodramatic means such as staged terrorist events, the theater of violence in the mass media, overt demonstrations of power, victimage, mystification, etc.[45] but also the many writings of Kenneth Burke.[46]

At the other end of the emotional spectrum Epicurus gave much importance to *friendship,* as he believed it was the most important basis of human happiness. He emphasized companionship, honesty, generosity, goodness and kindness to friends, along with prudence, self-sufficiency, serenity, simplicity and restraint. Because he appeared to give little importance to kinship or to society as a socially constructed reality, and as he believed in and supported the atomic theory of Democritus, he was compelled to find a social explanation for "the temporary association of individuals within larger systems characteristic of nature, where 'everything flows'". There may at some time be found a quantum explanation to complement the psychological importance we give today to the attraction between people that results in temporary communities or groups. Epicurus, however, offered friendship as the philosophical explanation for the role of such attraction. And in his garden, friendship was extended to all: to women, slaves, young and old. There, associations relied solely on human volition, rather than on coercion, and hence the importance of friendship to maintain the sense of cohesion.

In this context, without fear, and with equality and freedom and with the search for happiness based on wisdom, logic and simplicity, Epicurus saw no place for glory, for success and fame, for wealth and greed, or for power and conquest. *"Λάθε Βιώσας"* (Live inconspicuously, unobtrusively): avoid behavior and ambitions that bring only banalities and mental distress. Live life here and now, with simplicity and respect for each other, but with joy and happiness.

How ironic! Almost the entire evolution of humanity since Epicurus has gone in the opposite direction, especially with the rise of economic theory, individualism and the technological society, which have brought a culture of egoism, competition, conquest and arrogance, and with ultimate consequences that may well circumscribe significantly, if not conclusively, human life on our planet. So it is not surprising that so many people today are looking to implement the values of Epicurus, with or without his name. There are scholars in all disciplines who are turning their attention towards the human and the spiritual, seeking to find a more reasoned philosophical and scientific approach to the current social reality.

9. Maslow's Developmental Theory of Human Needs

One such effort (without apparent reference to Epicurus), starting nearly half a century ago was that of Abraham Maslow,[47] who sought to formulate a theory of emotional needs as they develop throughout a normal (non-pathological) person's lifetime. In his well-known "hierarchy" he sought, through his clinical work, to develop an empirical theory that was dynamic and universal. He claimed that the first needs, first in importance and time, were the *physiological needs* of humans arising during infancy: needs for food, water, warmth, etc. These are the basic material needs, and essentially the only needs incorporated in economic theory where they are expressed solely in terms of money. Mainstream economic theory offers essentially no theoretical guidance as to how these needs would be insured for all people. The free market system has certainly not succeeded in doing this even in the advanced industrial countries, as the past 200 years have shown all too clearly. Surprisingly, they were not even identified as needs in scientific discussions and indices of development, including in the United Nations, until fairly recently, and only after a long campaign by Mahbub al Haq.[48, 49]

The second developmental need is the emotional need for *safety,* which is very important during the childhood years of human beings. It is the need for security, protection, stability, dependency, freedom from fear, anxiety, and chaos, need for structure, order, law, and limits, etc. It is a need that is satisfied primarily within the context of the loving family, *but which presupposes the security of the family in the larger society.* Again mainstream economic theory offers no guidance here. It is also a need whose satisfaction is undermined by the violence that is a daily presence in the media, even in children's cartoons. This violence serves broader political purposes by creating fear, often subconsciously, important for social control as mentioned above, but also necessary to justify the militarization of the global politico-economic system in which military armaments are the number one world trade commodity according to statistics provided by the United Nations.

The third need in human psychological development is the need for *affiliation or friendship* within a group, a very important need during adolescence when the child begins the search for autonomy. It is the need to belong somewhere outside the family, the need for loving relationships with friends, which will subsequently evolve into similar relationships with spouses, children and community. It is a need which could be satisfied through youth groups and clubs sponsored by schools, churches and other associations for young people. Among other things the young could discuss the ways in which the need for affiliation is much exploited in advertising, which is directed increasingly towards adolescents. Teenage children have a critical emotional need to belong to a reference group beyond the family and will do almost anything, which in current society, television, cinema and, in general, advertising, suggest are necessary to belong to such a group.

Later, during the early developmental years of adulthood people have an emotional need for esteem, specifically for self-esteem and social esteem. The first is expressed as a need for power, achievement, efficiency, ownership, capacity, confidence, independence and freedom, and the second for reputation, position, fame and glory, dominance, recognition, attention, importance, dignity and respect. Maslow's theory has been much used in management seminars and workshops in relation to this need, though how it can serve to counsel employees involved in a rapacious, predatory system where only the bottom line is of importance, remains a mystery.

It was also a need referred to by Adam Smith as approbation, though his examples reveal his failure to appreciate how different life in mass society would be from what he was experiencing during his time. One unfortunate development has been that most of the economists who have followed Smith have reduced the basis of such praise (often clouded by envy) to material or monetary terms, disregarding other forms of emotional and spiritual satisfaction sought by human beings. Unfortunately, Smith justified the search for approbation on the grounds that it would encourage people to continue to "cut the trees and plough the fields", with all the disastrous results we see today in the environment and in human psychology.

In any case, here it appears that Maslow diverges from Epicurus and his canon to live inconspicuously and unobtrusively. Or could it be that Epicurus understood something that Maslow did not take into account, i.e., that it is very difficult if not impossible to find real (authentic) esteem in a large-scale society? This is certainly true in the mass society of today, as evidenced by inquiries made on this topic. Current surveys show that few people express satisfaction in their work, which is, for the most part, the place where one must expect the need for esteem to be satisfied.[50]

Parenthetically, one might add that the Soviet system also ignored these emotional needs in defining the new socialist world. Material needs were guaranteed, but were ultimately understood as they were defined in the capitalist world. Thus, continuous increases in consumer goods and the necessary increases in industrial production that this entailed were to be the defining purpose of the new socialist society, with the same resulting environmental problems that have marked the history of capitalism.

At the same time, development was seen as an engineering problem in the same mechanistic framework as employed by the capitalist system, and was to be realized through central control, in this case the state instead of the corporation. Work, while guaranteed for everyone, turned out to be the same mindless process as portrayed by Charlie Chaplin and formalized by Taylorism under capitalism.

> *"The academic and business world are still largely dominated by the mechanistic Newtonian vision of reality and the Cartesian separation of the spiritual and the material."*

Thus, esteem needs, which can only be realized through worker participation at every stage in the decision-making process, were as frustrated under Soviet socialism as under capitalism. Joshua Horn[51] described the long painful process that worker participation entailed, based upon his experience in the post revolutionary medical system in China. But, if applied universally, this would have slowed down the accumulation of consumer goods that was to characterize the new utopia. Thus, apparently for this reason, it was rejected as 'inefficient' in the Newtonian framework that was employed in the centralized Soviet planning system.[52]

Meanwhile, the (illusion of) glory, much sought after by politicians and those who generally have a passion for money and power, cannot satisfy such needs. Is it perhaps that Epicurus believed that only in small-scale communities could one satisfy the need for esteem? Epicurus did not live in our present mass society, but he must have realized that it was necessary for people to know you well, and to truly respect you, so that you, yourself would realize that this was genuine esteem. And is this perhaps why so many people are now creating smaller communities in order to live a more fulfilling life?

At the final stage in one's emotional development, Maslow identified a higher need, the need for *self-actualization*. This is the need to become more and more idiosyncratically everything one is capable of becoming, from an ideal parent to an athlete, musician, carpenter or whatever. Normally, this need is met only very rarely in our contemporary society, according to Maslow, on the grounds that, apart from very exceptional people, most would have had to satisfy all the other developmental needs first in order to reach this level, and this would occur usually only after the age of fifty.[53, 54]

Indeed, Maslow's hierarchy is characterized by the concept of 'prepotency', which means that it is an interdependent system where lower needs must be generally satisfied before higher needs even become relevant. Hence, ordinarily, if a lower need is not satisfied at the appropriate age it could very well remain dominant and prevent the emergence of higher needs later in life. Thus, if during the years of infancy persons have not satisfied their need for food, these people will tend to remain psychologically at this level, and food will persist as an obsessive need throughout their lives, inhibiting the emergence of other higher needs. The same applies to the need for security in childhood, or friendship and affiliation in adolescence. If any one of these needs is not met at the appropriate age, it will tend to persist as an unmet psychological need throughout a person's life and block the emergence of later needs for esteem and self-actualization.[55]

With this in mind, the seemingly strange and erratic appearance of children's psychological needs, or lack of emotional intelligence according to Goleman,[56] in adult populations is explained. Different people have stayed at different stages in their psychological development, and hence the emotional immaturity characteristic of a significant proportion of the adult population, especially, the male need for power, perhaps because childhood safety needs were not satisfied. And one reason for this is that socioeconomic conditions plus the lack of philosophy throughout the educational system, throughout science and throughout (the technological) society in general, do not give attention to normal psychological development. That is, if we want people to be happy we must at some point put emotional and moral development alongside, if not ahead of economic growth, which, if we did, would cause a tectonic shift in the current scientific understanding of what is important in human life.

Meanwhile, it is not that this shift has not already started to take place. Since the time of Maslow, there has been an enormous amount of research on human happiness and well-being, or eudaemonia, as the Greeks referred to it. Neuroscientists, psychiatrists, psychologists, geneticists, philosophers and even physicists have been conducting research on every facet of human well-being. Much of this research has been summarized recently by C. Robert Cloninger in his book, *Feeling Good, the Science of Well-Being,*[57] which also includes his own research on the multi-dimensional, including spiritual, characteristics of well-being. Unfortunately, the academic and business world are still largely dominated by the mechanistic Newtonian vision of reality and the Cartesian separation of the spiritual and the material, and where even basic physiological needs have only recently been recognized as worth reporting alongside GDP, per capita income, etc. It is for this reason that we must struggle to make known the insights of Maslow, Cloninger, and many other scholars who are working to incorporate the *total* (spiritual and material) human being into our philosophy of science and society.

10. What Can We Do To Save Humans With (and from) Science?

We must appreciate that Maslow's hierarchy is *not* a deterministic theory in the Newtonian sense, nor is it expected that people reading about his theory would not be affected by it, as Descartes would have imagined. Therefore, the idea of prepotency can be utilized and then overcome through reflection on the hierarchy during adulthood. Just knowing about it may free persons from its hold, in the same sense that physical reality in the quantum world may be altered by scientists who are observing it.

Maslow, in the meantime, adds two more needs outside the prepotency framework: cognitive needs and aesthetic needs. These needs appear in all societies and all epochs, and are probably the key thing to examine if we wish to extract ourselves from the impasse of our present existence. To create a better social system we must first understand the problems in the current system and then be able to envision, think about, and generally create an image of a new social structure.

Thus, Maslow's developmental theory may be used in two ways:

First, it may be used as an approach to individual psychological therapy as part of a quest for personal well-being. Here it can be used to identify inadequacies in psychological development arising from unmet needs during infancy, childhood and adolescence that constitute obstacles to satisfaction of esteem and self-actualization needs later in life. This is something which most of psychological therapy is directed towards, in any case, either within similar or differing theoretical frameworks, including that of Dr. Cloninger, who has explored the need for cooperativeness and self-transcendence as necessary prerequisites not only to individual well-being but also to social well-being and, in the long run, the survival of our species.

Secondly, and equally important here, we must talk about the socioeconomic implications of Maslow's theory, and about the need to institutionalize, in the sociological meaning of the term, the satisfaction of these needs at the appropriate time in the emotional development of all members of society. Thus, our fixation on efficiency, productivity and growth in the material realm must give way to concern for growth in the emotional and spiritual realm. Instead of adding endless numbers of gadgets and widgets, especially of the military sort, we must seek to add more healthy and emotionally mature human beings. Epicurus' insights into happiness should also help to liberate us from this overbearing material realm, with additional untold benefits in our effort to stop degrading the environment (and each other).

Thus, economic theory must be directed to providing a minimum of food, clothing and shelter for all members of society, with the assurance that women (and men) will not be degraded socially for their absence from the "productive" sector during periods of early childhood development. The same requirement must apply to each stage in the emotional development of all persons such that the satisfaction of their need for security, love and affiliation is embodied in social institutions directed to that purpose. Here we must emphasize the importance of protecting the family where such needs are first and best satisfied, which would mean allowing flexible work schedules and avoiding punishment for either women or men who are engaged in this critical social function. At later stages, when esteem needs are relevant, work must be designed as an end in itself, and not just as a means to increase production and/or profit making. Obviously, questions of productivity and efficiency cannot be ignored in the work place, but they must be kept in perspective, not as ends in themselves, but as means to the greater well being of the overall population. Again, Epicurus, as well as the serious problem of environmental degradation, should help us to maintain a proper perspective on how much and what sorts of production of material goods and services are important to society. Finally, economists, themselves, will have to learn to arrange the numbers so that these radically different social goals can be achieved. It should be both a challenge and a great satisfaction as they relearn their science in the service of humankind, serving Apollo, the god of light and healing instead of Ares, the god of war.

Among other things, this will require a renewed understanding that all knowledge is relative. What we believe as true today may have been either unknown or fantasy yesterday, and may be either a falsehood or, more likely, only a partial truth tomorrow. This understanding of relativity has been increasingly more acceptable to science since the time of Einstein, Heisenberg and Bohr,[58] and in general has always been more or less known in the humanities and the arts. Indeed, the social role of art is to experiment with reality, opening prospects for other possible realities, either through criticism of the status quo, or through images of another, better reality.[59, 60, 61] If ordinary people and even more scientists begin to accept the relativity of knowledge with all its implications, as Berlin indicated above, and to *know when liberating ideas have become suffocating straitjackets,* then we can begin to build a better society. This is not, of course, to adopt the extreme relativist (often postmodern) position that implies that there is no such thing as true knowledge, and that, therefore, nothing matters. Newtonian physics has not been thrown out because of quantum physics; it still occupies an important, though now more limited position, which is the way of all growth: the more we know, the more we realize what we don't know.

As mentioned above, we live with a number of scientific and socio-political ideas from the 18th and 19th centuries. The liberating ideological and theoretical ideas of this era were the product of the efforts of merchants and industrialists to be freed from the control of landlords and kings, who claimed that they ruled with the blessing of divine right. Even the U.S. Constitution extended the idea of democracy solely to people with property! Only after prolonged struggles did workers acquire voting rights, and women only in the 1920s, and for blacks in America only in the 1960s, that is, just a few years ago! In spite of this, an American journalist has described the current U.S. system as still little more than a 'representative oligarchy', which is not far from the reality in Europe. If you look at the cost of elections around the world, for example, you will understand that only the rich or 'friends' of the rich, that is, of the oligarchy, may seek to become elected to higher political office. Many social scientists still insist on calling these systems 'democracies', disguising reality with such "Orwellian" euphemisms in their 'scientific' analyses.

Mainstream economic theory is even more disingenuous. It speaks of a 'free market' system that might have existed at some point in the 18th or 19th century before the inevitable effects of competition started producing winners and losers and 'the big fish began to eat the small'. The accumulated effect of these economic forces has produced ever fewer and larger firms, particularly in the developed countries and by extension in the rest of the world, as competitive capitalism has evolved into its present monopoly form.[62] The term 'free market' is a euphemism that obscures, among other things, the economic disparity between developed and less developed countries, a disparity that allows monopoly capital to enter freely into the less developed economies and pillage their resources, as well as their means of production and distribution, creating a permanent dependent status for these countries. It also obscures the ability of these few companies to control the prices and general market conditions for the products or services they provide.

Finally, and more recently, it obscures the evolution of the shift in economic power from the industrial to the financial sector where 'the financial tail is now wagging the industrial dog', and the subsequent and inevitable extension of the severe economic crisis beyond the financial sector into a worldwide depression at least as great as that of the 1930s. There are many other examples of anachronisms in economic theory, as it struggles with the 'straitjackets' of 19th century thought, without even mentioning the whole range of non-material human needs that do not appear anywhere in the economic and technocratic approach to the socioeconomic system.

11. Conclusion

Thus, to begin to change the system, humanism and philosophy would have to be reintroduced into society and science, that is into the educational system and the 'theater' of the media, where adult education takes place. With art, especially dramatic art, playing an important role, we can begin to envision a different reality where human beings and their emotional and moral needs would be given precedence, rather than our current preoccupation with profit making, consumerism, greed, jealousy, and fear. Not that we should ignore the positive values of science and economics, values such as logic, efficiency, rationality, etc. Simply, *these values should serve human needs rather than define them.*

Furthermore, we must seek to remove all the labels that we use, without thinking, to describe people and situations, labels that separate 'us' from 'them', even in the same society, the same city and the same neighborhood, cultivating hostility and intolerance, and creating a serious obstacle to a more humane society. This is likely a phenomenon that has derived, as Maslow might say, from the insecurity that ironically appears to have characterized the history of all the world since the acquisition of property accompanying the creation of surpluses provided by the domestication of plants and animals over the past 10,000 years, an insecurity that appears to have led to a craze for power and control that has characterized so many people (especially males) since that time.[63]

Indeed, as humankind seeks to attain the next level of spontaneous evolution to manage its global complexity, it should be inspired by better knowledge of the stages that have come before. Unlike the social Darwinist inspired belief that random mutation, competition, and adaptation create survivors, it is now seen to be a more "intentional" process that is inherent in quantum nature itself. This process leads to the ***increased cooperation*** that has allowed adaptation and survival, which in turn explains the evolution from prokaryotic uni-cellular organisms to multi-cellular organisms to proto-hominids and then to our own self-conscious organisms.[64] The increased control fostered by increased complexity is not accomplished by dominance but by increased communication among specialized components of the system. The current urge for control, which characterizes the early Newtonian conception of the universe and which has been carried over into society, is not what has allowed us to evolve into the self-conscious organisms that we are today. If we are to survive as such, and given that we have increasing knowledge about how the quantum universe is organized, we should like all the other elements of that universe to use that knowledge to find new cooperative means of surviving at the global level.

Maslow describes the process whereby children can become integrated, self-actualized adults. We now need to participate in creating a society that would allow the satisfaction of ***emotional*** needs, as they appear at each stage in human life. Epicurus, at the same time, has described a more modest material environment in which this process could evolve in a natural way, where humans could find the biological and psychological security and respect that would allow them to form a non-hostile identity, an identity that would not be threatened when confronted with other people and other identities in the same or other geographic and social space. Such an identity would not be restricted to 'us and them', so that the inevitable conflicts that occur in human society could be solved without resorting to violence.

Unlike the Pythagorean communities, as well as most subsequent utopian religious communities, where obligations are institutionalized, all facets of membership in the 'garden' of Epicurus were voluntary, such that the bonds were based on emotion, not law. The contributions and sharing to create a more egalitarian and just community were done in a spirit of friendship and not obligation. This process was facilitated by the principles of frugality and lack of vanity, which allowed social status and respect to be achieved without resorting to material wealth and fortune. It is this combination of the maximization of pleasure in the context of austerity that would allow the need for self-awareness and self-actualization to be satisfied without undue reference to material goods, wealth and money. Such a philosophy is particularly necessary today, because it would not only facilitate true psychological development, but would do so at a much lower environmental cost.

The philosophy of personal greed, which inspired the rise of capitalism, has brought us to an impasse with nature and with ourselves. Thus, we return to Epicurus not only to see how he sought to satisfy human needs, but also especially how he sought to create a community (society) that resembled the more democratic societies of 'hunters and gatherers'. There is no need to over-romanticize them, but at the same time these people had, for the most part, found ways to live modestly by sharing their limited wealth, without the need to create an identity so closely attached to property.[65] A 'possessive' identity arose with the domestication of plants and animals and with the idea of 'private property' (land and livestock), as mentioned above. Over time this definition of identity extended to larger geopolitical entities and led it towards a hostile dynamic with an extension from simple jealousy all the way to civil strife and eventually to international wars of conquest, thus turning it into a force for division rather than inclusion: 'You're either for us or against us', where there is no 'third way' and no space for compromise.[66]

Today, the courageous effort to create a common identity among all mankind is forced to struggle with the residue of human evolution over the past 10,000 years, to say nothing of the effects of a social Darwinist inspired predatory capitalist system and its economic theory institutionalized over the past several hundred years. This is a system where every thing and every person is an exploitable resource, and cooperative relations, even with nature, are very difficult, if not impossible to realize. It was precisely this hostility that Epicurus sought to combat with his emphasis on simplicity, equality and friendship in the garden, where property is something that we share as an outgrowth of people learning to develop faith in their fellow human beings.

Instead of helping us to use and develop our emotional and moral selves, mechanistic (social) science has tried to convince us that they are not necessary, that scientific logic would make them redundant, and that shrewdness would suffice. Instead of confronting the maxim of Plato, this science has sought to establish cunning as the highest human value. Can social scientists, especially economists, who have so much influence in today's world, produce a theory for a system that would maximize *security, friendship, and love?* If they can, perhaps the effort to satisfy needs for esteem and self-realization could evolve naturally within the same framework.

"Individual perspectives are always social in origin."

So, let us try to look more closely at the meaning of happiness, something that the welfare states have tried to do, although, as seen above, the effort has been blunted by an economistic view of the human being, even in the socialist countries.[67] But we must measure true need satisfaction, not some fabricated indices developed from existing data. We must ask the people, themselves, remembering that individual perspectives are always social in origin. Social scientists, psychologists and philosophers must all work together to create questionnaires and interview methods that can uncover true human feelings, and then develop indices that would measure such feelings. A significant change in scientific thought, and ultimately in society, would be required, if we were to succeed in such an effort. We need a new vision that would subordinate conventional economic signals to new human concepts. The beliefs of economists about efficiency would have to change to 'improving not only the material, but also the *emotional and moral circumstances of one person without worsening the emotional and moral circumstances of anyone else*'. All this must refer to new and more humane societies, simply because existing thoughts and behaviors are leading us to a dead end. Indeed, mainstream economic theory is not able to guarantee any of the above-mentioned needs; it appears at this time, at least, to guarantee that all the wealth, property and power will float to the top 1% of the population!

Often it is the more adventurous, the 'marginal', often younger scientists, who dare to risk their 'reputation' with such unorthodox thoughts and deeds. This, at least, is what the analysis by Thomas Kuhn[68] would predict when he speaks of 'scientific revolutions'. It is the young scientists who can experience the quantum or Gestalt shift from an old paradigm to a new one without the excessive emotional cost that older scientists are likely to experience. And it characterizes the adventurous people who are leaving the modernist rat race for life in more cooperative settings, whether in large cities or small towns, as they seek to rediscover the emotional and social skills necessary for harmonious living in a return to the 'Garden of Epicurus'. There they are seeking to find new ways of coexistence among themselves and with nature, ways necessary to found a new post-individualist society, where humans will be the measure, and money, science, mathematics, religion, etc., will be the lesser, though not unimportant means.

Author Contact Information
Email: g.gutenschwager@gmail.com

Notes

1 Ernst Schumacher, *Small Is Beautiful: Economics As If People Mattered* (New York: Harper and Row, 1973).

2 Bruce Rosenblum and Fred Kuttner, *Quantum Enigma: Physics Encounters Consciousness* (London: Duckworth Overlook, 2011).

3 Bruce Lipton and Steve Bhaerman, *Spontaneous Evolution: Our Positive Future (and a way to get there from here)* (London: Hay House, 2011).

4 Hugh Dalziel Duncan, *Culture and Democracy: the Struggle for Form in Society and Architecture in Chicago and the Middle West during the Life and Time of Louis H. Sullivan* (Totowa: Bedminster Press, 1965).

5 Stuart Ewen, *Captains of Consciousness: Advertising and the Social Roots of the Consumer Culture* (New York: McGraw-Hill, 1976).

6 Alan Nasser, "Fiscal Policy as Class Politics: What Keynes Really Prescribed," *Counter Punch* 19, No. 19 (2012):1–1.

7 With a full Introduction by Engels written in 1895. Karl Marx, *The Class Struggles in France, 1848–50* (New York: International Publishers, 1895).

8 Theo Colborn, Dianne Dumanoski and John Peterson Meyers, *Our Stolen Future: Are We Threatening our Fertility, Intelligence, and Survival—A Scientific Detective Story* (New York: Penguin Books, 1996).

9 C. B. Macpherson, *The Political Theory of Possessive Individualism: Hobbes to Locke* (Oxford: Oxford University Press, 1962).

10 Richard B. Norgaard, *Development Betrayed: the End of Progress and a Co-evolutionary Revisioning of the Future* (London: Routledge, 1994).

11 Neva Goodwin, "An Overview of Climate Change," *Real World Economics Review* No. 46 (2008): 110–135. http:www.pae-con.net/PAEReview/issue46/Goodwin46.pdf

12 Richard Stivers, *The Culture of Cynicism: American Morality in Decline* (Oxford: Blackwell, 1994).

13 Gertrude Himmelfarb, *The Demoralization of Society: from Victorian Virtues to Modern Values* (New York: Alfred A. Knopf, 1995).

14 Bruce Lipton and Steve Bhaerman, *Spontaneous Evolution: Our positive future (and a way to get there from here)* (Carlsbad: Hay House, 2009).

15 Eamon Javers and Jim VandeHei, "The Stimulus Bill: Go Big or Go Home," *Politico* 28th January 2009.

16 Deepak Chopra and Leonard Mlodinow, *War of the Worldviews: Where Science and Spirituality Meet—and Do Not* (New York: Three Rivers Press, 2011).

17 John Maynard Keynes, *The General Theory of Employment, Interest and Money* (London: MacMillan, 1936).

18 Nuno Ornelas Martins, "Mathematics, Science, and the Cambridge Tradition," *Economic Thought: History, Philosophy and Methodology* 1, No. 2 (2012): 15–35.

19 William K. Tabb, "The Crisis: A View from Occupied America," *Monthly Review* 64, No. 4 (2012): 15–21.

20 Robert E. Lane, *The Loss of Happiness in Market Democracies* (New Haven: Yale University Press, 2000).

21 Isaiah Berlin, "Does Political Theory Still Exist," in *Philosophy, Politics and Society* (London: Basil Blackwell, 1962), 19.

22 Thomas Kuhn, *The Structure of Scientific Revolutions* (Chicago: University of Chicago Press, 1962, 1970).

23 Alan Macfarlane, *The Culture of Capitalism* (Oxford: Blackwell, 1987).

24 Henri Pirenne, *Medieval Cities* (Garden City: Doubleday, 1925).

25 Michael A. Lebowitz, *The Contradictions of "Real Socialism": The Conductor and the Conducted* (New York: Monthly Review Press, 2012).

26 Thomas Frank, *The Wrecking Crew: How Conservatives Ruined Government, Enriched Themselves and Beggared the Nation* (New York: Metropolitan Books/Henry Holt and Company, 2008).

27 Harry Magdoff, *The Age of Imperialism: the Economics of U.S. Foreign Policy* (N.Y.: Monthly Review Press, 1968).

28 Staffan Berenstam Linder, *The Harried Leisure Class* (New York: Columbia University Press, 1970).

29 Michael Perelman, *The Invisible Handcuffs of Capitalism: How Market Tyranny Stifles the Economy by Stunting Workers* (New York: Monthly Review Press, 2011).

30 Edward Fullbrook, *A Guide to What's Wrong with Economics* (London: Anthem Press, 2004).

31 Joel Magnuson, *Mindful Economics: How the U.S. Economy Works, Why It Matters, and How It Could be Different* (New York: Seven Stories Press, 2007).

32 John Quiggin, *Zombie Economics: How Dead Ideas Still Walk among Us* (Princeton: Princeton University Press, 2010).

33 Paul H. Ray and Sherry Ruth Anderson, *Cultural Creatives: How Fifty Million People Are Changing the World* (New York: Three Rivers Press, 2000).

34 Jonathon Dawson, *Ecovillages: New Frontiers for Sustainability. Schumacher Briefing, No. 12* (Totnes: Greenbooks, 2006).

35 Richard Moore, *Escaping the Matrix: How We the People Can Change the World* (Redwood City: The Cyberjournal Project, 2005).

36 Peter Berger and Thomas Luckmann, *The Social Construction of Reality: A Treatise in the Sociology of Knowledge* (New York: Doubleday, 1966).

37 Ray and Anderson, *Cultural Creatives.*

38 Ronald Inglehart, *Modernization and Postmodernization: Cultural, Economic and Political Change in 43 Societies* (Princeton: Princeton University Press, 1997).

39 Dawson, *Ecovillages.*

40 Moore, *Escaping the Matrix.*

41 Eric Brende, *Better Off: Flipping the Switch on Technology* (New York: Harper Collins Publishers, 2004).

42 Haralambos Theodorides, *Epicurus, The True Countenance of the Ancient World* (Athens: "Estias" Bookstore, 1981 [1954]).

43 "POW's Healthier than Peers," *Saint Louis Post Dispatch,* 13th November, 1977.

44 Thomas Paine, *The Age of Reason* (New York: Barnes and Noble, 2006).
45 Duncan, *Culture and Democracy.*
46 Kenneth Burke, *Counterstatement* (Berkeley: University of California Press, 1968).
47 Abraham Maslow, *Motivation and Personality* Second Edition (New York: Harper and Row, 1970).
48 Mahbub Al Haq, *Reflections on Human Development* (Delhi: Oxford University Press, 1999).
49 Paul Streeten, *First Things First: Meeting Basic Human Needs in the Developing Countries* (Oxford: Oxford University Press, 1981).
50 Gerard Huizinga, *Maslow's Need Hierarchy in the Work Situation* (Broninger: Walters-Noodhoff Publishers, 1970).
51 Joshua S. Horn, *Away with all Pests: an English Surgeon in People's China, 1954–1969* (New York: Monthly Review Press, 1969).
52 Lebowitz, *The Contradictions of "Real Socialism".*
53 Douglas T. Hall and Khalid E. Nougain, "An Examination of Maslow's Need Hierarchy in an Organizational Setting," *Organizational Behavior and Human Performance* 3, No. 1 (1968): 12–35.
54 Gerald Gutenschwager, *Planning and Social Science: A Humanistic Approach* (Lanham: University Press of America, 2004).
55 Huizinga, *Maslow's Need Hierarchy in the Work Situation.*
56 Daniel Goleman, *Emotional Intelligence* (New York: Bantam Books, 2005).
57 C. Robert Cloninger, *Feeling Good: The Science of Well-Being* (NY: Oxford University Press, 2004).
58 Fritjof Capra, *The Turning Point: Science, Society, and the Rising Culture* (N.Y.: Simon and Schuster, 1982).
59 Kenneth Burke, *Attitudes Toward History* (Boston: Beacon Press, 1961).
60 Duncan, *Symbols in Society.*
61 Duncan, *Symbols and Social Theory.*
62 Paul Baran and Paul Sweezy, *Monopoly Capital: An Essay on the American Economic and Social Order* (New York: Monthly Review Press, 1966).
63 Frederick Engels, *The Origin of the Family, Private Property and the State* ed. Eleanor Burke Leacock (N.Y.: International Publishers, 1972).
64 Bruce Lipton, *The Biology of Belief: Unleashing the Power of Consciousness, Matter and Miracles* (Carlsbad: Hay House, Inc., 2008).
65 Marshall Sahlins, *Stone Age Economics* (New York: Aldine de Gruyter, 1972).
66 William Ury, *The Third Side: Why We Fight and How We Can Stop* (New York: Penguin Books, 1999).
67 Michael A. Lebowitz, *The Contradictions of "Real Socialism".*
68 Kuhn, *The Structure of Scientific Revolutions.*

Gerald Gutenschwager, *Emeritus Professor, School of Architecture, Washington University, St. Louis, Missouri, USA; Research Fellow, Department of Planning and Regional Development, University of Thessaly, Volos, Greece*

In the Beginning

The Origin of the Successful Sustainability Agent

As we develop the moral aspect of our lives, we often adapt standards of right and wrong that serve as guides and deterrents for our conduct.

—Albert Bandura

Introduction

For our first discussion on the psychology of sustainability we will consider how one's "familial ecology"—drawing from Bronfenbrenner's (1986) ecology of the family—might influence our "sustainability inclination" (Chandler, 2017). Toward understanding why our earliest days and years likely influence our inclination to act sustainably, we will explore three areas of psychological research: parenting style (PS), attachment style (AT), and social value orientation (SVO).

First, it is important to keep in mind that the spectra of life experiences are inextricably linked and interdependent continua that constitute the essence of human ecology. Put another way, no experience occurs in isolation of another or all other experiences at any given time. This inextricable and dynamic relationship among experiences has profound implications as factors acting on, for example, a scarcity-abundance spectrum would likely affect an individual's experience on fear-courage and avarice-generosity spectra.

A myriad of factors can influence where we are within any spectrum. The ecology (i.e., sociocultural, socioecological, and environmental setting) of our family of origin, parenting style(s) experienced within that ecology, and the consequent attachment style that develops affect how we respond to those factors. Tantamount in importance, however, is that we understand that attachment style is plastic, that is it is not fixed, it can change and often does. If we know this, and we know a bit about attachment theory we can affect our attachment style positively along its continuum. Parenting and attachment styles can affect development of one's social value orientation. As you read the following sections, consider these relationships. Afterward, you will understand the basic premise on which the concept of a sustainability inclination rests, and that parenting, attachment, a social value orientation, has a composite effect on an individual's inclination to act sustainably.

Theories and Concepts in Context of Sustainability

Parenting Styles

In the early 1960s Diana Baumrind identified three types of parenting based on her research with preschool-age children. She later (ca. 1966) included "neglectful" as a fourth parenting style. These constructs have remained as accurate representations of parenting styles and of the general effect that these have on an individual's development into adulthood. Depending on social, cultural, and environmental factors, parenting style can have a significant effect on attachment style and social value orientation, which are believed to be important factors regarding individual sustainability inclination. Following are Baumrind's four types of parenting.

- Authoritative: Often referred to as "democratic parenting," it is a style that is characterized by parents or guardians establishing clear, somewhat flexible, age-appropriate boundaries within which the child can explore her or his environment safely. Discipline is measured and generally non-violent (i.e., no physical reprimand), and the level of punishment is commensurate to the type of misbehavior. Children in authoritative homes are allowed to share their thoughts and opinions.
- Authoritarian: Parenting that is characterized by rigid expectation of adherence to rules, and this expectation is typically enforced with shouting and physical punishment. Level of punishment typically does not match misbehavior. In authoritarian households children are to be seen not heard, and children are fearful to explore their environment.
- Indulgent/permissive: Parenting that is characterized by ill-defined and unsubstantial boundaries and expectations. Poor behavior is often met with a similar response as good behavior—provision of something wanted by the child—and there is no equitable effort-to-reward system. Children experiencing this style of parenting literally do not understand what justifies an equitable exchange and that they must be responsible for their actions. This parenting style cultivates entitlement, a lofty unrealistic sense of self, often resentment toward structure and work, as well as the indulgent/permissive parent(s) and their generation, as well as low self-efficacy and sense of agency.
- Neglectful: Parenting that is arguably the most detrimental style—although many will assert the same regarding indulgent/permissive. Children experience this style of parenting develop a sense of worthlessness. Children experiencing neglectful parenting have no trust foundation with their parents from which to explore the world (Mgbemere & Telles, 2013) and have difficulty forming relationships with others.

Attachment Theory

Attachment theory (AT) was developed by researchers John Bowlby (beginning late-1950s) and Mary Ainesworth (beginning early-1960s). Bowlby's early research at facilities for children with developmental disabilities and psychopathologies set him on a theoretical path not unlike Carl Jung's wherein he would come to question and eventually rule out Freudian theory that children's and eventually adult's psychopathologies arose from unconscious attempts to resolve guilt about aggression and libidinal drives, and to assert that psychosocial illness was much more the product of socioecological factors and especially the quality later referred to as "style" of child-mother attachment (Chandler, 2014).

Koren-Karie, Oppenheim, and Goldsmith (2007) reported that "the legacy of early attachment is reflected in children's and adult's relationships with others, self-regulation, and emotional openness" (p. 31). This single entry should draw attention to the importance of attachment to a disposition toward prosocial behavior in general and potentially an inclination toward sustainable behavior in particular.

Attachment Styles

While the terms used for some attachment styles vary from author to author, and are somewhat different from the original categories developed by Bowlby and Ainesworth, most AT researchers hold that there are four types of attachment: secure, avoidant or insecure/avoidant, anxious/ambivalent or insecure/resistant, and disorganized/disoriented.

- Secure attachment: With secure attachment the child grows up feeling that his or her caregiver will protect and provide for him or her and generally is allowed to and feels safe with exploring his or her environment. Research indicates that individuals with secure attachment demonstrate healthy interdependence (i.e., cooperation), manage stress well, and are confident (high esteem/efficacy).
- Avoidant or insecure/avoidant: Children with avoidant or insecure/avoidant attachment do not believe that their caregiver will protect or provide. Adults with this type of attachment have difficulty trusting others especially for support, are more likely to be individualistic or competitive, low in esteem and efficacy, and have difficulty managing stressful circumstances in healthy ways.
- Anxious/ambivalent or insecure/resistant: Children with anxious/ambivalent (insecure/resistant) attachment experience uncertainty about a caregiver's ability to provide and protect and/or interest in providing and protecting. Research indicates that adults with this attachment type have difficulty with commitment and managing stress, are more likely to be individualistic or competitive, and have low self-efficacy and self-esteem.
- Disorganized/disoriented: Children with disorganized/disoriented attachment believe that there is no tangible provision or protection. Depending on social and cultural factors this might be the most problematic style of attachment for an adult to maintain mental health and to engage healthily in society, as codependent and mistrusting relationships might be developed.

Social Value Orientation

Research suggests that a secure attachment is of critical importance regarding prosocial behavior (e.g., Chandler, 2011). While a prosocial perception is not exclusively cooperative it is typically the most conducive to sustainable behavior (Chandler, 2014). According to researchers (Messick & McClintock, 1968; Van Lange, DeBruin, Otten, & Joireman, 1997), social value orientation theory holds that individuals' perceptions of function of self-other relationships disposes them to favor, to a lesser or greater extent, outcomes that either benefit the self (proself) or the collective (prosocial; Chandler, 2017). There are three types of social value orientations:

- Cooperative: Where the individual seeks to maximize outcomes for self and others
- Individualistic: Where the individual seeks to maximize benefit for self with scant regard if any for another or others
- Competitive: Where the individual attends more to maximizing relative advantage of self-benefiting outcomes over others' outcomes

Conceptualizing Relationships Between Parenting, Attachment, Social Value Orientation, and Sustainability Inclination

The concept of a relationship between parenting, attachment, and social value orientation (Figure 2.1) was drawn from numerous sources (Bartholomew & Horowitz, 1991; Bowlby, 1988; Bretherton, 1992; Chandler, 2014; Merz & Consedine, 2009; Mikulincer et al., 2001; Schore

Parenting		Attachment		Social Value Orientation
Authoritative	→	Secure	→	Cooperative
↕		↕	?	↕
Authoritarian	→	Insecure-Avoidant	?	
↕		↕		Competitive
Indulgent-Permissive	→	Anxious/Abivalent Insecure/Resistant	?	↕
↕		↕	?	
Neglectful	→	Disorganized-Disoriented	→	Individualistic

Figure 2.1 Illustrates relationships between parenting, attachment, and social value orientation. Bi-directional arrows indicate continua and plasticity, single-direction arrows indicate a general trend or typical relationship, and a "?" indicates that the direction or relationship is difficult to predict.

& Schore, 2008, 2010; Van Lange et al., 1997; Van Lange & Kuhlman, 1994). Van Lange and colleagues (1997) were among the first to study attachment theory as a means to describe individual perception of place in and responsibility to society (Chandler, 2014). A "responsibility to society" can be understood as an inclination to act sustainability, especially when one considers that the characteristics of prosocial individuals align well with those of sustainability-minded individuals. Using social value orientation theory Van Lange and colleagues (1997) were able to describe how attachment style affects individual adoption of social value orientations. They demonstrated that individuals who experience secure attachment in childhood exhibited prosocial orientation where those who experienced either avoidant or anxious-ambivalent attachment became individualists or competitors. However, it is important to note that social value orientation, like attachment, is plastic.

Early research in the plasticity of social value orientation (Merz & Consedine, 2009; Mikulincer et al., 2001) found that prosocialness typically increases with age, intervention for prosocialness was effective with some populations more so than others, and inducement of secure attachment experience enhanced empathy (a characteristic of prosocialness) toward non-intimate others' needs irrespective of participants' attachment style. This is all to say that there is likely a relationship between an individual's attachment style and social value orientation with his or her inclination to act sustainably (Figure 2.2). Furthermore, one's sustainability inclination is also likely to be plastic, therefore subject to individual action, and can be improved through intervention.

Parenting		Attachment		Social Value Orientation
Authoritative	High	Secure	High	Cooperative
Authoritarian		Insecure-Avoidant		
				Competitive
Indulgent-Permissive		Anxious/Abivalent Insecure/Resistant		
Neglectful	Low	Disorganized-Disoriented	Low	Individualistic
		Sustainability Inclination		

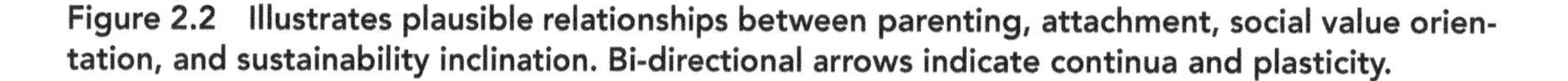

Figure 2.2 Illustrates plausible relationships between parenting, attachment, social value orientation, and sustainability inclination. Bi-directional arrows indicate continua and plasticity.

About the Feature Article

As you read *Bowlby's Ethological Theory of Attachment Behavior: The Nature and Nurture of Love for the Mother* consider the importance of understanding parenting, attachment, and social value orientation for developing a more comprehensive understanding of how you think, feel, and act toward yourself and others. In addition, ask yourself if a shift in your attachment experience would be beneficial to your social value orientation and how this might affect your inclination to act sustainability.

Finally, think about the Western cultural bias that Vicedo highlights in Bowlby's conclusion that a secure attachment essentially was limited to mother-child relationships, and how knowing that attachment experience can be achieved more broadly might help to improve an individual's sense of self and sustainability inclination.

References

Bartholomew, K., & Horowitz, L. M. (1991). Attachment styles among young adults: a test of a four-category model. *Journal of Personality and Social Psychology, 61*(2), 226.

Bowlby, J. (1988). A secure base. New York: Basic Books.

Bretherton, I. (1992). The origins of attachment theory: John Bowlby and Mary Ainsworth. *Developmental Psychology, 28(5)*, 759–775. doi:10.1037/0012-1649.28.5.759

Chandler, R. (2011). Implications of attachment theory on prosocial or sustainability behavior: An annotated bibliography. Unpublished.

Chandler, R. (2014). *I am the paradigm shift: A grounded theory of learners' sustainability outcome comprehension experience.* Ann Arbor, MI: ProQuest.

Chandler, R. (2017). I am the paradigm shift theory: Explaining students' sustainability outcome comprehension experience. *Psychology and Psychological Research International Journal,* 2(5), 1–12.

Merz, E. M., & Consedine, N. S. (2009). The association of family support and wellbeing in later life depends on adult attachment style. *Attachment & Human Development, 11*(2), 203–221.

Messick, D. M., & McClintock, C. G. (1968). Motivational basis of choice in experimental games. *Journal of Experimental Social Psychology, 4*(1), 1–25.

Mgbemere, B., & Telles, R. (2013). Types of parenting styles and how to identify yours. *Developmental Psychology at Vanderbilt.*

Mikulincer, M., Gillath, O., Halevy, V., Avihou, N., Avidan, S., & Eshkoli, N. (2001). Attachment theory and reactions to others' needs: Evidence that activation of the sense of attachment security promotes empathic responses. *Journal of Personality and Social Psychology, 81*(6), 1205–1224.

Koren-Karie, N., Oppenheim, D., & Goldsmith, D. (2007). Keeping the inner world of the child in mind: Using the insightfulness assessment with mothers in a therapeutic preschool. In D. Oppenheim and D. F. Goldsmith (Eds.), *Attachment Theory in Clinical Work with Children: Bridging the Gap Between Research and Practice* (pp. 31–57). New York: Guilford.

Schore, J. R., & Schore, J. N. (2008). Modern attachment theory: The central role of affect regulation in development and treatment. *Clinical Social Work Journal, 36*(1), 9–20.

Schore, J. R., & Schore, A. N. (2011). Clinical social work and regulation theory: Implications of neurobiological models of attachment. In *Adult attachment in clinical social work* (pp. 57–75). Springer, New York, NY.

Van Lange, P. A. M., De Bruin, E. M. N., Otten, W., & Joireman, J. A. (1997). Development of prosocial, individualistic, and competitive orientations: Theory and preliminary evidence. *Journal of Personality and Social Psychology, 73*(4), 733–746.

Van Lange, P. A. M., & Kuhlman, D. M. (1994). Social value orientations and impressions of partner's honesty and intelligence: A test of the might versus morality effect. *Journal of Personality and Social Psychology, 67(1),* 126–141.

COPYRIGHTED MATERIAL — DO NOT DUPLICATE, DISTRIBUTE, OR POST

READING 2

Bowlby's Ethological Theory of Attachment Behavior

The Nature and Nurture of Love for the Mother

Marga Vicedo

There is a growing realization that the way a mother feels about her child is the most significant feature of all in a child's development and in his attitude to those around him.—John Bowlby, "The Rediscovery of the Family" (1954)

Introduction

After his 1951 WHO report, John Bowlby continued developing his views about the instinctual nature of the mother-child relationship and the disastrous effects that maternal separation and deprivation have on children. Since Bowlby was British and spent his career in England, most historical research has focused on his influence within the English context. In addition, a large number of important works on the history of child rearing, adoption, the family, and changing conceptions of motherhood in the United States have briefly noted the impact of Bowlby's work, identifying him as the most important figure in postwar debates about the effects of maternal deprivation. Yet there is no study of Bowlby's influence in the United States.[1]

Here I examine the development of Bowlby's views and their scientific and social reception in the United States during the 1950s, a pivotal period in the evolution of his views and in debates about the social implications of his work. Bowlby's assertion that mother love is a biological need for children influenced discussions about whether mothers should work outside the home and supported a gendered division of parental care. Bowlby's influence, I propose, was heightened because the social interest in his views about the effects of maternal deprivation came at a crucial

Marga Vicedo, "Bowlby's Ethological Theory of Attachment Behavior: The Nature and Nurture of Love for the Mother," *The Nature and Nurture of Love: From Imprinting to Attachment in Cold War America*, pp. 69-92, 260-265, 289-314.

juncture in debates about women's role in modern society, and also because of the emotional effect his position had on mothers.

Not only was Bowlby important in the United States, but the United States was crucial for Bowlby. American agencies funded some of his research at the Tavistock Clinic. Bowlby also spent the 1957–58 academic year at the Center for Behavioral Studies at Stanford, a period seminal in the development of his ethological theory of attachment behavior. In addition, many researchers whose work Bowlby relied on were American, as were many who criticized his work.

Some American psychologists criticized the lack of convincing evidence that maternal deprivation had severe and lasting consequences for children's emotional development. These criticisms prompted Bowlby to rely heavily on animal behavior studies to support his views. As we saw in chapter 2, Lorenz encouraged his expectations that ethology would help him flesh out a biological account of the mother-child dyad. Bowlby established a naturalistic framework for the mother-infant dyad by combining specific ideas from psychoanalysis and from ethology. In his classic 1958 paper "The Nature of the Child's Tie to His Mother," Bowlby presented his ethological theory of attachment behavior. He argued that attachment to the mother is an innate biological need and consequently that separation from the mother or lack of mother love has catastrophic consequences for a child's development.

By claiming biology proved that a mother's heart determines the mind of her child, Bowlby's argument placed an unusually strong emotional and moral demand on mothers. As historians such as Ruth Bloch and Jan Lewis have shown, the power of mother love in shaping a child's mind is "the kernel of the emotionology of motherhood" in the United States. But this power was now shored up with the authority of biological science, since Bowlby presented mother love as a child's biological need and claimed the support of ethology for this view.[2]

From Natural Description to Social Prescription: Infants' Needs and the Tragedy of Working Mothers

When Bowlby's 1951 WHO report and its more popular 1953 version appeared, his main thesis about the importance of mother love fit well with the consensus developing within the American psychoanalytic community, as we saw in chapter 1. In fact Bowlby had already drawn on the studies of some American researchers, including David Levy and René Spitz, to support his views in the WHO report. However, Bowlby's study was not just one more work on maternal deprivation, for three reasons.

First, in his report Bowlby actively constructed a consensus by strategically emphasizing the common points among the researchers working on children. He relied on studies that covered a range of related but distinct issues: infants separated from their families owing to hospitalization of the mother or the infant; separation from the mother for short periods; permanent separation from mothers or the whole family; unsatisfactory maternal care; and faulty emotional attitude of the mother toward the child. But he included all those studies under the umbrella of "maternal care and love," obscuring the dissimilarities among the children and situations studied. In addition, he boosted this consensus by appealing to a standard epistemological tenet in science. He noted that one particular study on a topic cannot provide convincing proof of a conclusion, but the convergence of several studies done independently adds evidential support to individual conclusions. Thus his views were proved by the convergence of similar results "from many sources." This convergence, he often repeated, left "no doubt that the main proposition is true."[3]

The second reason is that Bowlby's WHO report, as a document backed by a respected international organization, gave his views a visibility and respectability that none of the previous studies enjoyed independently. On publication, it became the authoritative document of the consensus within a large field of research. The ideas of René Spitz, David Levy, Margaret Ribble, and Therese Benedek were well known among child analysts, but with Bowlby's report they gained greater visibility beyond psychoanalytic and psychiatric circles. Although Bowlby was not the only scientist moving toward a deterministic view of mother love, his views epitomize its strongest instantiation, and he became its most visible advocate.

The third reason is that Bowlby, more than any of the other researchers in the field, was active in drawing practical implications from his research. Bowlby had concluded his report with a clear prescription for mothers:

> The provision of constant attention night and day, seven days a week and 365 days in the year, is possible only for a woman who derives profound satisfaction from seeing her child grow from babyhood, through the many phases of childhood, to become an independent man or woman, and knows that it is her care which has made this possible.[4]

Furthermore, Bowlby continued, for the mother to provide constant devotion she needs a support group—the family.

For him the family was a "natural unit," essential for children's healthy development: "It is for these reasons that the mother-love which a young child needs is so easily provided within the family, and is so very, very difficult to provide outside it."[5] Bowlby referred to the family as the "natural home group," and he compiled a list of the reasons that the natural home group might fail to care properly for the child: illegitimacy, chronic illness, economic conditions, war, famine, death of a parent, desertion, imprisonment, divorce, and full-time employment of the mother. "Any family suffering from one or more of these conditions must be regarded as a possible source of deprived children," he argued.[6]

Could "full-time employment of the mother" really be equivalent to famine, war, or death of a parent? This was a simple corollary of Bowlby's position. If, as he believed, the constant presence of a loving mother is necessary for the child's mental health, her absence would be catastrophic.

The catastrophe was social as well as personal, according to his analysis. Lack of mother love led not only to psychopathology but also to socio pathology. "The proper care of children," Bowlby continued, is "essential for the mental and social welfare of a community." And "when their care is neglected, as happens in every country of the Western world to-day, they grow up to reproduce themselves. Deprived children, whether in their own homes or out of them, are the source of social infection as real and serious as are carriers of diphtheria and typhoid."[7] Thus, in fulfilling their natural role, women were doing the right thing toward their children, their families, and their communities. Mental health, achieved through emotional well-being, was as important for the social body as physical hygiene was for the organism. The health of the social body was thus in the hands, or rather the hearts, of mothers.

Through this line of argument, Bowlby revealed his concern not only about children, but also about group welfare, especially the maintenance of a distribution of parental roles that he believed would ensure the traditional social order and the very continuity of the species. In scholarly writings and conferences, Bowlby presented this position as conclusively proved by scientific research. From his standpoint, the implications were clear. A mother needed to stay home, for the sake of her child and society.

Through the WHO report and its coverage by the international press, Bowlby's ideas spread rapidly among scientific and public audiences. When Bowlby titled his piece in *Home Companion* "Mother Is the Whole World," the message reverberated across the globe. The *Johannesburg Star* in South Africa reported Bowlby as saying that "when deprived of a mother's care a child's development is almost always retarded physically, intellectually and socially." Another South African newspaper, *Cape Argus,* reported that "Social Behaviour Depends on Mother Love." "The Importance of a Mother's Love" was also covered in the *East African Standard* from Nairobi. The French reported that between the attitude of the mother and the future behavior of her children, there was "une relation de cause à effet quasi mathématique" (an almost mathematical relationship of cause and effect). The Italians put it more poetically: "Solo le˙ mani di una Madre possono plasmare il destino" (only the hands of a mother can shape destiny).[8]

For American women, Bowlby's message about the crucial role of mother love in children's development and the importance of the "natural home group" arrived at a time of major changes in women's roles and widespread social concern about the rising number of women working outside the home. After World War II, the patriarchal family gained support from numerous measures. As historian Nancy Cott has shown, the social benefits of the 1944 GI Bill of Rights, which assumed responsibility for veterans' economic well-being, helped to enhance "men's roles as husband-heads of households, as property owners, as job-holders and providers," since women were only about 2 percent of all military personnel. In addition, after the war the government showed little interest in continuing the limited support for child-care centers that had been provided during the war, when one and a half million mothers of small children entered the workforce to support the war effort.[9] Cold War propaganda also reinforced traditional gender roles within the American family, as historian Elaine Tyler May has documented.[10] When mounting domestic conflicts and international tensions grew, public and government rhetoric promoted "togetherness" as the key to security. All these measures encouraged the traditional separation of gender roles, with women at home and men in the workforce. A baby boom and sprawling suburbs attest to the impact of these measures of containment, even if, as the Cold War went on, "the rush to marry and buy homes, the reinscription of traditional gender roles, and the overinsistence on the pleasures of family life" revealed less "signs of self-satisfaction than defenses against uncertainty," as historian Gaile McGregor has argued.[11]

In this anxiety-filled environment, two social indicators raised concern about the malfunctioning of families and resulting harm to children. First, the numbers showed that postwar men and women were not adjusting to each other easily. Whereas in 1940 one marriage in six had ended in divorce, by 1946 one in four did. A million GIs were divorced by 1950.[12] The rising divorce rates fueled concerns about the social impact on children and adolescents. Second, the Children's Bureau record of Juvenile Court cases and the FBI compendium of police arrests pointed to a steep rise in juvenile delinquency during World War II, followed by a sharp decline and then another rise during the 1950s. Gallup polls and popular articles revealed increasing alarm about juvenile delinquency, the rise of gangs, and the decline of parental guidance. In 1953 the US Senate began extensive investigations about juvenile delinquency that lasted over a decade. These events helped sensationalize the issue and turn it into a national crisis. While politicians debated and called for data, models, and experts, the young drove the issue out into the open. Marlon Brando riding a motor cycle in *The Wild One* and James Dean cruising in a sports car in *Rebel without a Cause* became emblematic of reckless American youth. Their unorthodox ways raised fears of impending social and moral decay propelled by emotionally unstable adolescents.[13] In turn, heightened worries about juvenile delinquency drew further attention to dysfunctional families.

Growing fears about higher divorce rates and juvenile delinquency encouraged debate about the role of women in the new social order. The extent of this mid-century debate can be appreciated by looking at the rise of studies about women in the mid-fifties. Let's pick 1953, the year of Bowlby's best seller on maternal care and the initial Senate hearings on juvenile delinquency. That year alone saw the publication of the following important works: Alfred Kinsey, *Sexual Behavior in the Human Female*; Mirra Komarovsky, *Women in the Modern World*; Ashley Montagu, *The Natural Superiority of Women*; and the American translation of Simone de Beauvoir, *The Second Sex*. This selection gives us a sense of the expanding body of work on women's issues.[14] These academic treatises did not, however, provide a uniform answer to questions about women's nature and their functions in modern society.

Some contemporary studies and historical works have underscored the conflicting nature of the messages sent to women during the 1950s. As I noted in chapter 1, Komarovsky's earlier sociological research showing that contradictory social messages to be autonomous, independent, and mature, on the one hand, and dependent, subordinate, and childlike, on the other, created deep internal conflicts for many women. In her analysis of women's popular magazines from

1946 to 1958, historian Joanne Meyerowitz has documented the conflicting messages women received during this period as well. Some of these glorified domesticity, while others advocated individual striving and public service.[15] Increasingly, historical research on the 1950s has questioned the common images of domestic bliss and complacency about traditional gender roles. Scholarly studies on the nature and roles of women presented conflicting views that exposed the tensions bubbling beneath the superficial image of happy suburban domesticity. After all, if women were "naturally superior," as Montagu claimed, why were they treated as "the second sex," as Beauvoir argued?

As a short analysis of the reactions to *The Second Sex* reveals, at the core of these concerns about women's changing roles were deep anxieties about motherhood. Written by one of France's most important postwar philosophers, this tract offered an encyclopedic review of historical events and ideas that had led to the construction of woman as "the Other," the opposite of the male and masculine. The other is not only different, but inferior. As in any work of grand scope, many of Beauvoir's points could be debated. Yet almost all American reviewers, male and female, housewives and scholars, scientists and humanists, focused on her assertion that "no maternal 'instinct' exists" and what they saw as her denigration of mother hood.[16]

The concern about this issue reflected the widespread uneasiness created by the greatest increase in American history in mothers of young children going to work outside the home. By the mid-1950s a "silent revolution" had occurred, noted sociologists Alva Myrdal and Viola Klein. More and more married women of different social classes were entering the labor force. At first they sought paid work out of economic necessity and to support the war effort. But now, explained Myrdal and Klein, "the economic motive can no longer be separated from the ideological one; nor can the voluntary element be distinguished from the compulsory one." Between 1940 and 1960, the number of married women with paid jobs doubled, and working mothers increased by 400 percent. Over four million married women took jobs, accounting for 60 percent of all new workers. In 1940 working wives were mainly working class; by the end of the 1950s, many were educated and middle class.[17]

Because more mothers were joining the workforce, the need for child care had again nearly become a crisis even before the Korean War began in 1950, according to historian Sonya Michel. In 1953 the US Department of Labor published *Employed Mothers and Child Care*, a report on "a subject of vital national interest at a time when married women constitute the largest labor reserve in the country, and therefore may be expected to continue entering the labor force in ever-increasing numbers, and when 5¼ million mothers already are employed." Of those, two million were reported to have children less than six years old.[18]

In this context, research about the effects of maternal separation and deprivation attracted great interest. In her study of the child guidance movement, Kathleen Jones has identified a prewar shift that emphasized the psychology of the individual rather than the social networks and circumstances of "the troublesome child." After the war, congruent with the postwar American romance with psychology documented by historian Ellen Herman and the more general interest in social engineering examined by historians such as Mark Solovey, social and political decisions about day care and child rearing increasingly became framed as empirical questions about the emotional needs of children.[19]

Bowlby was thus addressing one of the major concerns of the postwar period in the United States. Backed by a prominent world organization, his views became a point of reference in discussions about the family, personality formation, and parental roles. Many social scientists in the United States had met Bowlby personally when he visited the country to elaborate on the WHO report. This report and its 1953 popular version were also widely reviewed in American journals.[20] In addition, one of Bowlby's closest collaborators, James Robertson, presented their work to American audiences through an influential film.

Robertson had worked at a number of odd jobs at the Hampstead Nurseries before moving to the Tavistock Child Development Research Unit in London to work with Bowlby in 1948. Supported by Bowlby and Anna Freud, he then applied to the Institute of Psychoanalysis for training and became an associate member of the British Psychoanalytical Society in 1953.[21] Under Bowlby's supervision, Robertson had started a project to observe the reactions of children separated from their families by hospitalization. Impressed by the effects on children and aware that his views might encounter resistance in the medical community, Robertson decided to make a film. In 1953, with support from the WHO, he took *A Two-Year-Old Goes to Hospital: A Scientific Film* on a six-week tour of the United States. The Children's Bureau in Washington, DC, worked out the itinerary, which included Yale and the psychoanalytical societies in Boston and New York.[22] The film was silent but was showed with a guide that listed the work being carried out in Bowlby's unit. At this point, Bowlby and Robertson were also writing a book about the effects of separation together with American psychologist Mary Ainsworth. Thus, Robertson's presentation of his film on separation in hospitals also helped disseminate Bowlby's views in the United States. In a 1954 letter to Anna Freud, Robertson told her that the film's best reception had been in America.[23]

Other indications of American interest in Bowlby's work come from his funding sources and connections. The Josiah Macy Jr. Foundation and the Ford Foundation generously supported the work that Bowlby's team carried out at the Tavistock Institute. Bowlby also held a fellowship at the Center for Advanced Study in the Behavioral Sciences in Stanford, California, in 1957–58. During his stay, he received numerous invitations to speak in different forums and visited several research centers in the country. Actively engaged with a circle of researchers that included many American psychologists, animal researchers, psychoanalysts, and workers in child development, Bowlby exerted influence well beyond England and the psychoanalytic establishment.

Although in the early and mid-1950s Bowlby's views were still pretty similar to those of other researchers, his status as the scientist behind the WHO report and his willingness to extract social prescriptions from his work made him a central reference in debates about women's work, maternal care, and children's emotions. His work was discussed widely, in policy conferences and the public media.

The Midcentury White House Conference on Children and Youth brought together Benjamin Spock, David Levy, Erik Erikson, Ashley Montagu, and other American psychologists, psychiatrists, and social scientists to address how children develop a healthy personality. The fifth in a series of decennial conferences started in 1909, it focused on "how to rear an emotionally healthy generation" and called attention to the children's "feelings." Earlier conferences had focused on the economic and social aspects of the problems American children encountered. Now, although the report from the meeting recognized that "emotional ill health may have economic, sociological, physical, psychological, and spiritual causes," it nevertheless underscored that "some of the chief ills of the present day are psychological."[24]

The conference also aimed to extract the policy implications of research on children's needs. One explicit goal was to find out the latest in research so that someone like Spock could then put it into a form understandable to the general public. Despite noting the tentative character of this knowledge and recognizing that there were several competing theories, the report claimed it was "well established that loving care is essential for the well-being of children." Both the discussion during the meetings and the final report focused largely on Erikson's views about child development, especially the importance of trust as a basic component of a healthy personality. Erikson, who had achieved national prominence with his *Childhood and Society*, emphasized that maternal love enables the child to develop a sense of self.[25] To support the view that mother love is determinant during infancy, the report referred to Bowlby's WHO report. Later, in the section "Effects of Deprivation of Maternal Care," it also appealed to Bowlby's WHO publication and quoted approvingly and at length his views about the detrimental effects of lack of mother love in infancy.[26]

Important scientists from other fields, including sociology and anthropology, appealed to Bowlby's work to defend the thesis that the child has an innate need for mother love. In "The Power of Creative Love," Harvard sociologist Pitirim A. Sorokin and his student Robert C. Hanson argued that motherly love is vital for babies. Even anthropologist Ashley Montagu, now best remembered for his opposition to biological explanations of behavior, argued that when researchers studied individuals incapable of showing love, it was "invariably found that something was lacking in their mother's relationship to them." Though Montagu had done no research on this topic, he recommended Bowlby's "admirable analysis" in the WHO report. Montagu also reported that children without love die, this time noting the investigations of David Levy. As an anthropologist, Montagu pointed to a variety of forms of love in different cultures, but he then claimed that they all would be "traceable to the need for the kind of love which is biologically determined, predetermined, to exist between mother and infant." The implications for mothers were serious: "To the extent to which women succeed or do not succeed in adequately loving their children, the boys and girls become inadequately loving men and women."[27]

The influence of Bowlby's views is also exemplified by Myrdal and Klein's treatment of the topic in *Women's Two Roles*. In the seemingly obligatory chapter on the "Effects of Mother's Employment on the Mental Health of Children," they discussed Bowlby's work and argued that "it would be scientifically inadmissible to apply conclusions drawn from cases of deprivation caused by emergency situations, such as death, abandonment or cruelty of the mother, or the separation through illness of mother or child, to cases where the mother is absent at regular intervals for a number of hours yet returns to the child each day and provides it with a home." They also denied the scientific validity of a lot of research on maternal deprivation and questioned its application to normal families with working mothers. Nevertheless, they concluded: "All we can do at present is to stress the undeniable fact that maternal love is a decisive element in any equation concerning young children." And later: "We therefore support the view that mothers should, as far as possible, take care of their own children during the first years of their lives."[28]

But could mothers' working outside their homes really endanger the health of their infants and even the whole nation? According to Bowlby, children's lack of mother love in their early years results in a number of social problems. He claimed that delinquency, among other things, could stem from a lack of maternal care. Was the rise of delinquency in America perhaps evidence that mothers were slacking? He included divorce as a problematic disruption of the natural home unit. And wasn't divorce becoming more prevalent in American society? Even more worrisome, Bowlby had presented "full-time employment of the mother" as equivalent to famine, war, or death of a parent.

Given that more and more women were entering the workforce, the question acquired social urgency: "Should a woman with children take a job?" asked the English *News Chronicle*. "The mother who stays at home gives her children a better chance," answered Bowlby.[29]

In the *New York Times*, Sloan Wilson, author of the best-selling novel *The Man in the Gray Flannel Suit* (later made into a successful movie starring Gregory Peck), contributed to the public debate with his declaration that married women with children should not have business careers. Instead, they should assume "executive wifehood," helping their husbands' careers. Bernice Fitz-Gibbon, the 1956 Woman of the Year in Business, mother of two and grandmother of three, responded that a career could make women better wives and mothers. So she encouraged women to take the "gay" rather than the gray flannel suit. In the ensuing debate, Wil-son cited psychiatrists' call for a "loving mother who has plenty of time to give her sons and daughters." David R. Mace, a professor of human relations, posed a simple question to Fitz-Gibbon: Had she ever heard of "Dr. John Bowlby, a psychiatrist of international reputation, whose impressive and well-documented report to the world's mental-health experts named maternal deprivation as a major cause of serious personality disorders?"[30]

The *Ladies' Home Journal* continued the discussion with a forum titled "Should Mothers of Young Children Work?" Besides Bowlby himself, the panelists in the forum included US secretary of labor James P. Mitchell, sociologist Mirra Komarovsky, Dr. Lynn White, a Jungian lay analyst, a mother and grandmother named Mrs. Florida Scott-Maxwell, Mrs. Roy Davis, a nurse and mother of four, and others. The article reported that while traditionally women had worked only out of economic necessity, at present they were going to work "by choice." But was this the right choice?

Although Secretary Mitchell argued that American women needed to be part of the workforce to maintain their current standard of living and to contribute to the national defense, he also claimed that "no nation should ever forget that the very primary, fundamental basis of a free society is the family structure—the home—and the most vital job is there." Should mothers, then, be denied the choice to work? In the midst of a Cold War in which the United States held up individual freedom as the basis for its superiority, Mitchell was not prepared to deny American women this freedom: "I think it is very right that we in this country have freedom of choice, unlike the Communist world, where there is no such thing." Nevertheless, he hoped that women workers would not be mothers, since the mother's place was "in the home." Mitchell thus defended the superiority of the American model by the somewhat ironic position that American women were free to do the wrong thing.

The women in the forum presented different viewpoints. Some who worked and had sitters reported that their children were doing fine. Others who stayed home felt that working women looked down upon them. Some said working was not always a matter of choice, for their families could not live well if they did not work. It was not a simple decision between the apron and the gay or gray flannel suit.

As for Bowlby, he repeated the advice he believed followed from his scientific work: "To deprive a small child of his mother's companionship is as bad as depriving him of vitamins." Seemingly aware of the boredom of suburban mothers, he recognized that most women "would like a more varied life than is available in the modern suburb," where "we have made it almost impossible for them to take care of their children happily and to combine this with some sort of career or job." His solution, though, was not to change social practices but to change social values, so that the home was given its proper place. To do that, "we must first ascertain who it is that holds the values we oppose. Personally, and this is pure prejudice, I think it is career women who look down on women who stay home." He further argued that group care was not mothering. Neither should children under three go to day care—though after that age, he realized, "part-time day care has its uses." Still, he insisted that children deprived of mothering would grow up to hate and mistrust, leading to a life of truancy and promiscuity.[31]

In turn, work by Bowlby and others on the effects of maternal deprivation helped support a division of parental roles, and consequently gender roles. For example, Ashley Montagu, a staunch supporter of Bowlby's work, contended in "The Triumph and Tragedy of the American Woman" that American women mistakenly believed equal rights implied equality of function. According to him, things were better in Europe, where a woman's life centered "upon the happiness of her husband and children, and this is likely to be satisfying to everyone concerned." Montagu, who had earlier defended the "natural superiority of women," now presented his interpretation of recent research on mother love to a general audience: "I put it down as an axiom that no woman with a husband and small children can hold a full-time job and be a good homemaker at one and the same time." For everybody's sake, Montagu hoped American women would realize that "being a good wife, a good mother, in short, a good homemaker, is the most important of all the occupations in the world."[32] Thus, some social scientists used children's alleged need for constant mother love to justify separate spheres and to reject what Montagu called "the equality of functions."

It is difficult to gauge how far studies of maternal deprivation and the WHO report influenced public opinion. According to historian Sonya Michel, the psychological discourse on maternal deprivation, including Bowlby's, represented the most vehement and explicit opposition both to maternal employment and to child care.[33] In the late 1950s, a National Manpower Council report showed that most Americans agreed that women with small children should not be working.[34] At the very least, it seems safe to assume that the scientific work helped shore up longstanding beliefs about infants' need for their mothers.

Yet during this period, several child psychologists working on maternal deprivation also began to question the validity of many of the studies Bowlby had relied on in his WHO report.

Challenging the Studies on Maternal Deprivation

Bowlby presented the notion of the mother as the psychic organizer as an empirical fact, though he recognized that research on this matter was inconclusive. In the WHO report, he rejected the studies that did not support his position, saying that only "three" studies presented evidence challenging his conclusions and that they lacked "high scientific quality."[35] Yet Bowlby also admitted that there were "still far too few systematic studies and statistical comparisons in which proper control groups have been used" that supported his views about mother love. He recognized that "relatively few studies taken by themselves are more than suggestive" and, furthermore, that there were different interpretations of the data. For example, psychologist William Goldfarb had asserted that deprived children "craved affection," whereas Bowlby described them as "affectionless." But the difference, according to him, was "probably more apparent than real." He also reported that some deprived children stole, but others didn't, as well as that two-thirds of the children deprived of mother love turned out to be "socially capable." This statement seems odd. If maternal love is as essential as vitamins and proteins, how could one explain these findings? But Bowlby rejected those results, saying that experts had not examined those children carefully. Perhaps "psychological troubles not leading to social incompetence were not recorded."[36] He did not specify what other "psychological troubles" he had in mind.

In spite of Bowlby's dismissal, there were significantly diverse interpretations of the data, as well as different views about the social implications of the results. Harvard psychiatrist Abraham Myerson implored scientists to "quit blaming mom," stressing that there was no scientific proof for considering mothers to be the cause of their children's neurosis. Based on an empirical study of 162 "farm children of old American stock," University of Wisconsin sociologist William H. Sewell found no correlation between infant training and personality development.[37] Furthermore, child psychologists were questioning the validity of Margaret Ribble's and René Spitz's work. Samuel Pinneau of the University of California presented the most comprehensive critical analysis.

Pinneau dealt first with the physiological evidence Ribble had provided to support her thesis that children whose mothers were not attuned and responsive to their emotional needs would develop gastrointestinal disturbances, tension, respiratory problems, anxiety, and disorganized neurological function. After examining dozens of studies, some of which failed to confirm Ribble's claims while others refuted them, Pinneau agreed with the conclusion of Harold Orlansky, a Yale anthropologist who had earlier made an extensive critical review of child studies. Pinneau adopted Orlansky's strongly worded assessment of Ribble: "It is unfortunate that such an influential writer has not attempted to draw a line between her empirical findings and her personal opinions."[38]

In his 1953 presidential address to the New York State Psychological Association, child psychologist L. Joseph Stone recognized the effectiveness of Pinneau's critique of Ribble by comparing its power to "a kind of hydrogen bomb." Owing to its awesome "destructive" impact, "not a paragraph is left standing for miles around." But although Stone agreed with the dismissal of Ribble's work, he still found the studies by Spitz and Bowlby convincing.[39]

But then Pinneau published a devastating critique of Spitz's work. Spitz had argued that infants separated from their mothers for over six weeks develop psychogenic disorders and literally wither away and die. Pinneau pointed out that it was difficult to evaluate Spitz's claims because he had not identified the specific sites of his studies—he only mentioned a nursery in a penal institution for delinquent girls and a foundling home. More troubling still, by comparing data Spitz offered in different reports about the same set of studies, Pinneau exposed great inconsistencies and shortcomings: Spitz had not specified the composition and training of the research staff, and he had presented contradictory data on the number of children studied and the parents' characteristics.[40]

In addition, Spitz had not determined the health of infants before or during his research, although he noted a lethal measles epidemic during his study of hospitalism. Owing to the loss of children through adoption, there was also a selective sampling bias in the foundling home. Furthermore, from the evidence presented, it was clear that the groups being compared differed substantially in economic background, constitution, and hereditary makeup. Pinneau pointed out that Spitz was inconsistent in presenting data about when the children were observed, and that he provided only cross-sectional but not longitudinal data. Pinneau also attacked the validity of the developmental scale Spitz used to obtain developmental quotients. After his thorough critique, Pinneau concluded: "The results of Spitz's studies cannot be accepted as scientific evidence supporting the hypothesis that institutional infants develop psychological disorders as a result of being separated from their mothers."[41]

As the evidence mounted against the view that maternal separation has devastating consequences on children, even researchers in Bowlby's own group reconsidered its effects. A 1956 paper by several members of his Tavistock group titled "The Effects of Mother-Child Separation: A Follow-up Study" noted that "some of the workers who first drew attention to the dangers of maternal deprivation resulting from separation have tended on occasion to overstate their case. In particular, statements implying that children who experience institutionalization and similar forms of severe privation and deprivation in early life *commonly* develop psychopathic or affectionless characters are incorrect."[42] This statement caused a stir, since it contradicted Bowlby's position in earlier papers and in the WHO study.

But Bowlby did not retreat. Almost two years later, responding to letters from perplexed readers who wondered whether he had changed his views, Bowlby published an explanatory note. He said he wanted to "discourage anyone from supposing that I have changed my position in any material way."[43] Instead, like child analysts Benedek, Levy, Spitz, and Ribble, who emphasized the natural foundation of the mother-child dyad, Bowlby turned to investigate its biological foundation.

Uniting Psychoanalysis and Ethology: The Nature of the Child's Tie to the Mother

At the end of the 1950s, Bowlby aimed to unify ethology and psychoanalysis, to synthesize both approaches into a single framework that explained the nature of a child's attachment to the mother as an instinctual relationship. At first glance it is hard to understand why Bowlby would be so enthusiastic about ethology. Lorenz's views on human behavior were loose extrapolations from his animal studies, based only on analogies and anecdotes. And Bowlby had already argued in the WHO report that his views about the significance of mother love in children were conclusively proved in humans. So what could be gained by finding out how ducks and geese raise their offspring?

Bowlby's turn to ethology was probably influenced by the mounting criticism directed during the mid-1950s toward the studies on maternal deprivation. In addition, he had already been searching for a naturalistic basis to support his views about the mother-child relationship. From early on in his career, Bowlby was interested in finding a biological foundation for the child's emotional needs. In his first papers he had discussed animal research on primates and considered this work relevant to explanations of human behavior. He looked at studies of animal behavior to compare their results with his observations of children.[44] Bowlby always wrote about the "natural" family unit, emphasized the natural basis of the mother-child dyad, and portrayed the child's emotional development as similar to embryological development. During the mid- to late 1950s he studied ethology and discussed its application to child development in numerous meetings with researchers such as those who had attended the WHO meetings described in chapter 2.

Furthermore, psychoanalysts had been struggling with the notion of instinct since Freud postulated that human drives originate from a somatic source. Freud said that one day biologists would help psycho analysts clarify this obscure concept.[45] On encountering ethology, Bowlby believed that day had arrived. He justified his turn to ethology by noting that the need to resort to biology had been "approved," even encouraged, by the founding father:

> In this context it is interesting to reflect on Freud's belief expressed over forty years ago (Freud 1915) that, for a further understanding of instinct, psychology would need to look for help from biology. As a result of developments in the biologically rooted science of ethology I believe the time has now come and that the psychoanalytic theory of instinct can be reformulated.[46]

The next year Bowlby published "The Nature of the Child's Tie to His Mother," where he presented the main thesis for an ethological theory of attachment behavior. In this paper, Bowlby identified two major explanatory frameworks to account for children's attachment to their mothers. Psychoanalysts focused on the infant's gratification and emphasized the mother's role in providing both food and care. He noted that many psychoanalysts of different tendencies supported this theory of secondary drive, including Dorothy Burlingham, Anna Freud, Melanie Klein, Margaret Ribble, Therese Benedek, and René Spitz. However, he saw a discrepancy between their position and their empirical data. He noted that in "each case" they had "observed non-oral social interaction between mother and infant" and, "in describing it, however, each seems to feel a compulsion to give primacy to needs for food and warmth and to suppose that social interaction develops only secondarily and as a result of instrumental learning."[47]

As a major alternative to this widely held psychoanalytic position, he laid out the views of ethologists, "who have never assumed that the only primary drives were those related to physiological needs. On the contrary, all their work has been based on the hypothesis that in animals there are many in-built responses which are comparatively independent of physiological needs and responses, the function of which is to promote social interaction between members of the species." Thus ethologists focused on innate or instinctual social responses, present at birth, not derived by conditioning through the gratification of primary needs like the need for food.[48]

Bowlby then advanced his own theory of component instinctual responses, which he put forward as a synthesis of psychoanalysis and ethology. In his view, attachment behavior integrates several component instinctual responses that at first are independent. The instinctual responses, which mature at different times during the first year of life and develop at different rates, bind the child to the mother and contribute to the reciprocal dynamic of binding mother to child. Five instinctual responses compose attachment behavior. The baby is the active partner in three of them: sucking, clinging, and following. The other two, crying and smiling, serve to "activate maternal behaviour."[49]

Bowlby adopted the ethological, and specifically Lorenzian, conception of instinct. He noted that, rather than using the "cumbersome term 'species-specific behaviour pattern,'" as ethologists did, he would call them "instinctual responses."[50] But Bowlby emphasized that he was using instinct in the ethological sense, not the psychoanalytic sense. He explained that in ethology instincts were "behaviour patterns ... common to all members of a species and determined in large measure by heredity. They are conceived as the units out of which many of the more complex sequences are built. Once activated the animal of which they form a part seems to be acting with all the blind impulsion with which, as analysts, we are familiar."[51]

He also adopted the concept of social releaser from Lorenz. As an example of how the system of social releasers and instincts works in bonding the child to the mother, Bowlby described the baby's smile: "However activated, as a social releaser of maternal behavior it is powerful. Can we doubt that the more and better an infant smiles the better is he loved and cared for? It is fortunate for their survival that babies are so designed by Nature that they beguile and enslave mothers."[52]

Bowlby thus presented the mother-child dyad as a biological system. In this system, each part complements the other, as designed by evolution. Not only is the child tied to the mother; the mother is tied to the child. Furthermore, he argued that "the nature of the child's tie to his mother" is a natural bond required for the survival of the species.

By appropriating the ethological framework, Bowlby argued for the biological significance of his theory and then claimed support for it from biology:

> I wish to emphasize that it is a main part of my thesis that each of the five instinctual responses which I am suggesting underlie the child's tie to his mother is present because of its survival value. ... The theory of Component Instinctual Responses, it is claimed, is rooted firmly in biological theory and requires no dynamic which is not plainly explicable in terms of the survival of the species.[53]

As Evelyn Fox Keller has shown in her discussion of molecular biology's reliance on the social authority of physics after World War II, a discipline can benefit from associating itself with another discipline that has higher social status and scientific standing.[54] In this case, by presenting his attachment theory as a synthesis of psychoanalysis and ethology, Bowlby bestowed on it the authority of biological knowledge. In addition, as ethology became very successful after World War II, attachment theory also gained momentum from the popularity of ethology and, specifically, Lorenz's studies of imprinting. As I showed in chapter 2, Lorenz visited the United States on several occasions and his views on parental care in animals received public acclaim.

Bowlby was aware of the advantage conferred on his views by the association with ethology. When he was finishing writing "The Nature of the Child's Tie," in the fall of 1957, he reported from Palo Alto: "As it happens this paper is going to come in for quite a lot of discussion in the next week or two. It is being circulated to one of the seminars and looks like being read more widely. ... By an unexpected but fortunate coincidence, Konrad Lorenz is going to be here next week for a couple of days. He will stay with us and give some sort of lecture on Tuesday, so ethology and all that seems likely to be in the news."[55]

In the following spring, Bowlby publicized his views in the East Coast. The trip included a visit to Mary Ainsworth in Baltimore, the debate at the *Ladies' Home Journal*, a broadcast on mental care and child care in New York, and more academic visits in Orange Park, New York, and New Haven. He was also hired for five days as a consultant by the National Institute of Mental Health, half-time for the Adult Psychiatry Unit and half-time for the Child Development Studies. Here, he also presented his work on what he called "ETHO-PSYCHO-ANALYSIS." He reported that his ideas were "greeted with some enthusiasm." In addition, he presented "The Nature of the Child's Tie" to the Western New England Psychoanalytic Society. Again, he sent home good news: "The paper was well received, partly perhaps because ethology is not unknown in these parts. Fritz Redlich is an old friend of Konrad Lorenz and has spent time at Konrad's place. So far I have given the paper 4 times in U.S.A. and have had fewer bricks hurled at me in all 4 times together than in London last summer."[56]

Riding on the coattails of ethology's success in the United States, Bowlby's views about the biological foundation of the mother-infant dyad attracted widespread interest. His timing was right. His presentation of the ethological theory of attachment dovetailed nicely with Lorenz's defense of the instinctual nature of human social behavior. Thus, in the United Sates, Bowlby found fertile ground for the idea that ethology could provide a sound framework to understand the attachment of a child to his mother.

But in turning attachment into a biological construct and presenting the mother-child dyad as a natural unit, Bowlby also had to confront one of the most vexing questions for his position: Is the natural mother the only one who can provide adequate child care? After the publication of his WHO report, this issue had been at the center of the social discussions about the role of mothers and the impact of child care. Bowlby had been ambiguous about this. In his 1958 foundational paper, he confronted the issue.

The Power of Natural Love

One of the most controversial issues in Bowlby's writings about the mother-child relationship concerned whether only biological mothers could provide their children with the necessary love and care. Could several people do so? Could fathers?

In his work, Bowlby explored only maternal separation and deprivation. However, sometimes he added a note saying that he was referring to the mother, mother substitute, or mother figure—to the person taking care of the infant, who might not be the biological mother. Aware that this was one of the most controversial implications of his theory, Bowlby was often ambiguous about whether a mother substitute is as good as the natural mother. However, when he situated his views within a biological framework, he was forced to confront the issue: Is the biological mother the one best suited to care for her child?

If evolution had designed the mother-child dyad as a unit, did that imply that biological mothers are the only ones able to provide good care, since they are the ones designed by nature for the role? In his 1958 paper charting the nature of the child's tie to the mother, Bowlby described attachment responses as "mother-oriented," though he said it was evident that this was so "only potentially." Each response could in principle focus on an object other than the mother. But in practice "this is improbable, since all or most of the consummatory stimuli which terminate them habitually come from the mother-figure." Even here, Bowlby talked about a mother "figure," but as he developed his views, his writings indicated that only the mother was designed by nature to provide specific responses to her child's demands.[57]

To clarify his position, Bowlby drew a parallel with the English monarchy:

> It is for this reason that the mother becomes so central a figure in the infant's life. For in healthy development it is towards her that each of the several responses becomes directed, much as each of the subjects of the realm comes to direct his loyalty towards the Queen; and it is in relation to the mother that the several responses become integrated into the complex behaviour which I have termed "attachment behaviour," much as it is in relation to the Sovereign that the components of our constitution become integrated into a working whole.[58]

Thus, not only the laws of nature but the functional rules of a well-ordered society required that authority be invested in a single figure—the queen in society, the mother at home. To ensure social order, the mother thus needs to fulfill her own natural role, as has been proved by the well-functioning designs of nature and society. Bowlby continued:

> We may extend the analogy. It is in the nature of our constitution, as of all others, that sovereignty is vested in a single person. A hierarchy of substitutes is permissible but at the head stands a particular individual. The same is true of the infant. Quite early, by a process of learning, he comes to centre his *instinctual responses* not only on a human figure but *on a particular human figure*. Good mothering from any kind woman ceases to satisfy him—*only his own mother will do.*[59]

In his picture, a hierarchy of authority is necessary for the proper functioning of the natural and the social orders: "The tendency for instinctual responses to be directed towards a particular individual or group of individuals and not promiscuously toward many is one which I believe to be so important and so neglected that it deserves a special term: monot-ropy."[60]

Bowlby's analogy between the family and the English monarchy is potent. It helped drive home the point that, without a central authority figure at home, the family unit would disintegrate.

The mother as queen of the home ensures family stability, much as the British queen ensures social order.

Further, it helped him avoid the charge that he was committing the naturalistic fallacy. Although initially it looks as if Bowlby is claiming monotropy should be a rule of society because it is a law of nature, a second look shows that his argument is more complex. If he said only that mothers are best able to provide good care because they are the ones designed by nature for the role, one could ask, But why should society follow the designs of nature? Moral philosophers have often pointed out the fallacy of going from natural descriptions to moral prescriptions. But what Bowlby said is that not only nature, but also society has shown the functional desirability of monotropy. Thus, in establishing an analogy between the mother-child dyad and the English monarchy, he justified the moral authority of the natural order by appealing to the social order as much as he justified the social order as based on a division of parental roles rooted in the designs of nature.

The turn to biology helped Bowlby legitimize a normative view of motherhood that he had already presented in his WHO report. But turning the child's love for the mother as well as the mother's love for her child into a biological instinct had far-reaching consequences for our understanding of mother love, mothers' work, and gender roles.

The biologizing of love had important implications for mothers. Never before had maternal love been categorized as a child's biological necessity. Nor had the mother been identified as a psychic organizer. In earlier times, a mother could enable or constrain her children's capacities. Mothers could temper, control, and educate their children. But now, according to Bowlby, children have a uniform, universal need for a specific type of mother love, while a mother's feelings determine her children's minds.

Second, although the mother acquires a central role in a child's emotional development, mother love is devalued. In arguing that the mother is designed to fulfill her child's instinctual needs, Bowlby transformed maternal love and care from a personal choice entailing devotion, work, patience, dedication, and not a few renunciations into a natural product of a woman's biological constitution. Furthermore, when maternal feelings are understood as the products of biology, they are removed from the realm of intelligence and freedom, and thus from the realm of behaviors that deserve moral recognition. Bowlby thought he had an upbeat message for mothers: "The normal mother can afford to rely on the prompting of her instincts in the happy knowledge that the tenderness they prompt is what the baby wants."[61] But when Bowlby noted that the normal mother is the unthinking and natural mother who is driven by her instincts, he divested maternal care of choice and, therefore, of moral value.

Third, Bowlby's view of mother love as a child's biological need justified gendered parental roles in a way that had a profound emotional hold on mothers. It is important to grasp not only the logic of an argument but also its emotional force. A mother was now called on to stay home not to fulfill society's desire for social order, but to fulfill her children's natural needs. The emotional power arises because women were not being asked to sacrifice their personal desires for the greater good of the social organism. Early in the Cold War, the rhetoric of containment helped to justify the separation of spheres. But as time went on, even that was unnecessary. If the mother is her child's psychic organizer, she needs to stay home, regardless of whether the times bring war or peace.

Thus, at a crucial period in reassessing parental roles in American society, Bowlby's views about the biological need for mother love represented a strong emotional argument supporting separate parental and gender roles. Although by the 1950s companionate marriage was often touted as an ideal, the different parental roles assigned to men and women made this ideal practically unattainable and socially undesirable. There was an increasing call for fathers to be kind, gentle, and loving to their children, but there was no broad effort to reassess the roles of mother and father. The traditional family unit seemed necessary, as Bowlby and many others pointed out. A father's main role was to provide financial support. As historian Robert L. Griswold has argued, "To support children financially while fostering their sex-role adjustment became the essence of 'maturity,' 'responsibility,' and manhood itself." In the 1950s the father remained the breadwinner, while the mother was responsible for child rearing. The emotional force of appealing to children's biological need for love justified the traditional division of labor with mother at home and father at work.[62]

Conclusion

In the United States Bowlby became an important voice in the scientific and social debates about children's needs and their consequences for the distribution of parental roles. I have argued that the impact of his views about the significance of mother love for child development needs to be understood in the context of the widespread anxiety about changing gender roles and working mothers during the early Cold War years.

By situating discussions about child development in their scientific and social context, I have provided an explanation for the high visibility of Bowlby's work and the corresponding neglect of his critics. Bowlby's ideas about mother love and the implications he drew about the importance of the nuclear family resonated with pervasive social concerns about gender roles in midcentury America. Since American child analysts had already made the role of the mother in helping her child develop the capacity to love into a central public concern, Bowlby was able to gain immediate prominence in ongoing discussions about parental roles. Amid the Cold War emphasis on the benefits of gendered parenting and the nuclear family, the numerous criticisms of the empirical evidence Bowlby used to support the essential role of mother love remained peripheral.

Furthermore, I have argued that Bowlby introduced a crucial new element in the history of justifications for gender roles by claiming that mother love was a biological need for children. Although the significance of mother love had already been part of the history of emotionology in the United States, his appeal to biology to justify the child's innate need for the mother secured it to a new scientific foundation, one that held a tremendous emotional power.

Understanding Bowlby's interpretation of "the *nature* of the child's tie to his mother" and interpreting its scientific and cultural reception during the 1950s cannot be done without locating its place in the debate about the mother's *social* tie to her child. Bowlby appealed to biology to claim that his position was based on scientific knowledge independent of social views and contingent historical factors. But the development and impact of scientific pronouncements about mother love have to be understood in the context of the changing concerns about women's participation in the workforce and the recurring debate about the distribution of parental roles. Questions about the nature of mother love and children's needs remained entangled with the question "Who should rear the children and how?"

Notes

1 On Bowlby, see references in chapter 1. On Bowlby's influence in the United States, see Barbara Ehrenreich and Deirdre English, *For Her Own Good: 150 Years of the Experts' Advice to Women* (New York: Anchor Books, 1978), 229; Mari Jo Buhle, *Feminism and Its Discontents: A Century of Struggle with Psychoanalysis* (Cambridge, MA: Harvard University Press, 1998), 162; Ann Hulbert, *Raising America: Experts, Parents, and a Century of Advice about Children* (New York: Vintage Books, 2003), 204–5; Christina Hardyment, *Dream Babies: Three Centuries of Good Advice on Child Care* (New York: Harper and Row, 1983), 236; Elaine Morgan, *The Descent of the Child: Human Evolution from a New Perspective* (London: Penguin, 1996), 118; Carl N. Degler, *At Odds: Women and the Family in America from the Revolution to the Present* (New York: Oxford University Press, 1980), 471; Julia Grant, *Raising Baby by the Book: The Education of American Mothers* (New Haven, CT: Yale University Press, 1998), 211; Maxine L. Margolis, *Mothers and Such: Views of American Women and Why They Changed* (Berkeley: University of California Press, 1984), 70; Molly Ladd-Taylor and Lauri Umansky, introduction to *"Bad" Mothers: The Politics of Blame in Twentieth-Century America*, ed. Molly Ladd-Taylor and Lauri Umansky (New York: New York University Press, 1998), 1–28, esp. 14; John Byng-Hall, "An Appreciation of John Bowlby: His Significance for Family Therapy," *Journal of Family Therapy* 13 (1991): 5–16; Barbara Melosh, *Strangers and Kin: The American Way of Adoption* (Cambridge, MA: Harvard University Press, 2002), 75, credits Bowlby with having influenced the change in standards of placement by adoption agencies. Melosh notes the appearance of Bowlby's report in 1951 and also the fact that by 1955 "half of all agencies were placing children less than a month old." It is not clear whether Melosh thinks Bowlby's report was the main cause of that change or just one factor among others. The trend in child adoption had gone from two years to one year to six months. A contemporary study documented the shift toward adopting younger children, based on the data provided in the 1952 Child Welfare League of America report, and discussed the influence of Bowlby. See J. Richard Wittenborn, assisted by Barbara Myers, *The Placement of Adoptive Children* (Springfield, IL: Charles C. Thomas, 1957), 4; and Ellen Herman, *Kinship by Design: A History of Adoption in the Modern United States* (Chicago: University of Chicago Press, 2008), 133.

COPYRIGHTED MATERIAL — DO NOT DUPLICATE, DISTRIBUTE, OR POST

2 Ruth Bloch, "American Feminine Ideals in Transition: The Rise of the Moral Mother, 1785–1815," *Feminist Studies* 4 (1978): 101–26; Jan Lewis, "Mother's Love: The Construction of an Emotion in Nineteenth-Century America," in *Mothers and Motherhood: Readings in American History*, ed. Rima D. Apple and Janet Golden (Columbus: Ohio State University Press, 1997), 52–71.

3 John Bowlby, *Child Care and the Growth of Love*, ed. Margery Fry (Harmondsworth, UK: Pelican, 1953), 18, 50; see also 34–35. This is an abridged version of John Bowlby, "Maternal Care and Mental Health," *Bulletin of the World Health Organization* 3 (1951): 355–534. On the history and significance of objectivity in science, see Lorraine Daston and Peter Galison, *Objectivity* (Cambridge, MA: MIT Press, 2007).

4 Bowlby, *Child Care*, 75–76.

5 Ibid., 76.

6 Ibid., 84.

7 Ibid., 181.

8 John Bowlby, "Mother Is the Whole World," *Home Companion* (London), 1952, 29–33. Newspaper clippings in PP/BOW/A.4/1, "Presscuttings April 1952–May 1953," and PP/BOW/A.4/2, "Press cuttings 1953–1954." John Bowlby Papers, Wellcome Library, London. This is only a small sample of the many reviews Bowlby collected.

9 Nancy Cott, *Public Vows: A History of Marriage and the Nation* (Cambridge, MA: Harvard University Press, 2000), 191; Steven Mintz and Susan Kellogg, *Domestic Revolutions: A Social History of American Family Life* (New York: Free Press, 1988). On day care, see also Mary Frances Berry, *The Politics of Parenthood: Child Care, Women's Rights, and the Myth of the Good Mother* (Harmondsworth, UK: Penguin, 1994).

10 Elaine Tyler May, *Homeward Bound: American Families in the Cold War Era* (New York: Basic Books, 1988). See also Ruth Feldstein, *Motherhood in Black and White: Race and Sex in American Liberalism, 1930–1965* (Ithaca, NY: Cornell University Press, 2000).

11 Gaile McGregor, "Domestic Blitz: A Revisionist Theory of the Fifties," *American Studies* 34 (1993): 8.

12 Cott, *Public Vows*, 189. See also Mintz and Kellogg, *Domestic Revolutions*, 170–71.

13 On delinquency and family life during the Cold War, see James Gilbert, *A Cycle of Outrage: America's Reaction to the Juvenile Delinquent in the 1950s* (New York: Oxford University Press, 1986), and Mintz and Kellogg, *Domestic Revolutions*.

14 Alfred C. Kinsey et al., *Sexual Behavior in the Human Female* (Philadelphia: W. B. Saunders, 1953); Mirra Komarovsky, *Women in the Modern World: Their Education and Their Dilemmas* (Boston: Little, Brown, 1953); Ashley Montagu, *The Natural Superiority of Women* (New York: Macmillan, 1953); Simone de Beauvoir, *The Second Sex* (New York: Vintage Books, 1953).

15 Joanne Meyerowitz, "Beyond the Feminine Mystique: A Reassessment of Postwar Mass Culture, 1946–1958," *Journal of American History* 79 (1993): 1455–82; McGregor, "Domestic Blitz"; Joanne Meyerowitz, ed., *Not June Cleaver: Women and Gender in Postwar America, 1945–1960* (Philadelphia: Temple University Press, 1994). On mothers, see Wini Breines, "Domineering Mothers in the 1950s: Image and Reality," *Women's Studies International Forum* 8 (1985): 601–8; Margolis, *Mothers and Such*, chap. 3; and Mintz and Kellogg, *Domestic Revolutions*. On the rise of scientific authority in the

realm of child rearing, see Rima D. Apple, *Perfect Motherhood: Science and Childrearing in America* (New Brunswick, NJ: Rutgers University Press, 2006), and Peter N. Stearns, *Anxious Parents: A History of Modern Childrearing in America* (New York: New York University Press, 2003).

16 Beauvoir, *Second Sex*, 570. See Therese Benedek, review of *The Second Sex*, by Simone de Beauvoir, *Psychoanalytic Quarterly* 22 (1953): 264–67; Marjorie Grene, review of *The Second Sex*, by Simone de Beauvoir, *New Republic* 128 (March 9, 1953): 22–23; and "A Senior Panel Takes Aim at *The Second Sex*," *Saturday Review* (February 21, 1953): 26–31, 41. The panel of reviewers included a psychiatrist, Karl Menninger; a writer, Philip Wylie; an educator, Ashley Montagu; a housewife, Phyllis McGinley; an anthropologist, Margaret Mead; and a public official, Olive R. Goldman.

17 Alva Myrdal and Viola Klein, *Women's Two Roles: Home and Work* (Lon-don: Routledge and Kegan Paul, 1956), 78, 83.

18 Sonya Michel, *Children's Interests/Mothers' Rights: The Shaping of America's Child Care Policy* (New Haven, CT: Yale University Press, 1999), 151; *Employed Mothers and Child Care*, Bulletin of the Women's Bureau 246 (Washington, DC: GPO, 1953), iii, 1.

19 Kathleen W. Jones, *Taming the Troublesome Child: American Families, Child Guidance, and the Limits of Psychiatric Authority* (Cambridge, MA: Harvard University Press, 1999); Ellen Herman, *The Romance of American Psychology: Political Culture in the Age of Experts* (Berkeley: University of California Press, 1995); Mark Solovey, *Shaky Foundations: The Politics-Patronage-Social-Science Nexus in Cold War America* (New Brunswick, NJ: Rutgers University Press, 2013).

20 See chapter 1.

21 James Robertson, application to the Institute of Psychoanalysis for training, dated April 26, 1950, box 86, folder 18 ("Robertson, James, 1950–53"), Anna Freud Papers, Sigmund Freud Collection, Manuscript Division, Library of Congress, Washington, DC.

22 Robertson to Anna Freud, February 5, 1953; Anna Freud to Robertson, February 20, 1953, box 86, folder 18 ("Robertson, James, 1950–53"), Anna Freud Papers.

23 Robertson to Anna Freud, November 21, 1954, box 86, folder 19 ("Robertson, James 1954–56"), Anna Freud Papers.

24 Helen Leland Witmer and Ruth Kotinsky, eds., *Personality in the Making: The Fact-Finding Report of the Midcentury White House Conference on Children and Youth* (New York: Harper and Row, 1952), xvi.

25 Ibid., 4–5; Erik Erikson, *Childhood and Society* (New York: Norton, 1950).

26 Witmer and Kotinsky, *Personality in the Making*, 93–96.

27 Pitirim A. Sorokin and Robert C. Hanson, "The Power of Creative Love," in *The Meaning of Love*, ed. Ashley Montagu (New York: Julian Press, 1953), 125; Ashley Montagu, "The Origin and Meaning of Love," in Montagu, *Meaning of Love*, 4, 4, 5, 18, 19. On Montagu's views on human nature, see Nadine Weidman, "An Anthropologist on TV: Ashley Montagu and the Biological Basis of Human Nature, 1945–1960," in Mark Solovey and Hamilton Cravens, eds. *Cold War Social Science* (New York: Palgrave Macmillan, 2012), 215–32.

28 Myrdal and Klein, *Women's Two Roles*, 125, 126, 127.

29 Clipping in Bowlby's Papers, PP/BOW/K.11/28.

30 "That Woman in Gray Flannel: A Debate," *New York Times*, February 12, 1956; Sloan Wilson, *The Man in the Gray Flannel Suit* (New York: Simon and Schuster, 1955).

31 "Should Mothers of Young Children Work?" *Ladies' Home Journal* 75 (November 1958): 58–59, 154–56, 158–61.

32 Ashley Montagu, "The Triumph and Tragedy of the American Woman," *Saturday Review* 41 (September 27, 1958): 14, 35, 34, 14.

33 Michel, *Children's Interests*, 155.

34 Margolis, *Mothers and Such*, 219.

35 Bowlby, *Child Care*, 43–44.

36 Ibid., 50, 41, 43.

37 Abraham Myerson, "Let's Quit Blaming Mom," *Science Digest* 29 (1951): 11; William H. Sewell, "Infant Training and the Personality of the Child," *American Journal of Sociology* 58 (1952): 150.

38 Harold Orlansky, "Infant Care and Personality," *Psychological Bulletin* 46 (1949): 12, used in Samuel R. Pinneau, "A Critique of the Articles by Margaret Ribble," *Child Development* 21 (1950): 222.

39 L. Joseph Stone, "A Critique of Studies of Infant Isolation," *Child Development* 25 (1954): 14.

40 Samuel R. Pinneau, "The Infantile Disorders of Hospitalism and Anaclitic Depression," *Psychological Bulletin* 52 (1955): 429–52.

41 Ibid., 447; see also ibid., 453ff. for Spitz's reply.

42 John Bowlby et al., "The Effects of Mother-Child Separation: A Follow-up Study," *British Journal of Medical Psychology* 29 (1956): 242.

43 John Bowlby, "A Note on Mother-Child Separation as a Mental Health Hazard," *British Journal of Medical Psychology* 31 (1958): 248.

44 Bowlby, *Child Care, 69;* E. F. M. Durbin and John Bowlby, *Personal Aggressiveness and War* (New York: Columbia University Press, 1939), includes an appendix on the social life of monkeys and apes.

45 Sigmund Freud, "Instincts and Their Vicissitudes" (1915); in *The Standard Edition of the Complete Psychological Works of Sigmund Freud*, translated under the general editorship of James Strachey in collaboration with Anna Freud and assisted by Alix Strachey and Alan Tyson, 24 vols. (London: Hogarth, 1953–74), 14:121–22. On this, see chapter 5.

46 John Bowlby, "An Ethological Approach to Research in Child Development," *British Journal of Medical Psychology* 30 (1957): 239.

47 John Bowlby, "The Nature of the Child's Tie to His Mother," *International Journal of Psychoanalysis* 39 (1958), 354.

48 Ibid., 358.

49 Ibid., 351.

50 Ibid., 362.

51 Ibid., 361.

52 Ibid., 367.

53 Ibid., 369.

54 Evelyn Fox Keller, "Physics and the Emergence of Molecular Biology: A History of Cognitive and Political Synergy," *Journal of the History of Biology* 23 (1990): 390. On the history and significance of objectivity in science see Daston and Galison, *Objectivity.*

55 Bowlby to Dugmore, October 19, 1957, PP/BOW/B.2/2. Bowlby Papers.

56 Bowlby sent reports of his trips for circulation to his research group. See: Copy of letter from Dr. Bowlby, Bowlby to Jock, January 18, 1958; and Bowlby to Jock, April 11/13, 1958, which includes the passage quoted here. PP/BOW/B.2/2. Bowlby Papers.

57 Bowlby, "Nature of the Child's Tie," 369.

58 Ibid., 369–70.

59 Ibid., 370; emphasis added.

60 Ibid.

61 Bowlby, *Child Care,* 17.

62 Robert L. Griswold, *Fatherhood in America: A History* (New York: Basic Books, 1993), 186.

Bibliography

Primary and Secondary Works

Apple, Rima D. *Perfect Motherhood: Science and Childrearing in America.* New Brunswick, NJ: Rutgers University Press, 2006.

Apple, Rima D., and Janet Golden, eds. *Mothers and Motherhood: Readings in American History.* Columbus: Ohio State University Press, 1997.

Beauvoir, Simone de. *The Second Sex.* New York: Vintage Books, 1953.

Benedek, Therese. Review of *The Second Sex,* by Simone de Beauvoir. *Psychoanalytic Quarterly* 22 (1953): 264–67.

Berry, Mary Frances. *The Politics of Parenthood: Child Care, Women's Rights, and the Myth of the Good Mother.* Harmondsworth, UK: Penguin, 1994.

Bloch, Ruth. "American Feminine Ideals in Transition: The Rise of the Moral Mother, 1785–1815." *Feminist Studies* 4 (1978): 100–126.

Bowlby, John. "Maternal Care and Mental Health," *Bulletin of the World Health Organization* 3 (1951): 355–534.

———. *Child Care and the Growth of Love,* edited by Margery Fry. Harmondsworth, UK: Pelican, 1953.

———. "The Rediscovery of the Family." 1954. In *Rediscovery of the Family and Other Lectures: Sister Marie Hilda Memorial Lectures 1954–1973,* edited by John Bowlby et al., 1–7. Aberdeen, UK: University of Aberdeen Press, 1981.

———. "An Ethological Approach to Research in Child Development." *British Journal of Medical Psychology* 30 (1957): 230–40.

______. "The Nature of the Child's Tie to His Mother." *International Journal of Psychoanalysis* 39 (1958): 350–73.

______. "A Note on Mother-Child Separation as a Mental Health Hazard." *British Journal of Medical Psychology* 31 (1958): 247–48.

Bowlby, John, Mary Ainsworth, Mary Boston, and Dina Rosenbluth. "The Effects of Mother-Child Separation: A Follow-up Study." *British Journal of Medical Psychology* 29 (1956): 211–47.

Breines, Wini. "Domineering Mothers in the 1950s: Image and Reality." *Women's Studies International Forum* 8 (1985): 601–8.

Buhle, Mari Jo. *Feminism and Its Discontents: A Century of Struggle with Psychoanalysis*. Cambridge, MA: Harvard University Press, 1998.

Byng-Hall, John. "An Appreciation of John Bowlby: His Significance for Family Therapy." *Journal of Family Therapy* 13 (1991): 5–16.

Cott, Nancy F. *Public Vows: A History of Marriage and the Nation*. Cambridge, MA: Harvard University Press, 2000.

Daston, Lorraine, and Peter Galison. *Objectivity*. Cambridge, MA: MIT Press, 2007.

Degler, Carl N. *At Odds: Women and the Family in America from the Revolution to the Present*. New York: Oxford University Press, 1980.

Durbin, E. F. M., and John Bowlby. *Personal Aggressiveness and War*. New York: Columbia University Press, 1939.

Ehrenreich, Barbara, and Deirdre English. *For Her Own Good: 150 Years of the Experts' Advice to Women*. New York: Anchor Books, 1978.

Employed Mothers and Child Care. Bulletin of the Women's Bureau 246. Washington, DC: GPO, 1953.

Erikson, Erik H. *Childhood and Society*. New York: Norton, 1950.

Feldstein, Ruth. *Motherhood in Black and White: Race and Sex in American Liberalism, 1930–1965*. Ithaca, NY: Cornell University Press, 2000.

Freud, Sigmund. "Instincts and Their Vicissitudes." 1915. In *Standard Edition*, 14:117–40.

______. *The Standard Edition of the Complete Psychological Works of Sigmund Freud*. Translated under the general editorship of James Strachey in collaboration with Anna Freud and assisted by Alix Strachey and Alan Tyson. 24 vols. London: Hogarth, 1953–74.

Gilbert, James. *A Cycle of Outrage: America's Reaction to the Juvenile Delinquent in the 1950s*. New York: Oxford University Press, 1986.

Grant, Julia. *Raising Baby by the Book: The Education of American Mothers*. New Haven, CT: Yale University Press, 1998.

Griswold, Robert L. *Fatherhood in America: A History*. New York: Basic Books, 1993.

Hardyment, Christina. *Dream Babies: Three Centuries of Good Advice on Child Care*. New York: Harper and Row, 1983.

Herman, Ellen. *The Romance of American Psychology: Political Culture in the Age of Experts*. Berkeley: University of California Press, 1995.

______. *Kinship by Design: A History of Adoption in the Modern United States*. Chicago: University of Chicago Press, 2008.

Hulbert, Ann. *Raising America: Experts, Parents, and a Century of Advice about Children*. New York: Vintage Books, 2003.

Jones, Kathleen W. *Taming the Troublesome Child: American Families, Child Guidance, and the Limits of Psychiatric Authority*. Cambridge, MA: Harvard University Press, 1999.

Keller, Evelyn Fox. "Physics and the Emergence of Molecular Biology: A History of Cognitive and Political Synergy." *Journal of the History of Biology* 23 (1990): 389–409.

Kinsey, Alfred C., Wardell B. Pomeroy, Clyde E. Martin, and Paul H. Gebhard. *Sexual Behavior in the Human Female.* Philadelphia: W. B. Saunders, 1953.

Komarovsky, Mirra. *Women in the Modern World: Their Education and Their Dilemmas.* Boston: Little, Brown, 1953.

Ladd-Taylor, Molly, and Lauri Umansky, eds. *"Bad" Mothers: The Politics of Blame in Twentieth-Century America.* New York: New York University Press, 1998.

Lewis, Jan. "Mother's Love: The Construction of an Emotion in Nineteenth-Century America." In *Mothers and Motherhood: Readings in American History,* edited by Rima D. Apple and Janet Golden, 52–71. Columbus: Ohio State University Press, 1997.

Margolis, Maxine L. *Mothers and Such: Views of American Women and Why They Changed.* Berkeley: University of California Press, 1984.

May, Elaine Tyler. *Homeward Bound: American Families in the Cold War Era.* New York: Basic Books, 1988.

McGregor, Gaile. "Domestic Blitz: A Revisionist Theory of the Fifties." *American Studies* 34 (1993): 5–33.

Melosh, Barbara. *Strangers and Kin: The American Way of Adoption.* Cambridge, MA: Harvard University Press, 2002.

Meyerowitz, Joanne. "Beyond the Feminine Mystique: A Reassessment of Postwar Mass Culture, 1946–1958." *Journal of American History* 79 (1993): 1455–82.

———, ed. *Not June Cleaver: Women and Gender in Postwar America, 1945–1960.* Philadelphia: Temple University Press, 1994.

Michel, Sonya. *Children's Interests/Mothers' Rights: The Shaping of America's Child Care Policy.* New Haven, CT: Yale University Press, 1999.

Mintz, Steven, and Susan Kellogg. *Domestic Revolutions: A Social History of American Family Life.* New York: Free Press, 1988.

Montagu, Ashley. *The Natural Superiority of Women.* New York: Macmillan, 1953.

———. "The Origins and Meaning of Love." In *The Meaning of Love,* edited by Ashley Montagu. New York: Julian Press, 1953.

———. "The Triumph and Tragedy of the American Woman." *Saturday Review* 41 (September 27, 1958): 13–15, 34–35.

Morgan, Elaine. *The Descent of the Child: Human Evolution from a New Perspective.* London: Penguin, 1996.

Myerson, Abraham. "Let's Quit Blaming Mom." *Science Digest* 29 (1951): 10–15.

Myrdal, Alva, and Viola Klein. *Women's Two Roles: Home and Work.* London: Routledge and Kegan Paul, 1956.

Orlansky, Harold. "Infant Care and Personality." *Psychological Bulletin* 46 (1949): 1–48.

Pinneau, Samuel R. "A Critique of the Articles by Margaret Ribble." *Child Development* 21 (1950): 203–28.

———. "The Infantile Disorders of Hospitalism and Anaclitic Depression." *Psychological Bulletin* 52 (1955): 429–52.

Sewell, William H. "Infant Training and the Personality of the Child." *American Journal of Sociology* 58 (1952): 150–59.

Solovey, Mark. *Shaky Foundations: The Politics-Patronage-Social-Science Nexus in Cold War America.* New Brunswick, NJ: Rutgers University Press, 2013.

Solovey, Mark, and Hamilton Cravens, eds. *Cold War Social Science: Knowledge Production, Liberal Democracy, and Human Nature*. New York: Palgrave Macmillan, 2012.

Sorokin, Pitirim A., and Robert C. Hanson. "The Power of Creative Love." In *The Meaning of Love,* edited by Ashley Montagu. New York: Julian Press, 1953.

Stearns, Peter N. *Anxious Parents: A History of Modern Childrearing in America*. New York: New York University Press, 2003.

Stone, L. Joseph. "A Critique of Studies of Infant Isolation." *Child Development* 25 (1954): 9–20.

Weidman, Nadine. "An Anthropologist on TV: Ashley Montagu and the Biological Basis of Human Nature, 1945–1960." In *Cold War Social Science: Knowledge Production, Liberal Democracy, and Human Nature*, edited by Mark Solovey and Hamilton Cravens, 215–32. New York: Palgrave Macmillan, 2012.

Wilson, Sloan. *The Man in the Gray Flannel Suit*. New York: Simon and Schuster, 1955.

Witmer, Helen Leland, and Ruth Kotinsky, eds. *Personality in the Making: The Fact-Finding Report of the Midcentury White House Conference on Children and Youth*. New York: Harper and Row, 1952.

Wittenborn, J. Richard, assisted by Barbara Myers. *The Placement of Adoptive Children*. Springfield, IL: Charles C. Thomas, 1957.

Archives Consulted

John Bowlby Papers, Western Manuscripts and Archives, Wellcome Library, London.

Anna Freud Papers, Sigmund Freud Collection, Manuscript Division, Library of Congress, Washington, DC.

CHAPTER 3

Who We Are and Who We Can Be

We look backward to our parents and forward to our children and through their children to a future we will never see, but about which we must care.

—Carl Jung

Introduction

Toward understanding a few things about how and why we have come to be who we are now and how we can, to varying extents, determine who we want to be in the future, we will explore lifespan development research in general, and the development of psychosocial experience and types of reasoning in particular. Lifespan development is an area of research that provides insight as to how psychological, social, cultural, and ecological factors through the lifespan shape our sense of self and psychosocial experience. How we develop along the lifespan, and in particular our psychosocial experience, is important in context of how/if we understand our role in and capability to improve human dignity and affect a sustainable human ecology.

As you are reading this chapter it is important to keep in mind that the relationship we have with our selves affects our relationship with others and by extension our relationship with Earth. When talking about this topic in class I refer to the sum of all factors affecting our self-relationship as our "intrapersonal ecology" and the sum of all factors affecting our self-other relationship as our "interpersonal ecology." The combined intrapersonal and interpersonal ecological experience constitutes our human ecology. Finally, as you are reading please keep in mind what we discussed in Chapter 2 "In the Beginning" about parenting, attachment, and social value orientation, and the connections that were identified with these in the context of improving human dignity and affecting a sustainable human ecology.

Theories and Concepts in Context of Sustainability

Lifespan Development

Lifespan development research involves scientists from virtually every field of psychology, sociology, physiology, and medicine. Lifespan development researchers seek to understand and explain how and why we change throughout the lifespan and our role in this change. Research has revealed that to some extent we can decide and direct how we want to change psychologically and socially throughout our lifespan. It is this "control" of our psychosocial evolution that is of interest to some psychologists and of particular importance in the context of developing approaches for improvement of human dignity and affecting a sustainable human ecology.

There are many predictable physiological and psychological developments that occur along our lifespan; however, psychological development is susceptible to sociocultural and socioecological factors as well as intentional change along the way. Therefore, individual differences can be considerable. Attachment theory researchers attest that attachment style can change for better or worse anywhere along the lifespan. Similarly, lifespan development researchers say that generally an individual can significantly alter their mental processes (i.e., their thinking), change their self-perception, values, social value orientation, and so on if they so desire and apply the effort necessary. This is why lifespan development researchers refer to development along the lifespan as being "plastic"; that is our thinking, therefore our emotions and our actions, are malleable, that is if we want to change our thinking, feeling, and emotions we can do so with intention and effort.

As we shift our conversation to psychosocial development it is important to remember that this development is also plastic and reciprocal. Generally, what I mean by this is that as we age we continue to draw unconsciously and consciously from experiences of the past to not only help make sense of the present but to also formulate possible future scenarios. It is this cognitive relationship between past experience, present assessment, and formulation of future scenarios that necessitates our employment of reflective judgment. By this I mean that we must thoughtfully and honestly not only recall past experiences (reflect), but we must do so with the intent to develop a cause-and-effect understanding (judgment) of past events. With care reflective judgment can provide us with an accurate understanding as to how and why we came to be who we are in the present as well as who we want to be in the future.

Psychosocial Development

As we enter the discussion of the development of our psychosocial experience (i.e., psychosocial stages) it is essential to remember that, as with all life experiences, each psychosocial experience or stage exists on a continuum. For example, an individual in middle adulthood will not be completely either generative or stagnant, but will typically experience something closer to one or the other. Moreover, since all life experience continua are interrelated, factors influencing one continuum will likely influence other continua. Again, a middle-aged individual, for example, who is experiencing a prolonged sense of abundance (on a scarcity-abundance scale) might in response experience increased generativity.

As you read the short descriptions of Erikson's psychosocial stages of development (McLeod, 2018) first consider how parenting and attachment might affect an individual's psychosocial experience. Second, review these stages of experience in context of the lifespan timeline presented in Figure 3.1. Now reflect, for example, on when you first remember being concerned about the environment, an endangered species, or marginalized people. What was your age and what was happening in your life then? What in general was your psychosocial experience and why? What was your social value orientation then, what is it now, and why? Finally, as you read these descriptions, and drawing from what you have learned thus far, consider which psychosocial stage would likely bolster one's experience of dignity as well as facilitate an individual's willingness or even ability to understand his or her role in creating a sustainable human ecology and to act on that understanding.

Psychosocial Stages of Development

Basic trust vs. mistrust: During this stage, the infant is uncertain about the world in which he or she lives. To resolve these feelings of uncertainty, the infant looks toward his or her primary caregiver for stability and consistency of care. If the care the infant receives is consistent, predictable and reliable, he or she will develop a sense of trust, which will carry with him or her to other relationships, and he or she will be able to feel secure even when threatened. Success in this stage will lead to the virtue of hope.

Autonomy vs. shame and doubt: Between the ages of 18 months and 3 years old, children begin to assert their independence, by walking away from their mother, picking which toy to play with, and making choices about what they like to wear, to eat, and so on. Success in this stage will lead to the virtue of will.

Initiative vs. guilt: In ages 3–6 children assert themselves more frequently. These are particularly lively, rapid-developing years in a child's life. According to Bee (1992), it is a "time of vigor of action and of behaviors that the parents may see as aggressive" (p. 90). Success in this stage will lead to the virtue of purpose.

Industry and competence vs. inferiority: In ages 6–11 children are at the stage where they will be learning to read and write, to do sums, to do things on their own. Teachers begin to take an important role in children's lives as they teach children specific skills. A balance between competence and modesty is necessary. Success in this stage will lead to the virtue of competence.

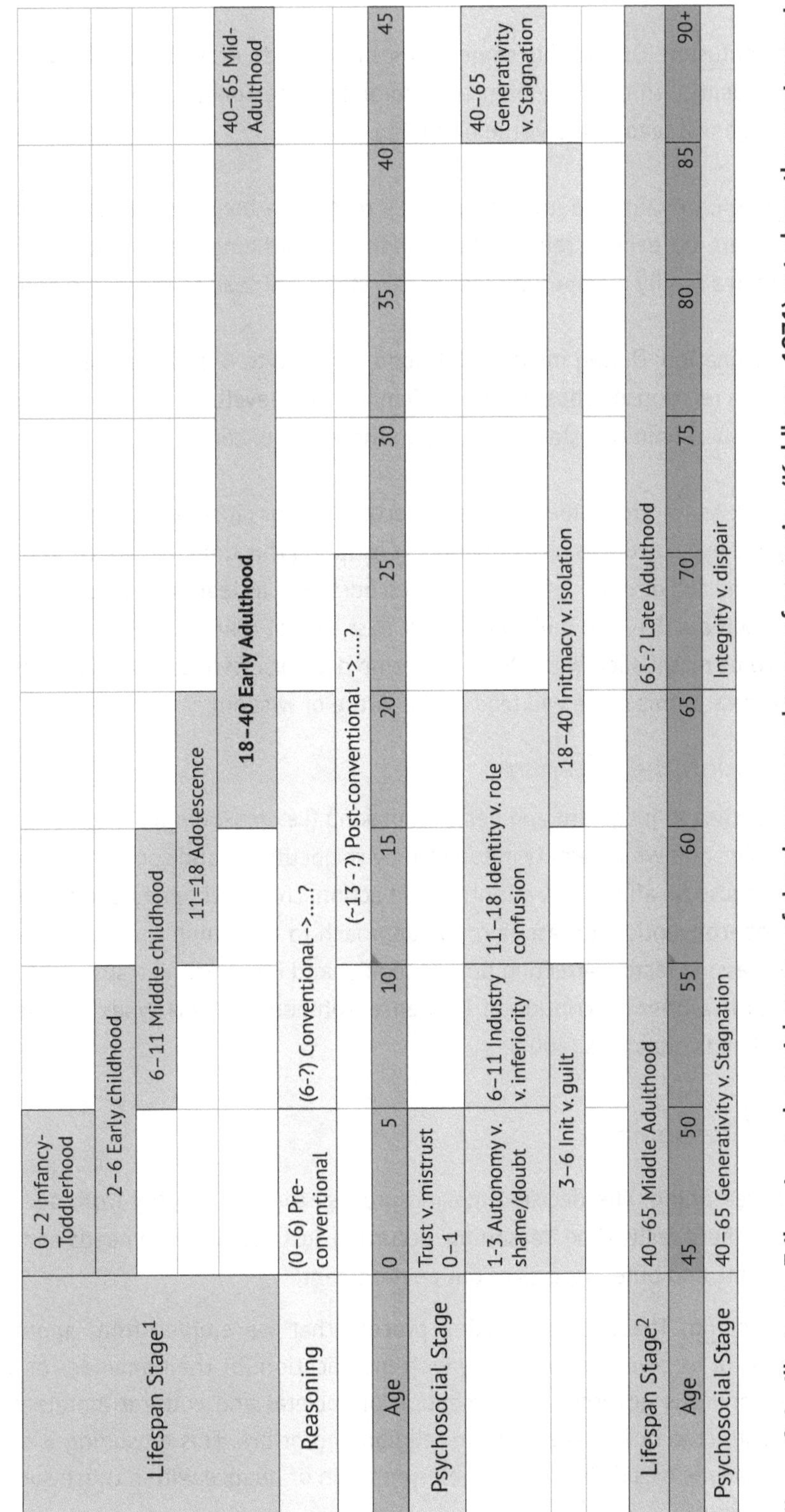

Figure 3.1 Illustrates Erikson's psychosocial stages of development and types of reasoning (Kohlberg, 1971) set along the most recent lifespan development timeline.

Identity vs. role confusion: During this stage (ages 11–18), adolescents search for a sense of self and personal identity, through an intense exploration of personal values, beliefs, and goals. Success in this stage will lead to the virtue of fidelity.

Intimacy vs. isolation: In young adulthood (ages 18 to 40) we begin to share ourselves more intimately with others. We explore relationships leading toward longer-term commitments with someone other than a family member. Success in this stage will lead to the virtue of love.

Generativity vs. stagnation: During middle adulthood (ages 40 to 65), we establish our careers, settle down within a relationship, begin our own families and develop a sense of being a part of the bigger picture. Success in this stage will lead to the virtue of care.

Integrity vs. despair: As we grow older (65+) and become senior citizens, we tend to slow down our productivity and explore life as retired people. It is during this time that we contemplate our accomplishments and can develop integrity if we see ourselves as leading a successful life. If we see our lives as unproductive, feel guilty about our past, or feel that we did not accomplish our life goals, we become dissatisfied with life and develop despair, often leading to depression and hopelessness. Success in this stage will lead to the virtue of wisdom.

Reasoning Through the Lifespan

We develop approaches to judgment and decision making (i.e., reasoning) along our lifespan or at least up to a point, and while largely influenced by sociocultural and socioecological factors, how we reason can also be affected by attention and action. The latter appears to be particularly true regarding post-conventional reasoning, the approach to reasoning that is likely the most important for addressing factors affecting human dignity and for affecting a sustainable human ecology. Following is a brief description of Lawrence Kohlberg's (1971) types of reasoning as adapted by Seifert and colleagues (2008).

Three Types of Reasoning

Pre-conventional reasoning: The decision-making process that we employ from age 0 to approximately age 6. There really is no "reasoning" occurring, just responses to needs and wants as moderated by parents and other aspects of our environment.

Conventional reasoning: The decision-making process that we employ from approximately age 6 and for most of us continue to employ with modification for the remainder of our lives. Conventional reasoning is governed by perception of societal and cultural morals or norms, for example, as instructed or interpreted from religion and/or law. This reasoning is said to be legalistic and typically leaves little room for interpretation or nuance within those societal and cultural morals or norms.

Post-conventional reasoning: The decision-making process that we might begin to employ in earlier adolescence or at a later point in life and that is directed by one's perception of the common good and the needs of society as a whole. Laws and societal perception of morals are respected and upheld as long as these to do not compromise the collective good and especially the needs of individuals of least means. Research indicates that less than 10% of the U.S. population employs this approach to decision making (Taylor, 2007). This limited presence of post-conventional reasoning likely explains in part why as a society we are moving so slowly toward the improvement of human dignity and a sustainable human ecology.

About the Feature Article

As you read the feature article *The Influence of Decision-Making Styles on Early Adolescents' Life Satisfaction*, consider your lifespan development experience in general and in particular how you have made decisions in the past. Do you make decisions differently now than you did a year or 4 years ago? What do you think has influenced your decision-making style(s)? Finally, consider Cenkseven-Onder's (2012) connection with decision-making style and life satisfaction. Do you see this connection in your personal lifespan development experience?

References

Bee, H. L. (1992). The developing child. London: HarperCollins.

Kohlberg, L. (1971). Stages of moral development. Moral Education, *1*(51), 23–92.

McLeod, S. (2018). Erik Erikson's stages of psychosocial development. *Simply Psychology.* Retrieved from https://www.simplypsychology.org/Erik-Erikson.html

Seifert, T., Goodman, K., Lindsay, Jorgensen, J. D., Wolniak, G, Pascarella, E., & Blaich, C. (2008). The effects of liberal arts experiences on liberal arts outcomes. *Research in Higher Education*, *49(2)*, 107–125. doi:10.1007/s11162-007-9070-7

Taylor, K. (Speaker). (2007). *Constructive development theory* (DVD Recording No. P6215D). Baltimore: Laureate Education, Inc.

READING 3

The Influence of Decision-Making Styles on Early Adolescents' Life Satisfaction

Fulya Cenkseven-Önder

FULYA CENKSEVEN-ÖNDER
Çukurova University

In this study, I examined decision-making styles and satisfaction in different life domains in early adolescence, and the influence of gender difference in relation to making decisions. The Multidimensional Students' Life Satisfaction Scale (Huebner, 1994) and the Adolescent Decision-making Scale (Mann, Harmoni, & Power, 1989) were completed by 918 early adolescents (432 girls, 486 boys) who were students at a school in a city in southern Turkey. Some gender differences regarding satisfaction with various life domains and decision-making styles were noted. It was found that, with the exception of the panic style, decision-making styles are predictors of life satisfaction. The results are discussed in relation to previous research. Finally, study limitations and possible directions for further research are outlined.

Keywords: life satisfaction, decision-making styles, early adolescents.

Over the last decade a considerable amount of research on positive psychology has consisted of subjective well-being studies (Seligman & Csikszentmihalyi, 2000). Subjective well-being includes life satisfaction as well as positive and negative affect

Fulya Cenkseven-Önder, "The Influence of Decision-Making Styles on Early Adolescents' Life Satisfaction," *Social Behavior and Personality*, vol. 40, no. 9, pp. 1523-1536.

COPYRIGHTED MATERIAL — DO NOT DUPLICATE, DISTRIBUTE, OR POST

components (Diener, 1994; Huebner, 1991). In this study, I examined life satisfaction, which is the cognitive component of subjective well-being (Diener, 1994). Diener defines *life satisfaction* as "*a global judgment that people make when they consider their life as a whole*" (p. 107). Life satisfaction includes people's satisfaction with their immediate living environment, the will to change their life, the satisfaction that they expect in the future, and the opinions of their relatives about the person's life. The domains of satisfaction may include job, family, leisure, self, and one's neighborhood (Diener & Lucas, 1999). Huebner considered life satisfaction to be a multidimensional concept referring to perceived satisfaction with family, friends, school environment, and self. In this study, life satisfaction is understood as a multidimensional concept.

Life satisfaction studies are usually confined to adults. However, during the last decade interest in children and adolescents' life satisfaction has increased (Huebner, 1997). There is evidence to suggest that low life satisfaction in adolescents is related to lack of effective decision-making skills and, thus, to aggressive behavior (Valois, Paxton, Zullig, & Huebner, 2006), depression (Huebner, Funk, & Gilman, 2000), risky sexual behavior (Valois, Zullig, Huebner, Kammermann, & Drane, 2002), and substance abuse (Zullig, Valois, Huebner, Oeltmann, & Drane, 2001). To provide a specific example, Commendador (2007) found that adolescents' risky health and sexual behaviors were correlated with inadequate decision-making skills. Several researchers (Mann, Harmoni, & Power, 1989; Schvaneveldt & Adams, 1983) have demonstrated that early adolescence is critical in the development of decision-making skills. Acquiring the skill to decide efficiently will allow adolescents to select what is best for them in their lives and to augment their life satisfaction (Resnick, 1987). However, in spite of its importance, few studies (Cenkseven-Önder & Çolakkadıoğlu, 2009; Deniz, 2006) have been conducted in which the relationship between life satisfaction and decision-making skills has been examined.

Decision making can be defined as *the process of choosing between different alternatives while in the midst of pursuing a goal* (Miller & Byrnes, 2001). People use different decision-making styles (Friedman & Mann, 1993; Janis & Mann, 1977) which are the approaches individuals take when they need to make a decision (Janis & Mann, 1977) and they differ in terms of perceived effort and efficiency (Payne, Bettman, & Johnson, 1993). Janis and Mann state that effective decision making consists of seven steps: (a) identifying the problem; (b) generating alternatives; (c) considering the possible consequences of the alternatives; (d) collecting information in order to improve one's ability to evaluate the alternatives; (e) evaluating the advantages and disadvantages of the alternatives; (f) identifying the appropriate alternative; and (g) employing the decision made, making plans, and evaluating the consequences.

Janis and Mann (1977) consider four decision-making styles in their conflict model; namely, complacency, panic, cop-out, and vigilance. *Complacency* is *behaving as if no decision needs to be made when confronted by a situation that needs a decision.* The individual does not consider any other alternatives and waits for the problem to solve itself. *Panic* is *making a decision in order to relieve stress and reduce conflict when confronted by a situation in which a decision must be made but there is not enough time to think carefully. Cop-out* is *postponing a decision or passing it on to someone else.*

The individual using this style escapes from the conflict created by the need for a decision by either doing nothing or not taking responsibility. *Vigilance* is *carefully researching a series of alternatives and evaluating the positive and negative sides of the alternatives when confronted by a situation that needs a decision.* Individuals using this style are confident and optimistic regarding correct decision-making and consider the options carefully (Friedman & Mann, 1993). Janis and Mann classify these styles as adaptive or maladaptive decision making. Complacency, panic, and cop-out are maladaptive styles, whereas vigilance is adaptive. Conflict theory also includes self-esteem regarding the decision-making skills of the individual. Self-esteem in decision-making is positively related to high global self-esteem and vigilance, whereas low self-esteem is related to low self-confidence, high stress, and maladaptive styles (Mann et al., 1989).

In this study, I examined early adolescents' decision-making styles and their perceived satisfaction with different life domains. I also examined the decision-making styles of this group to determine whether or not gender difference influenced how the decision was made. There are inconsistent results related to decision-making styles and life satisfaction in terms of gender differences. For example, Friedman and Mann (1993) and Güçray (1998) found that, compared to women, men reported significantly higher levels of self-esteem in regard to decision making and greater use of the decision-making styles of vigilance and complacency, whereas women reported significantly greater use of the panic and cop-out styles of decision-making than did men. However, there are also studies in which men have reported greater use of the cop-out style of decision making than have women (Bacanlı & Sürücü, 2006), and also studies in which women have reported greater use than men of the vigilance style (Brown & Mann, 1990). Correspondingly, some researchers have found significant differences in level of life satisfaction, with females having a higher level of satisfaction than males (Köker, 1991), some researchers have found that men had a higher level of life satisfaction compared to women (Neto, 1993), and other researchers have found no significant difference in life satisfaction of men and women (Huebner, 1991). These inconsistent results may point to the conclusion that in dimensions of decision-making styles or life satisfaction the gender effect may differ in different societies and research groups. It is, therefore, important to study the gender effect in a Turkish sample.

Adolescents using adaptive styles make more efficient decisions with regard to their families, friends, and living environment. I assumed that this could increase perceived life satisfaction in terms of school, family, friends, living environment, and self. The influence gender differences have on well-being increases during adolescence because of psychosocial and biological changes (Piko, 2001).

I hypothesized that self-esteem in decision-making and the vigilance style would be positively related to dimensions of life satisfaction but would be negatively related to maladaptive styles. I sought answers to the following research questions: (1) Do satisfaction with various life domains, self-esteem in regard to decision-making, and decision-making styles in adolescents vary according to gender? (2) Do self-esteem in regard to decision-making and decision-making styles predict satisfaction within various life domains? (3) Are there any gender differences in the relationship among self-esteem in decision-making, decision-making styles, and life satisfaction?

Method

Participants

Participants were 918 middle school students in a city in southern Turkey, of whom 432 were girls and 486 were boys. The students were between 13 and 15 years of age ($M = 13.63$, $SD = .67$). Table 3.1 contains the participants characteristics. The questionnaires took 35 minutes to fill in and were completed in classes under teachers' supervision.

Table 3.1 Participants' Characteristics

VARIABLES	*n*	%	VARIABLES	*n*	%	VARIABLES	*n*	%
Gender			**Mother's schooling**			**Father's schooling**		
Female	432	47.1	Illiterate	111	11.2	Illiterate	42	4.6
Male	486	52.9	Primary	318	34.6	Primary	255	27.8
Grade			Middle	141	15.4	Middle	173	18.8
6th	113	12.3	High	195	21.2	High	238	25.9
7th	397	52.9	University	153	16.7	University	210	22.9
8th	408	44.4						

Instruments

Multidimensional Students' Life Satisfaction Scale (MSLSS)

The MSLSS (Huebner, 1994) is a 40-item self-report instrument that assesses satisfaction across five specific life domains of family, school, friends, self, and living environment. In addition, the MSLSS allows for an overall assessment of an adolescent's life satisfaction. All questions on the MSLSS are responded to using a 4-point Likert scale ranging from *never* (1) to *almost always* (4). The MSLSS was adapted into Turkish by Çivitçi (2007). The Turkish form consists of 36 items. Cronbach's alpha coefficients were between .82 and .85 for the subscales and .92 for the total score.

Adolescent Decision-making Scale (ADMS)

Mann et al. (1989) developed the ADMS in order to measure the frequency of use of the four decision-making styles and the level of self-esteem in decision-making. The 30-item scale consists of five subscales: self-esteem, vigilance, panic, cop-out, and complacency. The response scales range from *always true for me* to *never true for me*. ADMS was adapted into Turkish by Çolakkadıoğlu and Güçray (2007). Cronbach's alphas varied between .65 and .79. Test-retest correlations were between .80 and .86 for the subscales.

Data Analysis

Means and standard deviation distributions were investigated. One-way analyses of variance (ANOVAs), Pearson product moment correlations, and regression analyses were performed.

Histogram and normality assumptions were examined and found to be satisfactory. The analysis was carried out using SPSS version 13.0.

Results

Gender Differences in Life Satisfaction and Decision-making Styles

In order to assess differences in life satisfaction and decision-making styles as a function of gender, a series of ANOVAs were conducted. As shown in Table 3.2, the girls reported being more satisfied with their friends and their school, and having greater general satisfaction than did the boys. Girls reported making use of the vigilance and panic decision-making styles significantly more often than did boys. Boys reported using complacency and cop-out decision-making styles significantly more often than did the girls.

Table 3.2 Means and Standard Deviations for MSLSS And ADMS Subscales by Gender

	FEMALE (n = 432)		MALE (n = 486)		WHOLE SAMPLE (n = 918)		SKEWNESS	KURTOSIS	F
	M	*SD*	*M*	*SD*	*M*	*SD*			
General satisfaction	3.26	.41	3.15	.43	3.20	.43	−.43	−.48	15.50*
Family satisfaction	3.31	.66	3.24	.62	3.27	.64	−.83	−.10	2.52
Friends satisfaction	3.52	.49	3.31	.56	3.41	.54	−.91	.12	37.18*
School satisfaction	3.16	.57	2.94	.58	3.04	.59	−.48	−.21	30.85*
Living environment satisfaction	3.02	.77	3.05	.63	3.04	.70	−.57	−.40	.39
Self-satisfaction	3.27	.56	3.22	.56	3.25	.56	−.58	−.37	1.90
Self-esteem	2.95	.50	3.01	.49	2.98	.49	.05	−.49	2.75
Vigilance	3.23	.53	3.04	.55	3.13	.55	−.39	−.44	26.37*
Panic	2.23	.65	2.10	.59	2.16	.63	.28	−.20	10.61*
Complacency	1.68	.47	1.82	.50	1.75	.49	.55	−.10	21.20*
Cop-out	1.72	.47	1.86	.48	1.80	.48	.49	−.13	19.65*

Note: * p <.001.

Relationships Between Decision-Making Styles and Life Satisfaction

In order to explore the relationship between adolescents' decision-making styles and their life satisfaction, a series of multiple regression analyses were conducted. Life satisfaction was significantly correlated with self-esteem in all domains (r =.22 to.45), as well as for the vigilance (r = .16 to .47), panic (r = −.08 to −.18), complacency (r = −.18 to −.30), and cop-out (r = −.18 to −.31) decision-making styles.

As shown in Table 3.3, all regression models were significant for the whole sample. All subscales of the ADMS, except for the panic decision-making style, significantly predicted satisfaction with

Table 3.3 Regression Models for Effect of Decision-making Styles on Life Satisfaction

	WHOLE SAMPLE		MALE		FEMALE	
VARIABLES	BETA	t	BETA	t	BETA	t
General satisfaction						
Self-esteem	.22	6.56***	.249	5.688***	.204	3.947***
Vigilance	.32	9.96***	.352	8.420***	.251	5.070***
Panic	.01	.14	-.021	-.479	.003	.054
Complacency	-.12	-3.51***	-.069	-1.601	-.167	-3.129**
Cop-out	-.07	-2.08*	-.113	-2.451*	.001	.012
	R_{adj}^2 = .29		R_{adj}^2 = .35		R_{adj}^2 = .22	
	F(5, 917) = 76.51***		F(5, 485) = 53.06***		F(5, 431) = 24.62***	
Family satisfaction						
Self-esteem	.13	3.73***	.115	2.396*	.152	2.783**
Vigilance	.27	7.72***	.332	7.247***	.196	3.737***
Panic	-.01	-.17	-.051	-1.068	.042	.772
Complacency	-.12	-3.42**	-.108	-2.278*	-.151	-2.680**
Cop-out	-.03	-.83	-.052	-1.029	-.010	-.167
	R_{adj}^2 = .17		R_{adj}^2 = .22		R_{adj}^2 = .12	
	F(5, 917) = 39.43***		F(5, 485) = 28.08***		F(5, 431) = 13.34***	
Friends satisfaction						
Self-esteem	.17	4.90***	.236	4.906***	.155	2.878**
Vigilance	.27	7.79***	.239	5.210***	.255	4.922***
Panic	.04	.99	-.019	-.391	.028	.506
Complacency	-.08	-2.10*	-.028	-.587	-.097	-1.746
Cop-out	-.09	-2.38*	-.109	-2.146*	.000	.000
	R_{adj}^2 = .19		R_{adj}^2 = .21		R_{adj}^2 = .14	
	F(5, 917) = 44.54***		F(5, 485) = 27.44***		F(5, 431) = 15.22***	
School satisfaction						
Self-esteem	.06	1.74	.089	1.768	.078	1.398
Vigilance	.25	7.14***	.251	5.186***	.216	4.047***
Panic	.03	.81	.018	.351	-.007	-.132
Complacency	-.07	-1.84	-.026	-.526	-.085	-1.478
Cop-out	-.10	-2.47*	-.126	-2.369*	-.017	-.286
	R_{adj}^2 = .13		R_{adj}^2 = .13		R_{adj}^2 = .09	
	F(5, 917) = 27.18***		F(5, 485) = 15.08***		F(5, 431) = 9.23***	
Living environment satisfaction						
Self-esteem	0.13	3.37**	.129	2.586**	.107	1.882
Vigilance	0.07	1.78	.210	4.401***	-.065	-1.194

(continued)

Table 3.3 Regression Models for Effect of Decision-making Styles on Life Satisfaction (*continued*)

	WHOLE SAMPLE		MALE		FEMALE	
VARIABLES	BETA	*t*	BETA	*t*	BETA	*t*
Panic	−0.06	−1.64	−.037	−.744	−.070	−1.214
Complacency	−0.12	−3.11**	−.095	−1.932	−.167	−2.830**
Cop-out	−0.02	−.52	−.103	−1.951	.035	.581
	$R_{adj}^2 = .07$		$R_{adj}^2 = .15$		$R_{adj}^2 = .04$	
	$F(5, 917) = 15.31$***		$F(5, 485) = 18.37$***		$F(5, 431) = 4.83$***	
Self-satisfaction						
Self-esteem	0.32	9.57***	.396	8.744***	.236	4.705***
Vigilance	0.31	9.71***	.263	6.081***	.357	7.412***
Panic	0.03	.99	.017	.391	.044	.859
Complacency	−0.01	−.22	.016	.365	−.036	−.697
Cop-out	−0.01	−.37	−.002	−.041	−.017	−.317
	$R_{adj}^2 = .28$		$R_{adj}^2 = .30$		$R_{adj}^2 = .26$	
	$F(5, 917) = 72.63$***		$F(5, 485) = 43.04$***		$F(5, 431) = 31.00$***	

Note: * $p < .05$, ** $p < .01$, *** $p < .001$.

friends and general satisfaction. The self-esteem, vigilance, and complacency decision-making styles were predictors of family satisfaction. School satisfaction was predicted by the vigilance and cop-out decision-making styles. Self-esteem and the complacency decision-making style predicted living environment satisfaction. Adaptive decision-making styles were predictors of self-satisfaction.

In order to assess gender differences in predicting life satisfaction, multiple regression models were run separately for boys and girls. As shown in Table 3, there were general gender differences for friends, school, and living environment satisfaction. High self-esteem, and the vigilance and cop-out decision-making styles predicted general satisfaction for boys. However, high self-esteem, and the vigilance and complacency decision-making styles predicted general satisfaction for girls. The cop-out decision-making style only significantly predicted satisfaction with friends and school for boys. Furthermore, high self-esteem and the vigilance decision-making style significantly predicted living environment satisfaction for boys, but only the complacency decision-making style predicted satisfaction with living environment for girls.

Discussion

In this study, some differences were observed in the life satisfaction of female early adolescents as compared to the life satisfaction of male early adolescents. General, school, and friends satisfaction scores were higher for girls than they were for boys. Although the results in a number of studies show that gender has no significant effect on life satisfaction (Huebner, 1991;

Nickerson & Nagle, 2004), the results in other studies show that, compared with males, females' life satisfaction is higher (Köker, 1991; Neto, 1993). Similar to the findings in this study, Huebner, Drane, and Valois (2000) and Nickerson and Nagle (2004) noted that female adolescents girls claimed to have greater school satisfaction than did adolescent boys. Pollack (1998) found that, compared with girls, boys' academic self-esteem was lower in early adolescence. Also, several researchers have indicated that boys get lower grades in school than do girls, and that they generally like nonacademic activities, such as watching television, sports, and playing games on the Internet more than do girls (see e.g., Halpern, 1997). It has also been found that boys have fewer feelings of belonging to their school than do girls (Goodenow, 1993). In my study the girls reported greater friend satisfaction than the boys did. According to Hortaçsu (1997), females love their friends more than do males; they share more secrets with them, and spend time with friends in smaller groups, whereas males spend time engaging in sports and similar activities with larger groups of friends. This may enable females to perceive more satisfaction with friendships as compared to males. In addition to this, male adolescents experience more peer pressure (Çiğdemoğlu, 2005) and bullying (Rigby, 2002) than do females, so these may be factors that cause males to have less satisfaction with friendships as compared to females.

In this study I found that females used the vigilance and panic decision-making styles more than did males, whereas males used complacency and cop-out styles more than did females. Vigilance is a decision-making style that requires more careful thinking and prudent behavior. Females are inclined to be more careful about details and try to behave more prudently according to their traditional gender roles, so this may be a factor in their use of the vigilance style. Some researchers have shown that females use the vigilance (Brown & Mann, 1990; Dülger, 2009; Kuzgun, 1992) and panic (Güçray, 1998; Kuzgun, 1992) decision-making styles more than do males. The fact that females use these two different styles may raise the following question: Do females have greater difficulty making a decision when the decision-making time is insufficient and stress is high? Further investigation of this subject is needed. The behaviors associated with the cop-out and complacency styles are related to maturity, and may be explained by the fact that males reach social and intellectual maturity much later than do females (Fischoff & Jacobs-Quadrel, 1995, as cited in Steinberg, 2007). A significant number of researchers have shown that males use the complacency (Dülger, 2009; Friedman, & Mann, 1993) and cop-out (Dülger, 2009) styles more than do females.

I observed that, according to the results of the regression analysis, the variables of vigilance decision-making style and self-esteem provided the most accurate explanation of adolescents' satisfaction with several life domains. An individual using the adaptive style of vigilance (Janis & Mann, 1977) attentively examines the relevant information, absorbs the information in a neutral manner, and evaluates the alternatives before making a decision. On the other hand, self-esteem in decision-making includes an individual's self-evaluation of his/her own decision and the satisfaction s/he has regarding that decision. Vigilance is a style in which effective decision-making steps are used, and findings in studies have shown that individuals who use this style have high self-esteem (Çolakkadıoğlu & Güçray, 2007; Güçray, 1998; Mann et al., 1989). Cenkseven-Önder and Çolakkadıoğlu (2009) found that these two variables are global predictors of adolescents' life satisfaction. Evidence shows that effective problem solving is related to well-being (Hamarta, 2009) and effective decision making (Mann et al., 1989). There is also evidence that individuals with greater life satisfaction are more effective problem solvers and are more resilient when they have to cope with stressful life events (Frisch, 2000). As problem solving is a part of decision-making sufficiency (Mann et al., 1989), I did not find it unexpected that individuals who use the vigilance style and have high self-esteem in decision-making also have a high level of life satisfaction. In addition to this, individuals who use the vigilance style have moderate stress levels at the time when they make a decision. A moderate level of stress enables individuals to be stimulated and motivated enough to fulfill all cognitive tasks, but does not harm cognitive activities (Janis & Mann, 1977). Therefore, a moderate level of stress is not likely to reduce an individual's life satisfaction.

Depression and life satisfaction are both indicators of psychological health and depression is negatively correlated with life satisfaction (Huebner et al., 2000). Results in empirical studies have shown that individuals who have a higher level of self-esteem regarding their decision-making skills and who use the vigilance style when making decisions, are less likely to have symptoms of depression than are individuals who use maladaptive decision-making styles (Okwumabua, Wong, & Duryea, 2003).

In this study, results showed that having high self-esteem with regard to decision-making and choice of decision-making styles predicts self-satisfaction better than does any other life satisfaction indicator. This result was similar for both boys and girls in my study. I found that high self-esteem and use of the vigilance style for making decisions were the best predictors of an individual's life satisfaction. Self-satisfaction also includes the happiness that results from an individual's characteristics. During adolescence, the effort to establish an identity leads adolescents to be more self-judgmental (Harter, 1993). If adolescents can make decisions by using effective decision-making steps in stressful situations and become happy with their decisions, it is possible that their self-satisfaction will also be high.

In this study, the maladaptive decision-making styles of panic, cop-out, and complacency (Janis & Mann, 1977) were identified as having a negative correlation with the perceived satisfaction of diverse life domains. Individuals who adopt maladaptive decision-making styles have a more external locus of control (Mann et al., 1989), so this may be a factor that decreases their life satisfaction. However, I found it interesting that, in my study, use of the panic style for making decisions was not a predictor of satisfaction in any life domain for either gender. The panic style is most often used in stressful situations when there is time pressure, and it may be that adolescents do not frequently encounter these kinds of situations. Therefore, it may not be a significant predictor of life satisfaction, which is affected by many variables. Similarly, in their study, Cenkseven-Önder and Çolakkadıoğlu (2009) found that the panic style was not a predictor of global adolescent life satisfaction.

In this study, I found that use of the complacency style of decision making was a predictor of adolescents' overall family, friend, and environment satisfaction, and the cop-out decision-making style was a predictor of total, friend, and school satisfaction. Individuals using the complacency style when making decisions can leave the problem as it is and ignore it since they either do not have the ability to solve it or do not know the logical way to solve it (Friedman & Mann, 1993). Therefore, they will not be able to make a decision in accordance with their needs. The fact that adolescents who are in need of independence are unable to make their own decisions in compliance with their needs may reduce the satisfaction they perceive from their family or friends. Similarly, solutions reached using the cop-out style to make decision do not fulfill the needs of the adolescent decision maker and may not match the goals of that individual. It is, therefore, possible that the adolescent who uses the cop-out style will be unhappy. Individuals using this style may have problems in their interpersonal relationships. They may experience problems because of lack of efficient decision-making regarding friends and school activities. In this case, it is possible that satisfaction with friends and school will decrease.

In separate analyses of boys and girls in my study, the level of self-esteem regarding decision making and the use of the vigilance style were predictors of boys' living environment satisfaction but were not predictors of girls' living environment satisfaction. The only predictor of environment satisfaction for the girls was use of the complacency style for making decisions. This difference between males and females may be related to cultural factors and traditional gender roles. Males are expected to think analytically and act rationally. Therefore, if they make effective decisions and are happy with their decisions, this will make them feel better about their environment and their satisfaction will increase. It may be that females using the complacency style to make decisions feel more intensely than males do that they are controlled by their environment, so they have a negative perception of the environment and feel unhappy as a result.

I noted that in my study the complacency style of decision making was a predictor of school satisfaction—but only for boys. The use of this style may cause problems such as little success in school activities. It is also known that low academic success is positively related to being unable to make effective decisions (Baiocco, Laghi, & D'Alessio, 2009) and that male adolescents' academic success rates are lower than are female adolescents' academic success rates (Halpern, 1997). In my separate analyses of boys and girls, I observed that the cop-out style was a predictor for boys' total, school, and friend satisfaction, but did not predict any kind of satisfaction for girls. In a male-dominated culture, males are expected to make their own decisions and are, therefore, thought to require less social support (Frydenberg & Lewis, 1991). The cop-out style may result in males having negative perceptions of themselves, and may also cause them to make more negative evaluations of their lives. Such behavior also decreases their perceived satisfaction with friendships and school.

There were some limitations in this study. Firstly, in several studies (e.g., Byrnes, Miller, & Reynolds, 1999; Poikolainen, Kanerva, & Lönnqvist, 1995) it has been found that the effectiveness of adolescents' decision-making skills increases with education and age. However, the research sample for this study was composed of early adolescents. The relationship between life satisfaction and adolescents' decision-making styles at different stages of adolescence was not examined. Longitudinal research will show how decision-making styles develop as adolescents grow up.

The data in this study were collected using self-report scales. Therefore, adolescents' low average score for the maladaptive styles may be a result of their perception of what would be socially desirable responses. It would be useful to collect data using different scales and methods (such as observation, interview, and behavioral decision-making scales) in future studies. In addition, the results obtained in this study define the relationship between life satisfaction and decision-making correlationally, rather than causally. The results should be assessed with these limitations in mind. Ethnic differences and socioeconomic status were not taken into consideration in this study. Thus, this study could be repeated using a sample with different demographic characteristics.

The findings in this study suggest that adolescents who make effective decisions and are happy with their decisions have high life satisfaction. I recommend that guidance courses be conducted in order to increase adolescents' effective decision-making skills, which will, in turn, help them increase their general life satisfaction and develop a healthy identity.

References

Bacanlı, F., & Sürücü, M. (2006). İlköğretim 8. sınıf öğrencilerinin sınav kaygıları ve karar verme stilleri arasındaki ilişkilerin incelenmesi [An examination of the relationship between test anxiety and decision-making styles of elementary school 8th grade students]. *Educational Administration: Theory and Practice, 45,* 7–35.

Baiocco, R., Laghi, F., & D'Alessio, M. (2009). Decision-making style among adolescents: Relationship with sensation seeking and locus of control. *Journal of Adolescence, 32,* 963–976. http://doi.org/ctr449

Brown, J. E., & Mann, L. (1990). The relationship between family structure and process variables and adolescent decision making. *Journal of Adolescence, 13,* 25–37. http://doi.org/bqrf4q

Byrnes, J. P., Miller, D. C., & Reynolds, M. (1999). Learning to make good decisions: A self-regulation perspective. *Child Development, 70,* 1121–1140. http://doi.org/czcmzg

Cenkseven-Önder, F., & Çolakkadıoğlu, O. (2009, October). *Ergenlerde öznel iyi olmanın yordayıcıları olarak karar verme ve problem çözme* [Decision-making and problem-solving as the predictors of adolescents' subjective well-being]. Paper presented at the XVIII National Congress of Education Sciences, Izmir, Turkey.

Commendador, K. (2007). The relationship between female adolescent self-esteem, decision-making, and contraceptive behavior. *Journal of the American Academy of Nurse Practitioners, 19,* 614–623. http://doi.org/bf45zd

Çiğdemoğlu, S. (2005). *Lise I. sınıf ögrencilerinin akran baskısı, özsaygı ve içedönüklük-dısadönüklük kisilik özelliklerinin okul türlerine göre incelenmesi* [An examination of peer pressure, self-esteem, and extrovert personality among ninth year students in different types of high school]. Unpublished Mmaster's thesis, Ankara University, Turkey.

Çivitçi, A. (2007). *Çok boyutlu öğrenci yasam doyumu ölçeğinin Türkçe'ye uyarlanması: Geçerlik ve güvenirlik çalışmaları* [The adaptation of the Multidimensional Students' Life Satisfaction Scale into Turkish: Validity and reliability studies]. *Eurasian Journal of Educational Research, 26,* 51–60.

Çolakkadıoğlu, O., & Güçray, S. S. (2007). Ergenlerde Karar Verme Ölçeği'ni Türkçe'ye uyarlama çalışması [The adaptation of the Adolescent Decision-making Questionnaire for the Turkish population]. *Eurasian Journal of Educational Research, 7*, 61–71.

Deniz, M. E. (2006). The relationships among coping with stress, life satisfaction, decision-making styles, and decision self-esteem: An investigation with Turkish university students. *Social Behavior and Personality: An international journal, 34*, 1161–1170. http://doi.org/d57wcq

Diener, E. (1994). Assessing subjective well-being: Progress and opportunities. *Social Indicators Research, 31*, 103–157. http://doi.org/cnd4xt

Diener, E., & Lucas, R. E. (1999). Personality and subjective well-being. In D. Kahneman, E. Diener, & N. Schwarz (Eds.), *Well-being: The foundations of hedonic psychology* (pp. 213–229). New York: Russell-Sage.

Dülger, Ö. (2009). *Ergenlerde algılanan sosyal destek ile karar verme davranışları arasındaki ilişkinin incelenmesi* [Correlation between decision-making behavior and the perceived social support of teenagers]. Unpublished Master's thesis, Marmara University, Turkey.

Friedman, I. A., & Mann, L. (1993). Coping patterns in adolescent decision-making: An Israeli-Australian comparison. *Journal of Adolescence, 16*, 187–199. http://doi.org/bpmx72

Frisch, M. B. (2000). Improving mental and physical health care through quality of life therapy and assessment. In E. Diener & D. R. Rahtz (Eds.), *Advances in quality of life theory and research* (pp. 207–241). London, England: Kluwer Academic Press.

Frydenberg, E., & Lewis, R. (1991). Adolescent coping: The different ways in which boys and girls cope. *Journal of Adolescence, 14, 119–133.* http://doi.org/d84232

Goodenow, C. (1993). The psychological sense of school membership among adolescents: Scale development and educational correlates. *Psychology in the Schools, 30*, 79–90. http://doi.org/b27t2v

Güçray, S. S. (1998). Bazı kişisel değişkenler, algılanan sosyal destek ve atılganlığın karar verme stilleri ile ilişkisi [Relations among some sociodemographic variables, perceived social support from family/friends, assertiveness, and the decision response style]. *Turkish Psychological Counseling and Guidance Journal, 2*, 7–16.

Halpern, D. F. (1997). Sex differences in intelligence: Implications for education. *American Psychologist, 52*, 1091–1102. http://doi.org/d3cvgn

Hamarta, E. (2009). A prediction of self-esteem and life satisfaction by social problem-solving. *Social Behavior and Personality: An international journal, 37*, 73–82. http://doi.org/b6g

Harter, S. (1993). Causes and consequences of low self-esteem in children and adolescents. In R. E. Baumeister (Ed.), *Self-esteem: The puzzle of low self-regard* (pp. 87–116). New York: Plenum.

Hortaçsu, N. (1997). İnsan ilişkileri [Human relationships]. İstanbul, Turkey: İmge Kitabevi.

Huebner, E. S. (1991). Correlates of life satisfaction in children. *School Psychology Quarterly, 6*, 103–111. http://doi.org/c27mks

Huebner, E. S. (1994). Preliminary development and validation of a multidimensional life satisfaction scale for children. *Psychological Assessment, 6, 149–158.* http://doi.org/bqpc8z

Huebner, E. S. (1997). Life satisfaction and happiness. In G. Bear, K. Minke, & A. Thomas (Eds.), *Children's needs II: Development, problems, and alternatives* (pp. 271–278). Washington, DC: National Association of School Psychologists.

Huebner, E. S., Drane, J. W., & Valois, R. F. (2000). Levels of demographic correlates of adolescent life satisfaction reports. *School Psychology International, 21, 281–292.* http://doi.org/cp39c2

Huebner, E. S., Funk, B. A., & Gilman, R. (2000). Cross-sectional and longitudinal psychosocial correlates of adolescent life satisfaction reports. *Canadian Journal of School Psychology, 16*, 53–64. http://doi.org/cv5rfq

Janis, I. L., & Mann, L. (1977). *Decision-making: A psychological analysis of conflict, choice, and commitment.* New York: Free Press.

Köker, S. (1991). *Normal ve sorunlu ergenlerin yasam doyumu düzeyinin karşılaştırılması* [Comparison of the life satisfaction of healthy and unhealthy adolescents]. Unpublished Master's thesis, Ankara University, Turkey.

Kuzgun, Y. (1992). Karar Stratejileri Ölçeği: Geliştirilmesi ve standardizasyonu [Decision Strategies Scale: Development and standardization]. In R. Bayraktar & I. Dağ (Eds.), *VII. National Psychology Congress Scientific Studies* (pp. 161–170). Ankara, Turkey: Turkish Psychologists Association.

Mann, L., Harmoni, R., & Power, C. (1989). Adolescent decision-making: The development of competence. *Journal of Adolescence, 12, 265–278.* http://doi.org/crmzmz

Miller, D. C., & Byrnes, J. P. (2001). Adolescents' decision-making in social situations: A self-regulation perspective. *Journal of Applied Developmental Psychology, 22, 237–256.* http://doi.org/dgc3j8

Neto, F. (1993). The Satisfaction With Life Scale: Psychometric properties in an adolescent sample. *Journal of Youth and Adolescence, 22*, 125–134. http://doi.org/cpkrnx

Nickerson, A. B., & Nagle, R. J. (2004). The influence of parent and peer attachments on life satisfaction in middle childhood and early adolescence. *Social Indicators Research, 66, 35–60.* http://doi.org/b6fpg3

Okwumabua, J. O., Wong, S. P., & Duryea, E. J. (2003). Depressive symptoms and decision-making among African-American youth. *Journal of Adolescent Research, 18*, 436–453. http://doi.org/dprb59

Payne, J. W., Bettman, R. J., & Johnson, J. E. (1993). *The adaptive decision maker.* New York: Cambridge University Press.

Piko, B. (2001). Gender differences and similarities in adolescents' ways of coping. *Psychological Record, 51*, 223–235.

Poikolainen, K., Kanerva, R., & Lönnqvist, J. (1995). Social class and defense styles among adolescents. *Journal of Adolescence, 18*, 669–677. http://doi.org/c2xnqc

Pollack, W. (1998). *Real boys: Rescuing our sons from the myths of boyhood.* New York: Holt.

Resnick, L. (1987). *Education and learning to think.* Washington, DC: National Academy Press.

Rigby, K. (2002). *New perspectives on bullying.* London, England: Kingsley.

Schvaneveldt, J. D., & Adams, G. R. (1983). Adolescents and the decision-making process. *Theory into Practice, 22*, 98–104. http://doi.org/dxgj4m

Seligman, M. E. P., & Csikszentmihalyi, M. (2000). Positive psychology: An introduction. *American Psychologist, 55*, 5–14. http://doi.org/dt4zs8

Steinberg, L. (2007). *Adolescence* (8th ed.). New York: McGraw-Hill.

Valois, R. F., Paxton, R. J., Zullig, K. J., & Huebner, E. S. (2006). Life satisfaction and violent behaviors among middle school students. *Journal of Child and Family Studies, 15*, 695–707. http://doi.org/dwtwrw

Valois, R. F., Zullig, K. J., Huebner, E. S., Kammermann, S. K., & Drane, J. W. (2002). Relationship between life satisfaction and sexual risk-taking behaviors among adolescents. *Journal of Child & Family Studies, 11,* 427–440. http://doi.org/fg458x

Zullig, K. J., Valois, R. F., Huebner, E. S., Oeltmann, J. E., & Drane, J. W. (2001). Relationship between perceived life satisfaction and adolescents' substance abuse. *Journal of Adolescent Health, 29,* 279–288. http://doi.org/bv42j3

Fulya Cenkseven-Önder, Psychological Counseling and Guidance Department, Çukurova University. Correspondence concerning this article should be addressed to: Fulya Cenkseven-Önder, Psychological Counseling and Guidance Department, Faculty of Education, Çukurova University, 01330 Balcalı, Adana, Turkey. Email: fulyac@cu.edu.tr

Human Ecology

No society can long sustain itself unless its members have learned the sensitivities, motivations and skills involved in assisting and caring for other human beings.

—Urie Bronfenbrenner

Introduction

The field of human ecology draws from multiple fields of sciences including but not limited to psychology, sociology, and anthropology for the study of our interaction with each other, as well as with natural and built environments. In general, human ecologists take a transdisciplinary approach to understanding and describing the human experience in context of our environments.

A comprehensive treatment of human ecology far exceeds the scope of this chapter, however, and in keeping with the premise that all human experience has an ecology, three human ecological concepts, intrapersonal ecology, interpersonal ecology, and environmental identity (Clayton, 2003) are of considerable importance in context of the psychology of sustainability. These three concepts allow us to understand the ecology of our experience individually, socially, and in the context of our environment.

Theories and Concepts in Context of Sustainability

Intrapersonal and Interpersonal Ecology

Sociologist and psychologists studying the relationship of individuals and groups to nature consider the self and identity much as these were described by G.H. Mead (Holland &

Lachicotte, 2007). This understanding has also come to include symbolic interactionism, the notion that development of meaning and perception of reality are construed and constructed as we interpret and experience the actions of others around us (Blumer, 1969; Stryker, 2008). The concepts of intrapersonal ecology and interpersonal ecology were developed from Meadian perspectives of self and identity, development of meaning and perception of reality as per symbolic interactionism, and from research in positive psychology (Seligman, 2002) pertaining to the effect our self-perception can have on our perception of others and the environment.

Simply put how we think, feel, and act toward ourselves (intrapersonal ecological experience) affects how we think, feel, and act toward others (interpersonal ecological experience). If we adopt an ecological perspective of the relationship between self and other it becomes much easier to understand the need for creating and maintaining a healthy human ecology. It is also important to understand that this relationship is reciprocal (Figure 4.1), meaning that the state or condition of human ecology affects the state or condition of intrapersonal and interpersonal ecologies and vice versa.

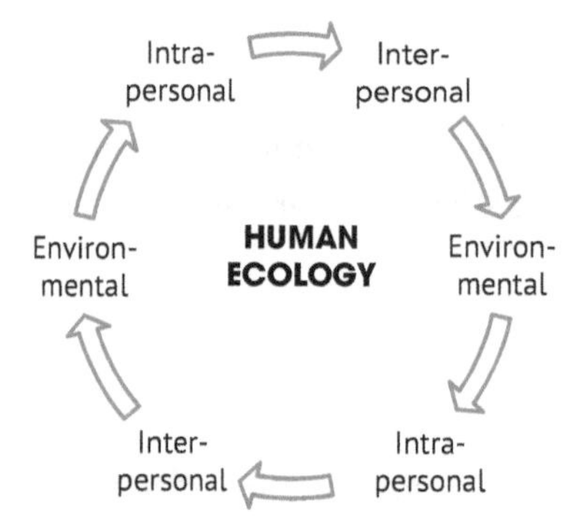

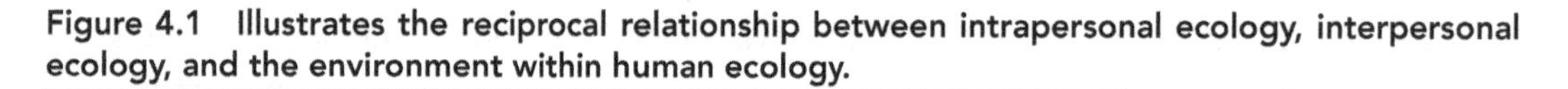

Figure 4.1 Illustrates the reciprocal relationship between intrapersonal ecology, interpersonal ecology, and the environment within human ecology.

Environmental Identity

Origins of environmental identity can be traced to the philosophy of deep ecology (Naess, 1973, 2010). "Deep ecology takes exception to the notion of human superiority in context of life on Earth, insists on a broadening of self to include nature such that one develops an ecological self" (Naess, 1995, p. 404). As the individual develops an ecological self he or she engages in a life that is characterized by increased ecologically continuous behavior that is sustainable behavior (Chandler, 2014, Devall, 1988; Devall & Sessions, 1988; Naess, 2010). Holding to the notion of an ecological self, sociologists and psychologists began to research the relationship of nature with identity and self (Holland & Lachicotte, 2007; Stryker, 2008; Stryker & Burke, 2000). This work would eventually yield the conceptualization of an environmental identity (Clayton, 2003). "Environmental identity arises from individuals' unique ways of thinking and communicating about, interacting with, and acting on behalf of nature" (Chandler, 2014, p. 45).

About Feature Articles

As you read the first article *Nature and Animals in Human Social Interactions* consider how you might incorporate a nonhuman animal or wild landscape into your intrapersonal ecological experience. How might doing so affect your sense of self and the interpersonal ecologies with which you interact.

The second reading in this chapter *Environmental Hermeneutics and Environmental/ Eco-Psychology: Explorations in Environmental Identity* is a fascinating discussion about how we interpret the environment around us and the affect that this interpretation has on the formation of environmental identity. While reading think about how you think about the environment around you. Is this process and perception different than how you perceive the environment in general or larger aspects of it, for example with Climate Change?

References

Blumer, H. (1969). *Symbolic interactionism: Perspective and method.* Berkeley, CA: University of California Press.

Chandler, R. (2014). *I am the paradigm shift: A grounded theory of learners' sustainability outcome comprehension experience.* Ann Arbor, MI: ProQuest.

Clayton, S. (2003). Environmental identity: A conceptual and operational definition. In S. Clayton & S. Opotow (Eds.), *Identity and the natural environment* (pp. 45–65). Cambridge, MA: MIT Press.

Devall, B. (1988). Simple in means, rich in ends: Practicing deep ecology. Salt Lake City, UT: Gibbs Smith.

Devall, B., & Sessions, G. (1985). Deep ecology. In C. Hanks (Ed.), *Technology and value* (pp. 455–459). Malden, MA. Wiley-Blackwell.

Holland, D., Lachicotte, Jr., W. (2007). Vygotsky, Mead, and the New Sociocultural Studies of Identity. In H. Daniels, M. Cole, & J. Wertsch (Eds.), *The Cambridge Companion to Vygotsky* (pp. 101–135). Cambridge: Cambridge University Press. doi: 10.1017/CCOL05211831040.005

Naess, A. (1973) The shallow and the deep, long-range ecology movement. A summary, Inquiry, 16:1–4, 95–100, doi: 10.1080/00201747308601682

Naess, A. (1995). Self-realization: An ecological approach to the world. In D. R. Drengson & Y. Inoue (Eds.), *The deep ecology movement: An Introductory anthology* (pp. 13–30). Berkley, CA: North Atlantic Books.

Naess, A. (2010). The deep ecological movement: Some philosophical aspects. In D. R. Keller (Ed.), *Environmental ethics: The big questions* (pp. 402–415). Malden, MA: Wiley Blackwell.

Seligman, M. E. (2002). Positive psychology, positive prevention, and positive therapy. *Handbook of Positive Psychology, 2*, 3–12.

Stryker, S. (2008). From Mead to a structural symbolic interactionism and beyond. *Annual Review of Sociology*, *34*, 15–31. Retrieved from http://www.annualreviews.org/doi/pdf/10.1146/annurev.soc.34.040507.134649

Stryker, S., & Burke, P. (2000). The past, present, and future of Identity Theory. *Social Psychology Quarterly, 63*, 284–297.

READING 4

Nature and Animals in Human Social Interactions

Fostering Environmental Identity

Susan Clayton

What We Ignore

As the premise of this volume suggests, humans ignore much of what goes on in the world. This is a necessary consequence of our limited perceptual and attentional capacities. In recent years research has provided dramatic and sometimes humorous examples of what people fail to notice: gorillas walking across a basketball court, a clown on a unicycle, the fact that a person we were speaking with has become someone else entirely (e.g., Hyman et al. 2009; Simons and Chabris 1999). Wrapped up in our internal monologues and goal pursuits, we are particularly inattentive to our environmental context. Robert Gifford coined the phrase "environmental numbness" to describe this phenomenon (see Gifford 2007). More recently, Peter Kahn's (1999) notion of "environmental generational amnesia" comments on the way each generation is oblivious to the environmental degradation that has taken place since the time of the previous generation, something that is also captured in the more general concept of "shifting baseline syndrome" (e.g., Papworth et al. 2008).

This lack of attention and awareness is worrying and dangerous when it encompasses our most pressing environmental problems. Recent polls show a decline in attention to climate change, for example, among the US and British populations (e.g., Jones 2010; Rosenthal 2010). Even among those members of the public who give some thought to environmental issues, the loss of biodiversity tends to get less attention than topics such as pollution. In a recent Gallup poll, only 31 percent said they were concerned about the extinction of plant and animal species (Jones 2010).

Of course, the failure to attend to these issues reflects more than cognitive limits. Emotional defenses also come into play: denial, for example, is a common response to big problems when people aren't sure what to do about them or don't perceive themselves as being able to solve them. Another emotional response is based on group identification. People can be angered if they perceive that their ways of life and social norms are being attacked and are likely to respond by dismissing the message (about environmental problems) and/or derogating the messenger (those who suggest we need to rethink the status quo). This is one reason why environmental discussions have become so politicized in the United States. The result, however, is a public that is largely unaware, inattentive, and unconcerned about the loss of species.

What We Value

This lack of attention to animal conservation does not connote a general apathy. People do care about nature, and about animals. According to the US Fish and Wildlife Service, for example, more Americans are participating in wildlife-related recreation; while the number of hunters and anglers is falling, a growing number of people report watching wildlife (31 percent, 21 percent are birdwatchers; USFWS 2009). Even stronger are attitudes toward animals that are closer to home. Approximately two-thirds of American households include pets (Walsh 2009). As an indication of how highly pets are valued from a purely economic perspective, total US pet expenditures for 2010 are projected to reach $47.7 billion (APPA 2010).

In systematic investigations, both Kellert (1996) and Manfredo (2008) have documented various ways in which we value wildlife. These range from abstract and objective, like a scientific interest or aesthetic appreciation, through utilitarian or moralistic values, to more emotionally based values like affection for nature and affection for individual animals. Both authors describe the possibility of mutualistic relationships between humans and animals; these relationships may be more likely when the animal possesses traits that are similar to humans.

In the middle ground between the domesticated animal-as-family-member and the wild animal, the popularity of zoos suggests that people value the experience of observing animals. Zoos and aquariums are very popular destinations, attracting more yearly visitors than all sporting events combined and more than any other type of informal learning environment; visitors to the zoo describe their experience as enjoyable (Clayton and Myers 2009). Zoo visits reflect not just a value for animals but also, significantly, a value for social interaction. Some of the primary motives reported behind zoo visits include the opportunity to spend time with friends and family. Klenosky and Saunders (2008) examined the factors that were implicated in whether visitors had a good time at the zoo and found two to be predictive: enjoyment and family togetherness.

In other words social motivations underlie many of the interactions people have with animals, from thinking about their pets as friends (95 percent) and/or family members (87 percent;

Walsh 2009) to bonding with family members in front of zoo exhibits or developing a sense of egalitarian relationship with wildlife.

Why the Disjunction?

What explains the simultaneous concern and lack of concern for animals? In part, this reflects a long-standing disjunction between humans and nature that seems to be a dominant theme in Western and perhaps particularly American culture. Nature is defined as what is free from human influence, and when we decide to protect nature we do so by removing it from a human sphere of influence. What is out of our daily experience, however, is all too easily ignored. And when it is ignored it becomes unfamiliar, scary, and potentially disliked (cf. Bixler and Floyd 1997).

Animals may be defined as the ultimate out-group: beings that are totally dissimilar, foreign, and unknowable. Crompton and Kasser (2009) review research showing that animal terms are often used to describe and disparage human out-groups and thus to indicate dissimilarity. Although pet owners form close attachments to "their" animals, it may be that in some cases animals who become part of the domestic sphere no longer represent wild nature. This is particularly evident to the extent that pets are treated more and more like people: wearing clothes, receiving medical care, eating from plates, and being house trained.

And yet even domesticated animals may provide an opportunity for people to be reminded of their love for the natural world. Several studies have found relationships between caring for pets and attitudes toward wild animals that attribute them with greater rights and moral standing (Kafer et al. 1992; Vining and Merrick 2006).

Why We Need to Connect Humans and Nature

People should be encouraged to make the connection between the things they value and the natural world as a whole, for three reasons. First, from an objective point of view, everything is connected: we can't draw a line between the human domain and the natural domain that will make a clear division between the domestic and the wild. Urban ecosystems are still ecosystems, and humans are still animals. Threats to one will affect the rest.

The objective truth, however, is the least important part of the issue. A second reason for making the connection is that human health is intricately dependent on the health of the natural environment. It is clear that our physical well-being requires healthy environments, including access to clean water and clean air, and food from organisms that have not become toxic due to contamination by manufactured chemicals. A growing body of evidence suggests that our mental well-being is also connected to the natural world (e.g., American Psychological Association 2009; Clayton and Myers 2009; Kuo and Faber Taylor 2004; Fuller et al. 2007; Wells

2000; Wells and Evans 2003): natural environments, and perhaps particularly healthy, diverse ecosystems, promote cognitive restoration and stress reduction. The potential benefits of relationships with animals has led to an increasing number of therapy programs in which children are given opportunities to interact with, or care for, a variety of animals.

A third reason to promote connections between the human realm and the rest of nature is in order to encourage people to care, actively, for their environment. Conserving nature and protecting species require people to act in ways that are not immediately, or obviously, connected to their own self-interest. Decades of research on prosocial behavior have shown that people are capable of profoundly altruistic behavior, sacrificing their own self-interest in order to promote the welfare of others. One of the best predictors of this type of altruism is the extent to which the person being helped is seen as similar to the helper, that, in fact, the helper is able to empathize with the one who needs help (e.g., Batson 1987).

Although most of the research has, unsurprisingly, studied humans helping other humans, several studies have shown that people are able to make this empathic connection to animals or even other elements of nature. My research has consistently found that a perception of animals as similar to humans is positively correlated with interest in protecting that animal or species (Clayton, Fraser, and Burgess 2008; Clayton, Fraser, and Saunders 2009). In an experimental manipulation, Schultz (2000) found that students who were explicitly told to take the perspective of an animal harmed by pollution showed a greater level of environmental concern than students who merely read about the problem without taking the animal's perspective. Berenguer (2007) showed a similar effect, not only when people were asked to take the perspective of a bird but also if they were asked to take the perspective of a tree!

Interestingly, a dispositional tendency toward empathy for other humans has been found to be associated with concern for animals, at least as reflected in vegetarianism (Filippi et al. 2010; Preylo and Arikawa 2008). Unfortunately, recent research also suggests that empathy as a whole may be declining (O'Brien, Hsing, and Konrath 2010). According to a meta-analysis, American college students are less likely to report that they try to take the perspective of another person than they were twenty or thirty years ago. If we are less inclined to empathize with other humans, it seems even more unlikely that we would try to take the perspective of a nonhuman animal.

What to Do

What is needed, then, is an emphasis on ways for people to make personal connections with nature. These connections can be found in opportunities to experience nature on a regular basis, through walks in the woods, bird watching, and other nonspectacular encounters with nonhuman nature. Research consistently shows that one of the strongest determinants of environmentalism as an adult is regular experience of the natural world as a child (Wells and Lekies 2006). Sheer familiarity with something tends to increase liking; in addition, repeated exposures allow us to learn more and feel more confident in our ability to navigate the wild or coexist with wildlife.

Humans are highly social animals, and their responses are correspondingly dependent on their social context. This is one reason why studies often find such disappointingly low correlations between individual attitudes or values and their behavior: conformity is a stronger determinant of behavior than principle. Connections to nature will be strongest when these connections are supported by, and have legitimacy within, a social context. Nature should be part of family outings and educational curricula. Neighborhoods should include pockets of public green space. City dwellers should encounter nature on their way to work.

Repeated encounters with nature and with animals, in social groups, allow people to recognize their connections with nature and their similarities with animals in a social context that validates those intersections, perhaps by providing experiences of shared emotional responses (e.g., Kals, Schumacher, and Montada 1999). The social context, in turn, can encourage people to link those emotional responses to a sense of responsibility and action.

Environmental Identity

My recent work has explored the concept of *environmental identity*: a sense of oneself as interdependent with the natural world, a self-concept that encourages cognitive and emotional connections between self and nature. Although everyone has the potential to have an environmental identity, just as everyone has the potential for an identity based on race or gender, people vary in the extent to which they consider it an important part of their self-definition. Using a questionnaire that was developed to measure this construct, I have found that people high in environmental identity are likely to have proenvironmental attitudes and to behave in more environmentally sustainable ways (Clayton 2003). They are also more sympathetic to the needs of animals and likely to support animal rights (Clayton 2008).

An environmental identity can be most effectively developed within a supportive social network. Early childhood experiences in nature are even more significant when they include a social component, such as the presence of a family member or other significant relationship (Chawla 1986; Kals, Schumacher, and Montada 1999); sharing nature with others provides a richer context for the interpretations of nature, emotional experiences, and self-understandings that constitute the environmental identity. Conversely, an unsupportive social context makes it harder to maintain a sense of oneself as a part of nature.

Fortunately, research suggests that many people value the opportunity to interact with others in a natural environment and experience nature in the presence of others—to develop, in other words, what Fraser has described as an *environmental social identity* (Fraser et al. 2009). An environmental social identity situates the sense of self as interdependent with nature within a social context that makes it a basis for a group identity as well: we are connected by our love of nature, care for animals, or work to promote conservation. Such an identity allows people to create or strengthen social ties based on shared values for nature, to gain social capital based on understanding of nature, to adopt a social role that emphasizes interactions with nature, and to enhance self-esteem and self-efficacy by working with others to take actions on behalf of nature.

In research on the environmental social identity of zoo volunteers, Fraser et al. (2009) found that both love of animals and the desire for social interaction were among the reasons to volunteer. Importantly, volunteers reported becoming more aware of, and committed to, conservation as a result of volunteering because of the ways in which their interactions with others solidified and amplified the initial support for animal conservation.

Social Interactions in Zoos

Zoo volunteers, as in the Fraser et al. (2009) study, are more committed to the protection of animals than the average person. But many average people are also motivated to cultivate an environmental social identity—that is, at a minimum, to have nature-based social experiences in which shared values are nurtured or expressed. Many families, for example, consider camping or hiking to be important to developing family bonds. A common way to create social experiences of nature can be found in zoos. As described above, zoos are a popular leisure destination and are particularly favored for family visits.

What do zoos do? Traditionally, they have been seen as providing educational information, but they do much more. They provide experiences that are emotionally engaging and socially significant. The animals themselves naturally arouse emotional responses of awe, amusement, even fear or disgust; these shared emotional experiences provide an important basis for strengthening bonds among the observers, and the observers can use the opportunity to discuss their relationship to the natural world.

Beyond strengthened social relationships, these experiences provide an opportunity to communicate shared values and conceptualizations of the human relationship with nature. Adult visitors often describe their motives for visiting as related to fostering wildlife appreciation or learning among the others in the group (Clayton and Myers 2009). In a recent qualitative study, Fraser (2009) interviewed parents about their motivation for taking children to the zoo. He reported four themes that emerged from the responses: encouraging altruism and empathy, promoting environmental values, enhancing self-esteem, and communicating cultural norms. Parents specifically valued the way in which the zoo facilitated bonding within the family and allowed them to talk to their children about respect, responsibility, care, and appreciation for nature. There is research suggesting that the development of empathy may be fostered by such experiences. For example, Kidd and Kidd (1996), in an observational study, found that the youngest children (three to five) took an egocentric perspective to animals in a petting museum, but the older children were increasingly likely to express concern (six to eight) and empathy (nine to twelve) for the animals.

Research I have conducted in zoos shows some fascinating and creative ways in which responses to the animal exhibits are used to reflect values and create shared social experiences. In order to explore the manifestations of environmental social identities, my colleagues and I observed people as they observed a variety of zoo exhibits. In a first set of studies (Clayton, Fraser, and Saunders 2009), we were most interested in emotional responses and in reactions that indicated awareness of similarity. We found that a significant proportion of comments reflected some sense of shared identity with the animals, as indicated by statements explicitly comparing humans and animals, taking the perspective of the animal, making inferences about what the animal was thinking, or imitating the animal. Importantly, survey data showed that a sense of connection to the animal was a strong predictor of wanting to know more about the animal and to help protect the species in the wild. A sense of connection was also significantly correlated with a happy response to the animals; similarly, Tunnicliffe (1996) found that more anthropomorphic comments about animals were made in a zoo than in a natural history museum, and that the number of anthropomorphic comments was related to the number of comments about liking the animals.

The tendency to imitate the animal may be significant, because some interesting recent work suggests that imitation might have a direct link to empathy. In a study of neurological processes, imitation of others led to greater activation of brain areas that are associated with action representation and that are in turn linked with the emotional response system (Carr et al. 2003). Thus the ways in which children hop like kangaroos, growl like tigers, and flap their arms like birds may be more important than we think in fostering emotional responses and an environmental identity.

In a second set of studies (Clayton, Fraser, and Burgess 2008), our focus was on the ways in which the animal exhibits prompted social interactions among visitors. We observed nonverbal and verbal interactions among 409 and 396 small (family or peer) groups, respectively. The most common responses were calling attention to the animal (seen in 84 percent of groups) and pointing to the animal (89 percent). We were struck by these seemingly banal behaviors: in the vast majority of groups, the response to the animal was to use it as a stimulus for a social interaction. People were not content to view the animal as solitary individuals; they wanted to share their awe, wonder, or amusement. Other common reactions included leaning together, found among almost 40 percent of the groups, and discussing the animal, found among almost 80 percent. (We distinguished between conveying actual information and merely discussing the animal in a descriptive way.) Thus the animal exhibits served to bring people together, physically and through conversation.

A further important type of response was a positive comment, which occurred among 47 percent of groups. This suggests that the exhibit was not just prompting a social interaction, but allowing the groups to affirm a shared value, that of appreciation for the animals. Some of the comments specifically articulated a human relationship to the animals, including, "She loves him!" "He's just like a human!" and "Don't you want to see your little cousin?" Overall, the observations indicated that at least some visitors were using their trip to the zoo to strengthen social bonds and to extend those bonds to at least loosely encompass the zoo animals.

This focus on positive experiences at the zoo should not obscure some of the tensions and ethical concerns associated with zoos. As Milstein (2009) recently described, zoos embody a dialectic between human mastery of nature and harmony with nature; between exploitation and idealism of nature; and, most centrally to this essay, between othering of animals and connection to animals. Thus we should be mindful of the extent to which certain zoo practices may promote disconnected and exploitative attitudes toward animals. However, as Milstein states, "ending zoos may miss an important opportunity to transform zoos and their reflection and production of nature-human relations" (31). Zoo practices have the potential, as I have found in my work, to encourage admiration, respect, and connection between humans and animals.

Such practices involve going beyond merely presenting the animal to situate it in contexts that are ecological, informational, and interactional. Situating it ecologically, as is already done by many zoos, involves providing a physical context of plants, geographical features, and in some cases other organisms. This allows the animal to behave in a way that is more normal, putting the focus on what the animal does as opposed to simply what it is, and may highlight the animal's needs in terms of food, shelter, and experience. Situating it informationally requires providing explicit information about the animal, not only a description of its physical appearance and habits but also information about its status in the wild. Finally, situating it interactionally means allowing zoo visitors to understand the ways in which people affect and are affected by the animal, giving them opportunities to make connections with the animal, and explaining how human activities intersect with, infringe on, or incorporate the species. This could include a discussion of how people are working to protect the animal in the wild or the things zoos do to keep the animals healthy.

From Caring to Conservation: The Need for Research

Appreciation and affection for animals, as pets or in the zoo, is quite common, and by itself it is clearly not enough. Many animal lovers find no dissonance between pampering their pets and eating animals kept in cruel conditions, or between admiring the elephants at the zoo and contributing to the destruction of their habitat. But the appreciation is a first step. We may not protect all the things we care for, but we are unlikely to protect the things we don't care for. What is important is the recognition, first, that people have the potential and even the proclivity to form emotional connections to nature—what E. O. Wilson (1984) famously characterized as biophilia—and, second, that a recognition of similarity enables empathy, which is associated with helping behavior. What we need is more research not only on ways to promote the connection but also on ways to translate the connection into actions that protect animals. Both of these links require attention to social networks and contexts and the ways in which social interactions nurture and sustain our respect for the natural world.

Zoos seem to be increasingly aware of the importance of fostering a sense of shared identity. Exhibits encourage people to recognize the similarities between themselves and other animals by, for example, describing shared physical traits and behavioral patterns. Bexell and colleagues (2009) encouraged participants in their wildlife conservation camp to take the perspective of animals, with promising effects on attitudes and behavior. But other signs may try to attract interest by stressing how bizarre and different animals are, or promote a sense of distance from the animal through the physical design of the exhibit, a strategy that may be associated with reduced interest in conservation (Clayton, Fraser, and Saunders 2009). Research can help provide information about the best way to present and describe animals in order to promote caring and concern rather than contempt or indifference.

Zoos may also be missing the opportunity to help visitors link their concerns to effective action. Although zoo visitors appear to trust and value the zoo as a source of information about environmental and conservation issues (Fraser 2009), results from at least one survey showed that visitors felt confused about what actions they could personally take to address these issues (Milstein 2009).

Conclusion: Conservation Psychology

Conservation psychologists are trying to use the methodological tools, theoretical understandings, and research results from psychology to encourage a healthy relationship between humans and nature, one in which people obtain the benefits that nature can provide for physical and mental well-being and people, in turn, protect ecosystems in which animal species can flourish. By participating in social interactions as well as representing the unknowable Other, animals bridge the gap between humans and nature and provide a powerful route for promoting both human and environmental health. By their charismatic attributes and behavior, animals attract our limited attention and remind us that nature deserves notice.

References

American Pet Products Association (APPA). 2010. "Industry Statistics and Trends." http://www.americanpetproducts.org/press_industrytrends.asp.

American Psychological Association Task Force on the Interface between Psychology and Global Climate Change. 2009. "Psychology and Global Climate Change: Addressing a Multi-Faceted Phenomenon and Set of Challenges." Washington, DC: Author. http://www.apa.org/science/about/publications/climate-change.aspx.

Batson, C. D. 1987. "Prosocial Motivation: Is It Ever Truly Altruistic?" In *Advances in Experimental Social Psychology*, vol. 20, edited by L. Berkowitz, 65–122. San Diego: Academic Press.

Berenguer, J. 2007. "The Effect of Empathy in Proenvironmental Attitudes and Behaviors." *Environment and Behavior* 39: 269–83.

Bexell, S., O. Jarrett, X. Ping, and R. Feng. 2009. "Fostering Humane Attitudes toward Animals." *Encounter* 22: 25–27.

Bixler, R., and M. Floyd. 1997. "Nature Is Scary, Disgusting, and Uncomfortable." *Environment and Behavior* 5: 202–47.

Carr, L., M. Iacoboni, M-C. Dubeau, J. Mazziotta, and G. L. Lenzi. 2003. "Neural Mechanisms of Empathy in Humans: A Relay from Neural Systems for Imitation to Limbic Areas." *Proceedings of the National Academy of Sciences* 100: 5497–502.

Chawla, L. 1986. "The Ecology of Environmental Memory." *Children's Environments Quarterly* 3 (4): 34–42.

Clayton, S. 2003. "Environmental Identity: A Conceptual and an Operational Definition." In *Identity and the Natural Environment*, edited by S. Clayton and S. Opotow, 45–65. Cambridge, MA: MIT Press.

———. 2008. "Attending to Identity: Ideology, Group Membership, and Perceptions of Justice." In *Advances in Group Processes: Justice*, edited by K. Hegtvedt and J. Clay-Warner, 241–66. Bingley, UK: Emerald.

Clayton, S., J. Fraser, and C. Burgess. 2008. "Defining Wild Animals: Visitor Conversations in Response to Zoo Exhibits." Paper presented at the meeting of the Society for Human Ecology, Bellingham, WA. September.

Clayton, S., J. Fraser, and C. Saunders. 2009. "Zoo Experiences: Conversations, Connections, and Concern for Animals." *Zoo Biology* 28: 377–97.

Clayton, S., and G. Myers. 2009. *Conservation Psychology: Understanding and Promoting Human Care for Nature*. Oxford: Wiley-Blackwell.

Crompton, T., and T. Kasser. 2009. *Meeting Environmental Challenges: The Role of Human Identity*. Surrey, UK: WWF.

Filippi, M., G. Riccitelli, A. Falini, F. Di Salle, P. Vuilleumier, et al. 2010. "The Brain Functional Networks Associated to Human and Animal Suffering Differ among Omnivores, Vegetarians, and Vegans." PLOS ONE 5 (5): e10847. doi:10.1371/journal.pone.0010847.

Fraser, J. 2009. "The Anticipated Utility of Zoos for Developing Moral Concern in Children." *Curator* 52: 349–61.

Fraser, J., S. Clayton, J. Sickler, and A. Taylor. 2009. "Belonging at the Zoo: Retired Volunteers, Conservation Activism, and Collective Identity." *Ageing and Society* 29: 351–68.

Fuller, R., K. Irvine, P. Devine-Wright, P. Warren, and K. Gaston. 2007. "Psychological Benefits of Greenspace Increase with Biodiversity." *Biology Letters* 3 (1): 390–94.

Gifford, R. 2007. "Environmental Psychology and Sustainable Development: Expansion, Maturation, and Challenges." *Journal of Social Issues* 63: 199–212.

Hyman, I., S. M. Boss, B. Wise, K. McKenzie, and J. Caggiano. 2009. "Did You See the Unicycling Clown?" *Applied Cognitive Psychology*. doi:10.1002/acp.1638.

Jones, J. 2010. "In U.S., Many Environmental Issues at 20-Year-Low Concern." March 16. http://www.gallup.com/poll/126716/Environmental-Issues-Year-Low-Concern.aspx.

Kafer, R., D. Lago, P. Wamboldt, and F. Harrington. 1992. "The Pet Relationship Scale: Replication of Psychometric Properties in Random Samples and Association with Attitudes toward Wild Animals." *Anthrozoös* 5 (2): 93–105.

Kahn, P. H., Jr. 1999. *The Human Relationship with Nature*. Cambridge, MA: MIT Press.

Kals, E., D. Schumacher, and L. Montada. 1999. "Emotional Affinity towards Nature as a Motivational Basis to Protect Nature." *Environment and Behavior* 31 (2): 178–202.

Kellert, S. 1996. *The Value of Life: Biological Diversity and Human Society.* Washington, DC: Island Press.

Kidd, A., and R. Kidd. 1996. "Developmental Factors Leading to Positive Attitudes toward Wildlife and Conservation." *Applied Animal Behavior Science* 47: 119–25.

Klenosky, D., and C. Saunders. 2008. "Put Me in the Zoo: A Laddering Study of Zoo Visitor Motives." *Tourism Review International* 11: 317–27.

Kuo, F., and A. Faber Taylor. 2004. "A Potential Natural Treatment for Attention-Deficit/Hyperactivity Disorder: Evidence from a National Study." *American Journal of Public Health* 94 (9): 1580–86.

Manfredo, M. 2008. *Who Cares about Wildlife?* New York: Springer.

Milstein, T. 2009. "Somethin' Tells Me It's All Happening at the Zoo: Discourse, Power, and Conservationism." *Environmental Communication* 3: 25–48.

O'Brien, E., C. Hsing, and S. Konrath. 2010. "Changes in Dispositional Empathy over Time in American College Students: A Meta-Analysis." Poster presented at the American Psychological Society meeting, Boston, MA. May.

Papworth, S. K., J. Rist, L. Coad, and E. J. Milner-Gulland. 2008. "Evidence for Shifting Baseline Syndrome in Conservation." *Conservation Letters* 2 (2): 93–100.

Preylo, B., and H. Arikawa. 2008. "Comparison of Vegetarians and Non-Vegetarians on Pet Attitudes and Empathy." *Anthrozoös* 21: 387–95.

Rosenthal, E. 2010. "Climate Fears Turn to Doubts among Britons." *New York Times*, May 24. http://www.nytimes.com/2010/05/25/science/earth/25climate.html?emc=eta1.

Schultz, P. W. 2000. "Empathizing with Nature: The Effects of Perspective Taking on Concern for Environmental Issues." *Journal of Social Issues* 56: 391–406.

Simons, D. J., and C. F. Chabris. 1999. "Gorillas in Our Midst: Sustained Inattentional Blindness for Dynamic Events." *Perception* 28: 1059–74.

Tunnicliffe, S. 1996. "Conversations within Primary School Parties Visiting Animal Specimens in a Museum and Zoo." *Journal of Biological Education* 30: 130–41.

US Fish and Wildlife Service (USFWS). 2006. "2006 National Survey of Fishing, Hunting, and Wildlife-Associated Recreation." http://library.fws.gov/pubs/nat_survey2006_final.pdf.

Vining, J. 2003. "Connection to Other Animals and Caring for Nature." *Human Ecology Review* 10: 87–99.

Vining, J., and M. Merrick. 2006. "Pet Keeping, Environmental Attitudes and Behavior, and Quality of Life." Paper presented at the 14th International Conference of the Society for Human Ecology, Bar Harbor, ME. October 18–21.

Walsh, F. 2009. "Human-Animal Bonds I: The Relational Significance of Companion Animals." *Family Process* 48 (4): 462–80.

Wells, N. 2000. "At Home with Nature: Effects of 'Greenness' on Children's Cognitive Functioning." *Environment and Behavior* 32: 775–95.

Wells, N., and G. Evans. 2003. "Nearby Nature: A Buffer of Life Stress among Rural Children." *Environment and Behavior* 35: 311–30.

Wells, N., and K. S. Lekies. 2006. "Nature and the Life Course: Pathways from Childhood Nature Experiences to Adult Environmentalism." *Children, Youth, and Environments* 16: 1–24.

Wilson, E. O. 1984. *Biophilia.* Cambridge, MA: Harvard University Press.

READING 5

Environmental Hermeneutics and Environmental/Eco-Psychology

Explorations in Environmental Identity

David Utsler

Introduction

Environmental hermeneutics is, as the subtitle of this book claims, an "emerging field." It is not the case that philosophical hermeneutics and environmental discourse have not been thought together before. But a "field" suggests a body of knowledge that is at once diverse yet coherent: Diverse, in that there are multiple perspectives and applications; coherent, in that there are recognizable characteristics that make environmental hermeneutics identifiable as a particular way of engaging environmental philosophy. Hermeneutics itself is widely recognized and understood to have multiple applications across a wide variety of disciplines and themes. Indeed, "environmental hermeneutics" might be simply defined as the elaboration of techniques useful for interpreting "the environment" in environmentally related disciplines.

While interpreting environments as a form of a text is certainly one facet of hermeneutical thinking, a broader, more nuanced description is necessary and springs from the purpose of philosophical hermeneutics itself. Richard Palmer writes,

> ... hermeneutics achieves its most authentic dimensions when it moves away from being a conglomeration of devices and techniques for text explication and attempts to see the hermeneutical problem within the horizon of a general account of interpretation itself.[1]

David Utsler, "Environmental Hermeneutics and Environmental/ Eco-Psychology: Explorations in Environmental Identity," *Interpreting Nature: The Emerging Field of Environmental Hermeneutics,* ed. Forrest Clingerman, et al., pp. 123-140, 334-337.

COPYRIGHTED MATERIAL — DO NOT DUPLICATE, DISTRIBUTE, OR POST

Palmer insisted on a broad conception of interpretation, by which he meant that in addition to the interpretation of texts, we seek to understand what is happening in the very act of interpreting itself. We interpret the world around us from the moment of waking until sleeping. "Interpretation is, then, perhaps the most basic act of human thinking; indeed existing itself may be said to be a constant process of interpretation."[2] Hermeneutics is an ongoing dialogical process between the interpreter and her world. This simply means that hermeneutics is not content with simple subject-object dichotomies but operates in the space of a dynamic complex of dialogical relations.

Like philosophical hermeneutics itself, an emerging environmental hermeneutics can and should likewise engage a wide variety of disciplines in a mutual reciprocity wherein environmental hermeneutics both contributes to and gains from such dialogue. The focus of this chapter is to realize this mutual reciprocity between environmental hermeneutics and environmental psychology/ecopsychology.[3] The reciprocal link this chapter will focus upon is the concept of "environmental identity."[4] I will follow the hermeneutical principle that all interpretation entails self-interpretation (a theme prominent in both Gadamer and Ricoeur, among others). Any environmental hermeneutics will likewise entail, explicitly or implicitly, self-interpretation in relation to environments—we can call this self-interpretation the environmental self. Likewise, environmental psychology is explicitly concerned with self-understanding in relation to environments and the ways in which such a relation shapes the psyche. I will proceed by first looking at a few ways that environmental identity has been conceived previously. I will then work out a more specifically hermeneutical understanding of environmental identity, drawing on the hermeneutics of Paul Ricoeur. In the section that follows, I will discuss the discipline of environmental psychology and the related thinking of those working in ecopsychology looking at how environmental identity is conceived therein. In the concluding section, I will argue that environmental identity in environmental psychology and ecopsychology is a psychological "environmental hermeneutics of the self." While it is valid to compare environmental hermeneutics and environmental psychology as distinct and complementary accounts of environmental identity, I will argue that there is also an instance of multidisciplinary accounts of the same reality.

Different Concepts of Environmental Identity

A concept of personal identity and the constitution of selfhood in relation to one's physical environment are not unique to hermeneutics. Some have termed it "ecological identity."[5] While various versions of ecological or environmental identity[6] have been defined and explicated somewhat differently, the unifying thread entails some form of self-understanding that derives from our relationship to the environment, whether "environment" is understood as "the earth," social or cultural environments, or built environments. For Mitchell Thomashow, ecological identity

> refers to all the different ways people construe themselves in relationship to the earth as manifested in personality, values, and sense of self. Nature becomes an object of identification. For the individual, this has extraordinary conceptual ramifications. The interpretation of life experience transcends social and cultural interactions. It also includes a person's connection to the earth, perception of the ecosystem, and direct experience of nature.[7]

Thomashow's definition shares features with a hermeneutical conception of environmental identity. In this quotation, he even notes "the interpretation of life experience" in terms of how we identify ourselves. While not an explicitly developed hermeneutical understanding, Thomashow recognizes that what he calls "life experience"—whether social, cultural, or in nature—is a process of interpretation.

Thomashow's definition of ecological identity pertains primarily to the individual. An individual and personal dimension to any conception of identity will be no less true than one derived from philosophical hermeneutics as well as other disciplines. But collective identities, even those pertaining to the environment, should also be considered. Insightful aspects of a collective environmental identity can be found in environmental justice literature in the work of Robert Melchior Figueroa.

Figueroa's development of the concept of environmental identity links identity to how individuals and communities understand themselves in terms of social location. For statistical purposes, communities are often defined in terms of abstractions, such as zip code or census data. In contrast, Figueroa argues that communities understand themselves in terms of "social location defined by cultural identity." This understanding is one way in which he defines environmental identity.[8] Figueroa expands upon his conception of environmental identity with the following:

> Recognition justice demands that we fully account for the situational aspects of group mobilization for environmental justice by understanding the individual and community environmental identities and environmental heritages at stake. An environmental identity is the amalgamation of cultural identities, ways of life, and self-perceptions that are connected to a given group's physical environment.[9]

For Figueroa, individual and community environmental identities are linked. This parallels very well with a hermeneutical conception of environmental identity that construes identity simultaneously in terms of the same and the other.

What is interesting in Figueroa's conception of environmental identity is that it is not only defined in terms of a relationship to the environment but it gathers all aspects of personal and communal identity that are connected to the physical environment of a person or group. This suggests a more dialogical understanding of the components of identity and self-understanding and (rightly, I think) assumes an integrated connection among them all. Such a conception, I would argue, is inherently hermeneutical in that it encompasses the play (or interplay) of multidimensional realities of existence. This aspect of a "given group's physical environment" would likewise make for an interesting dialogue between environmental justice studies and a "hermeneutics of place" as found in Forrest Clingerman's chapter in this volume. "Place" or "emplacement"[10] and social justice are linked together, which indicates an important dialogue between environmental hermeneutics and environmental justice that needs to take place.

A final hermeneutically interesting observation I would like to make concerning Figueroa's definition of environmental identity is how it is linked with what he calls "environmental heritage." He writes,

> Environmental identity is closely related to environmental heritage, where the meanings and symbols of the past frame values, practices, and places we wish to preserve for ourselves as *members of a community*. In other words, our environmental heritage is our environmental identity in relation to the community viewed over time.[11]

What is immediately striking is how environmental heritage here is clearly predicated on some form or another of narrative theory.[12] How else could Figueroa's definition of environmental heritage obtain if not in narrative form? Environmental heritage is not merely the recounting of bare historical data but clearly involves some sense of meaning in relation to place for the people who possess the particular heritage. Moreover, if environmental heritage is environmental identity narratively configured over time it also brings to the fore (as does narrative) the notion of memory.[13] Again, Clingerman's chapter in this volume takes up a dialectic of memory of the place of time and the time of place. Although Clingerman and Figueroa are doing very different things, it is clear that similar philosophical ideas form the underpinning of their work.

What is evident in just the two foregoing examples of the concept of environmental or ecological identity is that whether explicitly thought of in terms of hermeneutics, self-understanding, self-perception, and all the components that make for grasping identity and constituting selfhood in relationship to the environment involve interpretation. All forms of environmental identity are inherently hermeneutical or, at the very least, are best conceptually explained with the help of hermeneutics. Environmental identity is always an interpretation predicated upon a dialectic between the self and the other than self of one's (and/or a community's) environment. This claim will likewise show itself to be true of environmental identity as it is understood in environmental psychology and ecopsychology. Before turning to that discussion, I will continue this exploration in environmental identity by developing the concept from philosophical hermeneutics.

Nature as One's Other Self/Other than Self: A Hermeneutics of Environmental Identity

My conception of environmental identity will be developed primarily, and nearly exclusively, from the philosophy of Paul Ricoeur. I will occasionally make reference to Hans-Georg Gadamer, whose own hermeneutics provides a fruitful field for environmental identity. I have in other places used hermeneutics to construct an initial understanding of environmental identity.[14] The present chapter develops environmental identity somewhat more completely, before placing it into conversation with environmental psychology in the next section.

Identity and selfhood for Ricoeur are not static categories but are constituted in a complex, multidimensional way.[15] This will be important for our understanding of environmental identity. If identity is not formed dialogically in relation with others, but is actually opposed or contrasted with otherness (we identify *this* one precisely because it is not *that* one), then there can be no such thing as an environmental identity—that is, an identity that can be understood as originating in dialogue with an environment. Let us then establish that identity is not reducible to mere subjectivity or the psychic sphere, but is multidimensional. Ricoeur opens up his work devoted to the "hermeneutics of the self," *Oneself as Another*, with these words: "By the title *Oneself as Another*, I wish to designate the point of convergence between the three major philosophical intentions that influenced the preparation of the studies that make up this book."[16] Notice that the three philosophical intentions (which shall be discussed in a moment) converge at a point from which Ricoeur's conception of selfhood emerges. One's self is oneself "as another," not an isolated autonomous subject. The three "intentions" that converge are "the detour of reflection by way of analysis, the dialectic of selfhood and sameness, and finally the dialectic of selfhood and otherness."[17] Let us look at each of these features and how they reveal an environmental identity in turn.

The main point of the first intention is that we come to the self reflexively rather than in the "immediate positing of the subject."[18] The reflexive aspect is a series of detours back to the self, which simply means that the self does not know itself with immediacy. I can say "I am" but "who" is doing the saying? "Who speaks?" is a fundamental category of reflective analysis for Ricoeur. The answer to that question can only be answered through detours, which can in the case of any given person be limitless. Reflection can be upon where I am from, my race, my religion or lack of religion, my family, the people I choose as my friends, how and what I work at, how and what I play at, and so on infinitely. There is no immediate access to an "inner core" or an "I" apart from reflective analysis through these many detours that answer the question of who is speaking and, Ricoeur adds, acting, recounting (remembering) him- or herself, and who is responsible.[19] What the path of detours reveals is that one is identified in a complex of relations to and through the other (mostly at this point by way of contrast and comparison, of other people, other places, and other things).

Can the physical world, the "natural environment," of which today there is so much concern, be counted among detours of reflective analysis by which we identify ourselves? Does the question "who?" apply here? Are problems related to global climate change, pollution, clean water, agriculture, sustainability, and so forth matters to which identity are relevant? Certainly, each and every aspect of our physical environment will not become a source of identity. Yet, there are places or experiences of places or physical entities that we find meaningful in one way or another, and this meaningfulness gives us a sense of who we are or by which we identify ourselves. Some are more direct or intentional than others. For example, I have fond and vivid memories of my grandparents' farmhouse that had a large stream that ran through the land behind it and a large wood. I spent countless hours walking through or jumping over different parts of the water. In the summer when it was hot enough to leave an almost dry stream bed, I would find wet muddy places in the shade and play with the crawdads. I caught snakes (much to my mother's chagrin and perhaps terror), set traps in which I caught little to nothing, and generally explored again and again this place of solitude and natural richness. To this day, I count part of who I am in relation to these experiences. What I learned about the world and how it works in the multiple little ecosystems I would watch for hours ("all the busy little creatures chasing out their destinies"[20]) formed aspects of my personality and worldview. These experiences were detours that answered the question "who?" for me.

Other detours are less intentional. For example, we cannot exactly dictate where we are born and grow up. Yet, aspects of our physical environment (and other related ones) shape our sense of self. This can be so negatively as well. I think of classmates from high school that these many years later talk about "how glad I was to get out of that place! I'm never going back!" In part their identity is influenced by self-consciously *not* identifying with a particular place. This, too, is a detour by way of reflective analysis, even if the analysis resulted in a negative reaction to a place. A detour by way of negation is no less a detour. The point is that environments, including "natural" or biotic ones, can be among the detours from which we identify ourselves.

The second intention underlying *Oneself as Another* is the dialectic between sameness and selfhood. Ricoeur uses the Latin *idem* to refer to the former and *ipse* that latter. *Idem* as identity is sameness in both a numerical and qualitative sense.[21] Applied to the person, I am myself and not another. Over time, I am the same person. The young boy who once traversed the streams and woods now sits in front of his computer writing this chapter and all the years between these two events do not change that identification. The qualitative sense is simply that two things can be "interchangeable with no noticeable difference."[22] *Ipse* is identity that "implies no assertion concerning some unchanging core of the personality."[23] In contrast to sameness, *ipseity*, or selfhood, accounts for the dynamic, changing aspects of personality in the same person.

This dialectic between *idem* and *ipse* offers little to our understanding of environmental identity, but there is one insight worth mentioning that will figure into the later discussion of ecopsychology, especially as it relates to therapy. Sameness and selfhood, as Ricoeur defines them, imply that a single person can change. Why is this important? Many environmental identities (ways of interpreting oneself in relation to nature) are not always necessarily good. In the case of those who interpret nature as an endless supply of resources to be exploited, for example, it would be unfortunate if identity was nothing more than an inner core to which we had unmediated access, unrelated to anything external, and fixed. That identity is arrived at through detours is revelatory in that it matters what detours are taken and the disposition in which they are taken. New detours can refigure the self in ways more environmentally benign. And for those who experience violence, conflict, or any number of psycho-social troubles, nature can be healing (more on this later).

The third and final intention is the dialectic of selfhood with otherness that is opened up by *ipseity*. Ricoeur notes that remaining "within the circle of sameness-identity, the otherness of the other than self offers nothing original ..." but when otherness and self-hood are paired together it offers a way of being with

> otherness of a kind that can be constitutive of selfhood as such. *Oneself as Another* suggests from the outset that the self-hood of oneself implies otherness to such an intimate degree that one cannot be thought of without the other, that instead one passes into the other ... (oneself inasmuch as being other).[24]

Unlike the first intention where the other is a detour back to the self, keeping self and other distinct, the third intention refers to a more profound intimacy where one is oneself by virtue of being other. Can nature be such an other?

Beginning with Aldo Leopold at least, there is no shortage of writing that proclaims human oneness with the nonhuman world. Much nature writing has emphasized oneself as another (our unity with nature) at the expense of the self (our uniqueness and difference from all other things). The self, however, is prior to the "one's other self." Otherwise what would the other than self be other to? Even though it is the case that we may discover the self more profoundly through experiencing the other, the self was always already there to have the experience. The tension between separation and intimacy must not be forgotten. Retaining tensions such as this one is a hallmark of hermeneutical thinking. After noting these issues, we should not hesitate to understand nature in terms of the third intention. I have elsewhere considered this intimacy in terms of vital being and corporeality.[25] Tradition and culture also join the human and nonhuman together creatively:

> Relationships with the land are generated from and enhanced through cultural histories, stories, and songs. Through my family, I encountered and gathered my Rarámuri cultural history through morals, ecological lessons and observations. Cultural history is more than a story; it's a way of perceiving ourselves as part of an extended ecological family of all species with

> whom we share ancestry, origins, and breath; a way of acknowledging that life in our environment is viable only when we view the life surrounding us as family. This family, or kin, includes all the natural elements of the ecosystem.[26]

In this passage, Enrique Salmon indicates the relation of his family and culture to the land while also extending his family to include the land. This is no doubt the experience of many indigenous peoples: that life is only "viable" when one's environment is understood as family in terms of what humans share with nonhumans. Salmon says in the same essay that while the Earth has only one voice, it speaks in many languages. Yet, many of these languages are not heard. "The unheard includes not only plants and animals, places or open spaces, streamsides or oceanscapes: they include people. More specifically, the cultures of people who maintain a sustainable and enhancing relationship with their land are at risk."[27] This notion of "many languages" calls to mind Gadamer's famous phrase, "*Being that can be understood is language*." But it is what follows this phrase, typically not commented on, that is of interest here:

> The hermeneutical phenomenon here projects its own universality back onto the ontological constitution of what is understood, determining it in a universal sense as *language* and determining its own relation to beings as interpretation. Thus we speak not only of a language of art but also of a language of nature—in short, of any language that things have.[28]

Gadamer goes on to speak of the "book of nature"[29] and if we are to hear the unheard languages Salmon speaks of, we may say that the problem is one of translation. Just as Salmon extends the notion of family beyond blood to "all natural elements of the ecosystem" (all the while one can realize the different senses of family without conflating or confusing the two), Gadamer extends the notion of language from human language to the way that any being speaks or communicates itself (all the while one can realize the different senses of language without conflating or confusing the two). Interpreting nature as "kin," extending a sense of family to nature awakens the need and desire to understand the language of nature. But why the metaphor of language? Simply, the purpose of language is communication and the purpose of communication is mutual recognition and mutual understanding. Thus, living together with others, human and nonhuman, is a function of language. Gadamer says that "language is a medium where I and world meet or, rather, manifest their original belonging together."[30]

The purpose of the foregoing analysis is to show that the human relationship to nature falls under the scope of what Gadamer calls the universality of hermeneutics. Recognition of this relation leads one back to how nature can be understood as one's other self. Nature, indeed, can be thought of in terms of the third philosophical intention of *Oneself as Another*. We can experience nature as a dialectic of selfhood (*ipseity*) and otherness so that nature is understood in terms of the intimacy Ricoeur highlights. Truly, one cannot think of oneself without the other of nature.

It is evident that the three philosophical intentions in Ricoeur's hermeneutics of the self lend themselves to the understanding (interpretation) of the human relationship to nature and how one's identity can be constituted or understood in this relationship. Environmental identity as a hermeneutical enterprise fosters a way of thinking about and encountering nature. I would also contend that the hermeneutics of the self, shown to apply to the human/nature relationship, demonstrates that an environmental identity is not a component of identity one chooses to have or not. The question is whether I will be self-aware of that component of my identity and what kind of identity or sense of self it will be.

The value of a hermeneutically constructed theory of environmental identity will be further manifested as we explore environmental identity through the lens of environmental psychology and ecopsychology.

Environmental Psychology and Ecopsychology

Environmental psychology and ecopsychology are two different but complementary fields. Each is relevant for our explorations in environmental identity. Before continuing this exploration through these fields, a few words should be said concerning their differences.

Environmental psychology is a branch of psychology concerned with the interaction between humans and their environments. It considers human behavior within environments, the effect of people on their environments, and, reciprocally, the effect of environments on humans. Environmental psychology considers environments as relevant data to understand human behavior—how and why humans act.[31] Like environmental hermeneutics, environmental psychology does not limit its conception of environments but considers all forms of environments whether natural, cultural, and so on. The literature in environmental psychology continues to grow, such as in the *Journal of Environmental Psychology* and textbooks such as Robert Gifford's *Environmental Psychology Principles and Practice.*[32] I will focus on one book in particular, *Identity and the Natural Environment: The Psychological Significance of Nature,*[33] as I continue this exploration in environmental identity. My choice to concentrate on this single book is due to the explicit focus of the editors and many of the authors on "environmental identity." Hence the dialogue at hand is between two conceptions of environmental identity, one drawn from philosophical hermeneutics and another from environmental psychology.

Distinct from environmental psychology, ecopsychology is defined by one of its most prominent voices, Theodore Roszak, as the joining together of the "psychological and the ecological, to see the needs of the planet and the person as a continuum."[34] There has been a strained relationship between environmental psychology and ecopsychology. An article critical, although not totally dismissive, of ecopsychology from an environmental psychology perspective appeared in the *Journal of Environmental Psychology* in 1995 by Joseph P. Reser.[35] As recently as 2009, Reser gave an interview in the journal *Ecopsychology* in which he expressed his admiration for ecopsychology and his hope for it to become more conceptually clear.[36] This mixture of caution and acceptance seems to characterize the attitudes of other environmental psychologists. For example,

> [d]espite the occasional theoretical insights and individual observations to be found in its writings, ecopsychology is not so much a descriptive or empirical psychology as it is an ethical and practical outlook in response to the present environmental crisis; like deep ecology, ecopsychology constitutes a self-transformative practice, and indeed has been formulated as a therapeutic approach. At the same time, these normative philosophical perspectives are by no means irrelevant for more conventional scholarly or scientific approaches, and the packaging of ecopsychology as "psychology" may help it serve as a moral guide or inspiration to the field of environmental psychology proper.[37]

The primary and essential difference between environmental psychology and ecopsychology it seems is that the former is a recognized field of psychology, properly and academically speaking, and the latter is a response to the environmental crisis and a dialogue with psychology, but lacking a full conceptual and theoretical development. That is not to say that environmental psychology is not concerned with normative outcomes or that one cannot draw out normative implications from the findings of environmental psychology. My observation is not that environmental psychology is merely descriptive and empirical whereas ecopsychology is concerned with environmental and ecological ethics. The difference, as I understand it, has to do with origins. Environmental psychology is rooted in psychology with all its methods, practices, and theoretical foundations. Based on the data, environmental psychology can certainly bring one to draw normative conclusions.[38] Ecopsychology, on the other hand, arose as a response to the environmental crisis, not out of a psychological science later applied to such a crisis. And just as environmental psychology's theoretical origins do not preclude a normative aspect, ecopsychology's roots in ecological crisis do not preclude the development of stronger conceptual foundations. Perhaps both would be best served by dialogue where environmental psychology sees its normative possibilities realized, in part, in the efforts of ecopsychology, and ecopsychology would strive for great conceptual clarity with the aid of environmental psychology. For the purposes of the analysis here, my interest is that for both the self is constituted and interpreted in various ways in relationship to environments. The differences, however, are necessary to point out. For purposes of clarity, I will look at environmental identity with environmental psychology and ecopsychology in separate sections.

Environmental Identity and Environmental Psychology

Susan Clayton and Susan Opotow have edited an insightful volume, bringing together a diverse group of scholars, to explore the "psychological significance of nature."[39] What joins the essays in the volume together is that each investigates how it is that our understanding of the self affects how we understand (and behave toward) nature and how the experience of nature also shapes and develops who we are. If nature and the human psyche are connected in any way, then there are going to be ramifications concerning that connection. "Environmental identity" conceived in terms of psychology is going to matter for personal identity and for social identity in relationship to the natural world and, as such, will also entail social consequences. The editors and authors hope insight into the connection between the psyche and nature can result, personally and socially, in more positive environmental outcomes.

Clayton and Opotow recognize that both "identity" and "nature" are not simply defined univocal terms. Each is complex and multivalent. Hence they "propose an integrative construct of environmental identity that encompasses multiple meanings as well as a recognition of the dynamic nature of identity."[40] While they do not use the term, Ricoeur's *ipseity* comes to mind as a way to describe their conception of identity. The recognition that environmental identity is not static and across individuals can be very different based on numerous factors and influences reveals that identity in relation to environments is a matter of interpretation, a polysemic "surplus of meaning." They acknowledge that different environmental identities can lead to different types of action, some good and others not so good. Although their aim is to understand the psychological significance of nature, the essays in the volume comprise a psychological environmental hermeneutics of the self.

Following William James, Susan Clayton agrees that persons have many "selves." So for Clayton

> an environmental identity is one part of the way in which people form their self-concept; a sense of connection to some part of the nonhuman natural environment, based on history, emotional attachment, and/or similarity, that affects the ways in which we perceive and act toward the worlds; a belief that the environment is important to us and an important part of who we are. An environmental identity can be similar to another collective identity ... in providing us with a sense of connection, of being part of a larger whole, and with a recognition of similarity between ourselves and others.[41]

Environmental identity for Clayton is both a way we orient ourselves to the environment as well as being a product of interactions with our environment. This definition is similar to what was argued for previously. After all, it is not much of a leap to say that Clayton's account of environmental identity involves detour by way of reflective analysis, a dialectic of sameness and selfhood, and, especially in terms of the emotional attachment, the dialectic of selfhood and otherness—that is, all three features of Ricoeur's hermeneutics of the self.

Clayton's and Opotow's book contains a wide variety of essays, some more theoretical and others related to particular case studies. The thread that runs through them all is that nature is psychologically significant (as the subtitle of the book says). One final point here that I will mention (because it will come up again in ecopsychology) is the healing capacity of nature for psychological and social well-being. Two chapters, in particular, the first by Robert Sommer and the latter by Maureen E. Austin and Rachel Kaplan, raise this point in terms of trees, especially in the city.[42] Trees, it turns out, are important to those who dwell in cities and are not lost among the street lights, fire hydrants, and so on. Trees make places in the city meaningful. Sommer's chapter indicates the grief that some people in the city feel when they lose a tree. Austin's and Kaplan's chapter discusses the transformative character of introducing trees and other means of beautification to vacant lots. The effects are numerous from reducing crime to building stronger community identities.

Environmental Identity and Ecopsychology

James Hillman argues, "There is only one core issue for all psychology. *Where is the 'me'?* Where does the 'me' begin? Where does the 'me' stop? Where does the 'other' begin?"[43] For Hillman and other practitioners of ecopsychology, the "other" of nature is also a part of the "me." Beyond simple subject-object dichotomies, a chief insight of ecopsychology is its grasp of the complexities of embodied identity and that identity is not reducible to psyches and externals. He refers to "projective identification" meaning moments in which we attach ourselves to the other ("distant objects") so "fiercely that [we] believe [we] cannot live without them"[44] (this can obviously have both healthy and unhealthy connotations). The similarity of Hillman's observations with Ricoeur's third intention in the hermeneutics of the self is unmistakable.

The healing capacity of nature is a central theme in ecopsychology. Restoring the earth is to heal the mind, to borrow from the title of the book, *Ecopsychology: Restoring the Earth, Healing the Mind.*[45] In the area of environmental philosophy, J. Baird Callicott writes of "environmental wellness."[46] Callicott points out the interrelation of the wellness movement to environmental concerns. In contrast to other aspects of life over which we have a certain degree of autonomy (e.g., diet and exercise), Callicott further argues that because the environment is a "commons" it will take social and political means to make the environment a space for human wellness. He takes it as self-evident that the wellness of the environment is without negotiation necessary for human wellness. He writes,

> I don't think that you need to be a rocket scientist to figure out the environmental quality ... is essential to overall human health and well-being. The sight of a person jogging through smog-clogged city streets is as much of a

> visual oxymoron as the sight of a person jogging along smoking a cigarette. An ersatz environment of metal, glass, concrete, and asphalt; congested automobile traffic; drugs, poverty, homelessness, and the street crime they breed—all of these seriously compromise our physical, emotional, and spiritual wellness. Environmental wellness, in short, is a necessary condition for human health and well-being generally. We cannot pursue personal wellness unless we also work collectively and cooperatively to ensure improvement in our natural and fabricated environments.[47]

It is important here not to have one's attention diverted by the emphasis on physical health away from "emotional and spiritual wellness." In the previous quotation, Callicott points out that mental and emotional health is not just about having a positive outlook, but such health depends on several external factors as well.

By placing people in direct contact with nature in various ways, therapists have discovered that such contact leads to greater emotional and social well-being. The Gnome Project is one such enterprise that, among other things, has shown that children traumatized in war-torn or high-conflict areas are helped by direct contact with nature.[48] Interaction with nature seems to provide what we might call a hermeneutic reconfiguration of the self.

This foregoing discussion on health and wellness serves the purpose of highlighting the importance of developing environmental identity and, further, why a hermeneutics of environmental identity is relevant. Consider it the following way. It is reasonable to say that sensible people agree that health and wellness are better than being sick. Whatever people's varied and diverse conceptions of the "good life" might be, it is doubtful that many of them include mental or emotional sickness and distress. So if environmental hermeneutics can show us a theory of the self through environmental identity and ecopsychology can show us that identity is connected to nature, then we can argue for self-interpretation and self-development and growth in environmentally positive ways. Although in social life there is room for many different understandings and practices that constitute the "good life," there are others that do not. Environmental hermeneutics aided by the hermeneutically oriented conceptions of identity in ecopsychology (and this is just as true of environmental psychology) provides tools for critically understanding what the good life may be, to quote Ricoeur, "with and for others in just institutions."[49]

Conclusion

This exploration into different conceptions of environmental identity is intended to highlight the complementary nature of them all. Moreover, I am arguing that environmental psychology and ecopsychology and their accounts of environmental identity and self-understanding are instances of an environmental hermeneutics of the self. One of the things that makes environmental psychology and ecopsychology of interest to environmental hermeneutics is that, although there are many case studies and empirical data that undergird their conclusions, what remains inescapable is the inherent hermeneutical dimensions. Ricoeur, for example, has amply demonstrated the hermeneutical dimensions of psychoanalysis.[50] People interpret themselves in relationship to their environments and the way they do so is relevant. Environmental psychology and ecopsychology are hermeneutical in that they show how people understand themselves and how that understanding shapes and motivates action, which results in a rich consideration of what is ethical. As such, this essay provides another argument in support of the final chapter of this volume that wonders whether hermeneutics might save environmental ethics.[51] Because environmental hermeneutics can engage a wide variety of disciplines, it can only offer enrichment to environmental philosophy generally and environmental ethics specifically.

Environmental identity, I contend, is a genuine component of human identity. However, it is not understood in some direct and unmediated way. We cannot speak of some direct, intuitive access into the *eidetics* of environmental identity. Indeed, since it is a component of identity characterized by being "environmental," it is in its very constitution situated! Identity in general—and environmental identity in particular—is hermeneutical, that is, identity involves a process of interpretation to come into its own. To say that environmental identity is hermeneutical is to say two things: 1) All identity, following Ricoeur, is not grounded in the immediacy of the subject. An environmental identity is a component of identity that obtains in an indirect mediated manner on various levels of our relation and interrelation to the natural world. 2) Likewise, environmental identity is not perceived in a simple dichotomy of the human subject and the natural object. Rather, it is manifest in a complex set of meaningful relations that result in multiple forms of self-understanding. If Palmer is correct, interpreting nature and all environments is a fundamental action of human existence. And if we follow Gadamer that all hermeneutical understanding is self-understanding[52] and Ricoeur that the self is constituted in the act of interpretation,[53] then interpreting environments yields an environmental identity. Any and all other forms of environmental identity are at their root hermeneutical—that is, are fully grounded and more deeply explained in terms of a hermeneutic mentality.

Gadamer observes that hermeneutics operates in an intermediary place such that "its work is not to develop a procedure of understanding but to clarify the conditions in which understanding takes place."[54] So, for example, when environmental psychology highlights the impact of nature on personality and offers definitions of environmental identity, it is hermeneutical principles that make such activity possible. The various ways that environmental psychology construes environmental identity are conceptually undergirded by the hermeneutics of the self. On one hand, environmental psychology and ecopsychology are clearly distinct disciplines complementary to environmental hermeneutics offering insights unique to their respective fields. On the other hand, environmental psychology and ecopsychology constitute a particular kind or instantiation of an environmental hermeneutics of the self, offering an environmentally relevant interpretation of human behavior in relation to and in response to environments. I do not mean to say that environmental hermeneutics encompasses environmental psychology or ecopsychology. But insofar as hermeneutics clarifies the conditions within which understanding is possible generally, environmental psychology and ecopsychology manifests this reality particularly.

My conclusion is that environmental hermeneutics and environmental/ecopsychology have a good deal to offer one another and would mutually benefit from dialogue. A Gadamerian "fusion" of these respective horizons would not only be mutually beneficial on the level of each discipline but would ultimately be beneficial to the environment in which we dwell (and, as such, as Callicott would say, is beneficial to us). In other words, it is characteristic of all three of the areas that comprise the subject matter of this chapter to be most fully realized in application. Gadamer forcefully argues that concrete real-world factors belong to the domain of hermeneutics.[55] Hermeneutics applies not to an abstract world but is operative right in the midst of the concerns of society. Both environmental and ecopsychology are concerned, as are all forms of psychology, with concrete results in people's lives. Therefore, the dialogue between these areas is not intended just for their academic enrichment inside the walls of the academy but ultimately to impact and improve our world. The link discussed here of environmental identity has the power to transform our conceptions of self, such that our dependence upon the natural environment becomes abundantly and unequivocally clear. A rightly construed environmental identity on personal and collective levels may be one of many tools employed as a sensible and effective response to the present-day environmental crisis and the debates over how best to address it.

Notes

1 Richard Palmer, *Hermeneutics* (Evanston, Ill.: Northwestern University Press, 1969), 8.

2 Ibid., 9.

3 It is important not to conflate environmental psychology and ecopsychology. The differences between the two will be discussed later in this essay.

4 See David Utsler, "Paul Ricoeur's Hermeneutics as a Model for Environmental Philosophy," *Philosophy Today* 53 (2009): 173–178; also, "Who Am I, Who Are These People and What is this Place?: A Hermeneutic Account of the Self, Others, and Environments," in *Placing Nature on the Borders of Religion, Philosophy, and Ethics*, ed. Forrest Clingerman and Mark H. Dixon (Burlington, Vt.: Ashgate, 2011), 139–152.

5 Mitchell Thomashow, *Ecological Identity: Becoming a Reflective Environmentalist*, (Cambridge, Mass.: MIT Press, 1996). See also *The Perceived Self: Ecological and Interpersonal Sources of Self Knowledge (Emory Symposia in Cognition)*, ed. Ulrich Neisser (Cambridge: Cambridge University Press, 1993 [1996]).

6 The term "ecological identity" as it is typically used would seem to refer more narrowly to relationships to natural entities and systems whereas "environmental identity" would seem to encompass

broader notions of environment and could include or encompass an ecological component of identity. There is, of course, social ecology, going back to Murray Bookchin, which links environmental problems to social and political problems.

7 Thomashow, *Ecological Identity*, 3.

8 Robert Melchior Figueroa, "Debating the Paradigms of Justice: The Bivalence of Environmental Justice" (PhD diss., University of Colorado Boulder, 1999), 147. This is the unpublished PhD dissertation provided to me by the author.

9 Robert Melchior Figueroa, "Evaluating Environmental Justice Claims," in *Forging Environmentalism: Justice, Livelihood and Contested Environments*, ed. Joanne Bauer (New York: M. E. Sharpe, 2006), 371.

10 See Forrest Clingerman, "Beyond the Flowers and the Stones: 'Emplacement' and the Modeling of Nature." *Philosophy in the Contemporary World* 11 (2004): 17–24.

11 Figueroa, "Evaluating Environmental Justice Claims," 372; emphasis original.

12 For more on narrative and environmental hermeneutics, see Brian Treanor's chapter in this volume, "Narrative and Nature: Appreciating and Understanding the Nonhuman World." See also Treanor, "Narrative Environmental Virtue Ethics: *Phronesis* without a *Phronimos*, *Environmental Ethics* 30 (2008): 361–379.

13 Janet Donohoe's chapter in this volume, "The Betweenness of Monuments" takes up the issue of memory and history in a fashion complementary to Figueroa's idea of environmental heritage. What Donohoe has to say about monuments can bring much to bear on thinking of ways in which the environmental heritages of peoples that have been destroyed by environmental injustices can be preserved in memory.

14 See note 4.

15 See Paul Ricoeur, *Oneself as Another*, trans. Kathleen Blamey (Chicago: The University of Chicago Press, 1992).

16 Ibid., 1.

17 Ibid., 16.

18 Ibid., 1.

19 I am purposely, for the sake of space, leaving out a fuller discussion on narrative and memory that has much to do with this discussion. I refer the reader to the essays in this volume by Forrest Clingerman, Janet Donohoe, Martin Drenthen, and Brian Treanor.

20 Lyric from the song "Natural Science" by Rush. Lyrics by Neil Peart. Music by Geddy Lee and Alex Lifeson. From the album *Permanent Waves*, Mercury Records, 1980.

21 Paul Ricoeur, *Oneself as Another* (Chicago: The University of Chicago Press, 1995), 116.

22 Ibid.

23 Ibid., 2.

24 Ibid., 3.

25 I refer again to the two works cited in note 4.

26 Enrique Salmon, "Sharing Breath: Some Links between Land, Plants, and People," in *Colors of Nature: Culture, Identity and the Natural World*, ed. Alison H. Deming and Lauret E. Savoy (Minneapolis: Milkweed Editions, 2011), 196–197.

27 Ibid., 196. By linking at-risk cultures with an at-risk Earth, Salmon demonstrates the link between traditional environmental concerns and issues with environmental justice. That this link is demonstrated by indigenous cultures is indicative of the need to listen to the wisdom of others embedded in cultural narratives.

28 Hans-Georg Gadamer, *Truth and Method*, 2nd rev. ed., trans. Joel Weinsheimer and Donald G. Marshall (New York: Continuum Press, 2004), 470; emphasis original.

29 See Forrest Clingerman, "Reading the Book of Nature: A Hermeneutical Account of Nature for Philosophical Theology," *Worldviews: Global Religions, Culture, and Ecology* 13 (2009): 72–91.

30 Gadamer, *Truth and Method*, 469.

31 One could follow an intersection here between hermeneutics and psychology in that human action and its meanings are likewise a concern of hermeneutical inquiry.

32 Robert Gifford, *Environmental Psychology: Principles and Practice*, 4th edition (Colville: Optimal Books, 2007).

33 Susan Clayton and Susan Opotow, eds., *Identity and the Natural Environment: The Psychological Significance of Nature* (Cambridge, Mass.: MIT Press, 2003).

34 Theodore Rozak, *The Voice of the Earth: An Exploration in Ecopsychology*, 2nd edition (Grand Rapids: Phanes Press, Inc., 2001 [1992]), 14.

35 Joseph P. Reser, "Whither Environmental Psychology?: The Transpersonal Ecopsychology Crossroads," *Journal of Environmental Psychology* 15 (1995): 235–257.

36 Joseph P. Reser, "Joseph Reser: The Ecopsychology Interview," *Ecopsychology* 1 (2009): 57–63.

37 Steven J. Holmes, "Some Lives and Some Theories," in *Identity and the Natural Environment*, 34. In-text references omitted. See also Elizabeth Ann Bragg, "Towards Ecological Self: Deep Ecology Meets Constructionist Self-Theory," *Journal of Environmental Psychology* 16 (1996): 93–108.

38 Psychology's focus on the self and narrative theory in hermeneutics finds a meeting point here. As Paul Ricoeur, Richard Kearney, and others have observed, the self is discovered and constructed through narrative and narrative has ethical implications. One way in which environmental psychology can realize its inherent normative elements is to employ the ethical power of narrative.

39 Clayton and Opotow, *Identity and the Natural Environment*. See note 32.

40 Clayton and Opotow, "Introduction: Identity and the Natural Environment," in *Identity and the Natural Environment*, 8.

41 Susan Clayton, "Environmental Identity: A Conceptual and Operational Definition," in *Identity and the Natural Environment*, 45–46.

42 Robert Sommer, "Trees and Human Identity" and Maureen E. Austin and Rachel Kaplan, "Identity, Involvement, and Expertise in the Inner City: Some Benefits of Tree-Planting Projects," in *Identity and the Natural Environment*, 179–204 and 205–225.

43 James Hillman, "A Psyche the Size of the Earth: A Psychological Foreword," in *Ecopsychology: Restoring the Earth, Healing the Mind*, ed. Theodore Rozak, Mary E. Gomes, and Allen D. Kanner (San Francisco: Sierra Club Books, 1995), xvii; emphasis original.

44 Ibid.

45 Rozak et al., *Ecopsychology.*

46 J. Baird Callicott, "Environmental Wellness," in *Beyond the Land Ethic: More Essays in Environmental Philosophy* (Albany: State University of New York Press, 1999), 283–299.

47 Ibid., 285.

48 See http://sites.google.com/site/thegnomeprojectorg/home.

49 Ricoeur, *Oneself as Another*, 172.

50 See Paul Ricoeur, *Freud and Philosophy: An Essay on Interpretation*, trans. Denis Savage (New Haven, Conn.: Yale University Press, 1970). See also, Ricoeur, *The Conflict of Interpretations* (Evanston, Ill.: Northwestern University Press, 1974), 99–208.

51 See Paul van Tongeren and Paulien Snellen, "How Hermeneutics Might Save the Life of (Environmental) Ethics," in this volume.

52 Gadamer, *Truth and Method*, 251.

53 Paul Ricoeur, *From Text to Action: Essays in Hermeneutics II*, trans. Kathleen Blamey and John B. Thompson (Evanston, Ill.: Northwestern University Press, 1991), 119.

54 Gadamer, *Truth and Method*, 295.

55 Hans-Georg Gadamer, *Philosophical Hermeneutics*, trans. and ed. David E. Linge (Los Angeles: University of California Press, 1976), 31.

The Ecology of Understanding

Everybody is a genius. But if you judge a fish by its ability to climb a tree, it will spend its whole life thinking it's stupid.

—Albert Einstein

Introduction

After years of research on intelligence and an increasing dismay regarding the misrepresentation of intelligence by IQ tests, Howard Gardner (1983), an American developmental and educational psychologist, introduced multiple intelligences theory (MI). Gardner's research revealed that intelligence is an aggregation of intelligence types, the expression of these having subtle to remarkable individual, sociocultural, and socioecological differences (Gardner, 1983, 1993, 1995, 2006). As early as 1973 David McCelland (1993) of Harvard questioned the reliability, validity, and efficacy of intelligence testing for prediction of individual success and suitability for college. For over 30 years especially Gardner (1983, 1993, 1995, 2006), McCelland (1993), and Sternberg (1985, 1993, 2004, 2007, 2009a, 2009b) have brought to light the shortcomings of general intelligence (g) tests and proffered through substantive research that intelligence is a multifaceted ecological phenomenon that cannot be well understood through a "g-ocentric" (Sternberg & Wagner, 1993, p. 1) view of intelligence.

Theories and Concepts in Context of Sustainability

Intelligence is an aggregation of types or forms of intelligence. Intelligences are employed proportionately as per the demands of daily life such as in gathering food or gathering materials to exchange for food and helping others do the same. We also employ our intelligences when interacting with members of our community for managing built, natural, and social structures toward holistically improving the environment for our community. Intelligence facilitates self-awareness and the contemplation necessary to improve our self-other relationships, as well as our relationship with the environment that sustains us. Intelligence allows us to recognize extraordinary threat and extraordinary opportunity, and to develop successful responses to both.

Howard Gardner's (1983, 2006) multiple intelligence theory (MI) and Robert Sternberg's (1985, 2009a) triarchic theory of intelligence (TTI) reveal that our intelligence is comprised of remarkable diversity. Just as with every aspect of human and nonhuman animal experience, intelligence has an ecology and is part of an ecological system. We become inclined to employ certain intelligences more than others. Certainly this inclination has a genetic basis; however, it seems clear that how and why we employ our intelligences is strongly influenced by sociocultural and socioecological factors.

Generally, all intelligences are available to us to for use in problem solving and creating new ideas if we make the effort to engage them. Remember that just as in nature diversity is essential to success and resilience. One effective and rewarding way to engage our multiple intelligences is to work with others to solve problems in context and create new sustainability solutions.

When we work together we are taking a more ecological approach, something that I refer to as a "collective cognition." The long-term benefit of our collective cognition has been illuminated through research guided for example by social baseline theory (Coan, 2008). Suffice it to say that we are a resilient species in large part due to "putting our heads together." The question now is can we employ our intelligences toward creating a sustainable human ecology? A quick look at the types of intelligences identified by Gardner and Sternberg illustrates the remarkable diversity of our intelligence, and should give us a reason to be optimistic about our ability to create a sustainable human ecology and one that fosters dignity for all creatures.

Gardner identified nine intelligences: *Linguistic* is one's capacity to perform and apply reading, writing, and verbal tasks and meaning; *logical/mathematical,* the ability to perform relational construction of thoughts, ideas, or concepts in meaningful (i.e., logical) ways, and to perform and apply mathematical operations and principals; *spatial,* which includes such phenomena as "sense of direction" and seeing and manipulating physical and conceptual objects' fit and form to maximize their function or suitability; *musical,* which includes behaviors and capabilities that might commonly be thought of as all that is associated with musical talent; *bodily-kinesthetic,* the ability to movement in synchrony with sound and/or another person (i.e., dance), as well as capabilities required from some types of sports; *interpersonal,* the ability to recognize subtle emotional cues, to empathize, and to accurately discern another's motivation and intention; *intrapersonal,* the ability to be self-aware, to know, and to manage one's self in socially appropriate and self-respecting ways; *naturalist* the ability to discriminate among living things (plants, animals) as well as sensitivity to other features of the natural world (clouds, rock configurations); and *existential,* the sensitivity and capacity to address deep questions about human existence, such as the meaning of life, why we die, and how we get here.

Sternberg identified three higher-order functioning systems or intelligences: *componential intelligence,* which addresses acquisition, analysis, and synthesis of information, relational organization, logic, planning, and management of forms of intelligence; *experiential-creative intelligence,* which is the ability to employ and augment existing knowledge-associated responses in unfamiliar situations successfully; and *contextual intelligence,* which encompasses those aspects of cognition associated with survival and success within one's environment, which includes but is not limited to selection of compatible conditions and/or manipulation of conditions to be conducive to survival and success, and personal adaptation in general.

Finally, compare Sternberg's intelligences with Gardner's intelligences and you find a remarkable similarity. For example, componential intelligence includes Gardner's linguistic, logical-mathematical, and spatial intelligences; Gardener's logical-mathematical, spatial, and musical fit closely within Sternberg's experiential-creative intelligence, and the TTI construct of contextual-practical intelligence is clearly analogous to MI's naturalistic, intrapersonal, and bodily-kinesthetic intelligences. Similarities across these theories also convey a broader message; intelligence is multifaceted, "g IQ" cannot represent the diversity or ecology of our intelligence, and a multiple intelligence approach to understanding intelligence is essential for understanding complex sustainability problems and for developing effective solutions to those problems. Finally, a multiple intelligence perspective facilitates awareness that we are not only unique but also inextricably connected, and this understanding bolsters personal and societal experience of dignity.

About the Feature Article

As you read *In a Nutshell* from *Multiple Intelligences: The Theory in Practice*, pay particular attention to Gardner's comparison of IQ and MI, and consider the implications to human dignity if for example intelligence was understood ecologically and assessments took multiple intelligence into account.

References

Coan, J. A. (2008). Toward a neuroscience of attachment. *Handbook of attachment: Theory, research, and clinical applications, 2*, 241–265.

Gardner, H. (1983). *Frames of mind: The theory of multiple intelligences.* New York, NY: Basic Books.

Gardner, H. (1993). *Multiple intelligences: The theory and practice.* New York, NY: Basic Books.

Gardner, H. (1995). Reflections on multiple intelligences: Myths and messages. *The Phi Delta Kappan*, 77, 201–209.

Gardner, H. (2006). On failing to grasp the core of MI theory: A response to Visser et al. *Intelligence,* 34(5), 503–505.

McClelland, D. C. (1973). Testing for competence rather than for "intelligence." *American Psychologist, 28*(1), 1–14. doi.org/10.1037/h0034092

Sternberg, R. (1985). *Beyond IQ: A triarchic theory of human intelligence*. New York, NY: Cambridge University Press.

Sternberg, R., & Wagner, R. (1993). The g-ocentric view of intelligence and job performance is wrong. *Current Directions in Psychological Science*, *2*(2), 1–5.

Sternberg, R. J. (2004). Who are the bright children? The cultural context of being and acting intelligent. *Educational Researcher, 36*(3), 148–155.

Sternberg, R. J. (2007). Who are the bright children? The cultural context of being and acting intelligent. *Educational Researcher*, *36*(3), 148–155. doi: org/10.3102/0013189X07299881

Sternberg, R. J. (2009a). *Cognitive psychology* (5th ed.). Belmont, CA: Thompson Wadsworth.

Sternberg, R. J. (Speaker). (2009b). *Cognitive psychology* (DVD Recording No. P6235D). Baltimore: Laureate Education.

READING 6

In a Nutshell

Howard Gardner

The original scene: Paris, 1900—La Belle Epoque. The city fathers approached a talented psychologist named Alfred Binet with an unusual request. Families were flocking to the capital city from the provinces, and a good many of their children were having trouble with their schoolwork. Could Binet devise some kind of a measure that would predict which youngsters would succeed and which would fail in the primary grades of Paris schools?

As almost everybody knows, Binet succeeded. In short order, his discovery came to be called the "intelligence test"; his measure, the IQ, for "intelligence quotient" (mental age divided by chronological age and multiplied by 100). Like other Parisian fashions, the IQ soon made its way to the United States, where it enjoyed a modest success until World War I, when it was used to test over one million American military recruits. With its use by the U.S. armed forces, and with America's victory in the conflict, Binet's invention had truly arrived. Ever since, the IQ test has looked like psychology's biggest success—a genuinely useful scientific tool.

What is the vision that led to the excitement about IQ? At least in the West, people had always relied on intuitive assessments of how smart other people were. Now intelligence seemed to be quantifiable. Just as you could measure someone's actual or potential height, now, it seemed, you could measure someone's actual or potential intelligence. We had one dimension of mental ability along which we could array everyone.

Howard Gardner, "In a Nutshell," *Multiple Intelligences: The Theory in Practice, a Reader*, pp. 3-24, 277-292. Copyright © 2006 by Perseus Books Group. Reprinted with permission.

The search for the perfect measure of intelligence has proceeded apace. Here, for example, are some quotations from an advertisement for one such test:

> Need an individual test which quickly provides a stable and reliable estimate of intelligence in four or five minutes per form? Has three forms? Does not depend on verbal production or subjective scoring? Can be used with the severely physically handicapped (even paralyzed) if they can signal yes or no? Handles two-year-olds and superior adults with the same short series of items and the same format? Only $16.00 complete.

Now, a single test that can do all that is quite a claim. American psychologist Arthur Jensen suggests that we could look at reaction time to assess intelligence: a set of lights go on; how quickly can the subject react? British psychologist Hans Eysenck recommends that investigators of intelligence look directly at brain waves. And with the advent of the gene chip, many look forward to the day when we can glance at the proper gene locus on the proper chromosome, read off someone's IQ, and confidently predict his or her life chances.

There are also, of course, more sophisticated versions of the IQ test. One of them is the SAT. Its name originally stood for Scholastic Aptitude Test, although with the passage of time, the meaning of the acronym has been changed—it became the Scholastic Assessment Test, and, more recently, it has been reduced to the plain old SAT—just the initials. The SAT purports to be a similar kind of measure, and if you add up a person's verbal and math scores, as is often done, you can rate him or her along a single intellectual dimension. (Recently, writing and reasoning components have been added.) Programs for the gifted, for example, often use that kind of measure; if your IQ is in excess of 130, you're admitted to the program—if it's 129, "Sorry, no room at the inn."

Along with this one-dimensional view of how to assess people's minds comes a corresponding view of school, which I will call the "uniform view." A uniform school features a core curriculum—a set of facts that everyone should know—and very few electives. The better students, perhaps those with higher IQs, are allowed to take courses that call on critical reading, calculation, and thinking skills. In the uniform school, there are regular assessments, using paper and pencil instruments, of the IQ or SAT variety. These assessments yield reliable rankings of people; the best and the brightest get into the better colleges, and perhaps—but only perhaps—they will also get better rankings in life. There is no question that this approach works well for certain people—schools such as Harvard and Stan-ford are eloquent testimony to that. Since this measurement and selection system is clearly meritocratic in certain respects, it has something to recommend it.

The uniform school sounds fair—after all, everyone is treated in the same way. But some years ago it occurred to me that this supposed rationale was completely unfair. The uniform school picks out and is addressed to a certain kind of mind—we might call it provisionally the

IQ or SAT mind. I sometimes call it the mind of the future law professor. The more your mind resembles that of the legendary law professor Dr. Charles W. Kingsfield Jr., played on-screen by John Houseman in *The Paper Chase*, the better you will do in school and the more readily you will handle IQ-SAT-type measures. But to the extent that your mind works differently—and not that many of us are cut out to be law professors—school is certainly not fair to you.

I would like to present an alternative vision—one based on a radically different view of the mind, and one that yields a very different view of school. It is a pluralistic view of mind, recognizing many different and discrete facets of cognition, acknowledging that people have different cognitive strengths and contrasting cognitive styles. I introduce the concept of an individual-centered school that takes this multifaceted view of intelligence seriously. This model for a school is based in part on findings from sciences that did not even exist in Binet's time: cognitive science (the study of the mind) and neuroscience (the study of the brain). One such approach I have called the theory of multiple intelligences. Let me tell you something about its sources and claims to lay the groundwork for the discussions on education in the chapters that follow.

I introduce this new point of view by asking you to suspend for a moment the usual judgment of what constitutes intelligence, and let your thoughts run freely over the capabilities of human beings—perhaps those that would be picked out by the proverbial visitor from Mars. Your mind may turn to the brilliant chess player, the world-class violinist, and the champion athlete; certainly, such outstanding performers deserve special consideration. Are the chess player, violinist, and athlete "intelligent" in these pursuits? If they are, then why do our tests of "intelligence" fail to identify them? If they are not intelligent, what allows them to achieve such astounding feats? In general, why does the contemporary construct of intelligence fail to take into account large areas of human endeavor?

To approach these questions I introduced the theory of multiple intelligences (MI) in the early 1980s. As the name indicates, I believe that human cognitive competence is better described in terms of a set of abilities, talents, or mental skills, which I call *intelligences*. All normal individuals possess each of these skills to some extent; individuals differ in the degree of skill and in the nature of their combination. I believe this theory of intelligence may be more humane and more veridical than alternative views of intelligence and that it more adequately reflects the data of human "intelligent" behavior. Such a theory has important educational implications.

What Constitutes an Intelligence?

The question of the optimal definition of intelligence looms large in my inquiry. And it is here that the theory of multiple intelligences begins to diverge from traditional points of view. In the classic psychometric view, intelligence is defined operationally as the ability to answer items on tests of intelligence. The inference from the test scores to some underlying ability is supported by statistical techniques. These techniques compare responses of subjects at different ages; the apparent correlation of these test scores across ages and across different tests corroborates the notion that the general faculty of intelligence, called *g* in short, does not change much with age, training, or experience. It is an inborn attribute or faculty of the individual.

Multiple intelligences theory, on the other hand, pluralizes the traditional concept. An intelligence is a computational capacity—a capacity to process a certain kind of information—that originates in human biology and human psychology. Humans have certain kinds of intelligences, whereas rats, birds, and computers foreground other kinds of computational capacities. An intelligence entails the ability to solve problems or fashion products that are of consequence in a particular cultural setting or community. The problem-solving skill allows one to approach a situation in which a goal is to be obtained and to locate the appropriate route to that goal. The creation of a cultural product allows one to capture and transmit knowledge or to express one's conclusions, beliefs, or feelings. The problems to be solved range from creating an end for a story to anticipating a mating move in chess to repairing a quilt. Products range from scientific theories to musical compositions to successful political campaigns.

MI theory is framed in light of the biological origins of each problem-solving skill. Only those skills that are universal to the human species are considered (again, we differ from rats, birds, or computers). Even so, the biological proclivity to participate in a particular form of problem solving must also be coupled with the cultural nurturing of that domain. For example, language, a universal skill, may manifest itself particularly as writing in one culture, as oratory in another culture, and as the secret language composed of anagrams or tongue twisters in a third.

Given the desideratum of selecting intelligences that are rooted in biology and that are valued in one or more cultural settings, how does one actually identify an intelligence? In coming up with the list, I reviewed evidence from various sources: knowledge about normal development and development in gifted individuals; information about the breakdown of cognitive skills under conditions of brain damage; studies of exceptional populations, including prodigies, savants, and autistic children; data about the evolution of cognition over the millennia; cross-cultural accounts of cognition; psychometric studies, including examinations of correlations among tests; and psychological training studies, particularly measures of transfer and generalization across tasks. Only those candidate intelligences that satisfied all or a healthy majority of the criteria were selected as bona fide intelligences. A more complete discussion of each of these criteria and of the intelligences that were initially identified may be found in *Frames of Mind* (1983b), especially chapter 4. In that foundational book I also consider how the theory might be disproved and compare it with competing theories of intelligence. An update of some of these discussions is presented in *Intelligence Reframed* (1999a), and in the chapters that follow.

In addition to satisfying the aforementioned criteria, each intelligence must have an identifiable core operation or set of operations. As a neurally based computational system, each intelligence is activated or triggered by certain kinds of internal or external information. For example, one core of musical intelligence is the sensitivity to pitch relations, and one core of linguistic intelligence is the sensitivity to the phonological features of a language.

An intelligence must also be susceptible to encoding in a symbol system—a culturally contrived system of meaning that captures and conveys important forms of information. Language, picturing, and mathematics are but three nearly worldwide symbol systems that are necessary for human survival and productivity. The relationship of an intelligence to a human symbol system is no accident. In fact, the existence of a core computational capacity anticipates the actual or potential creation of a symbol system that exploits that capacity. While it may be possible for an intelligence to develop without an accompanying symbol system, a primary characteristic of human intelligence may well be its gravitation toward such an embodiment.

The Original Set of Intelligences

Having sketched the characteristics and criteria for an intelligence, I turn now to a brief consideration of each of the intelligences that were proposed in the early 1980s. I begin each sketch with a thumbnail biography of a person who demonstrates an unusual facility with that intelligence. (These biographies were developed chiefly by my longtime colleague Joseph Walters.) The biographies illustrate some of the abilities that are central to the fluent operation of a given intelligence. Although each biography illustrates a particular intelligence, I do not wish to imply that in adulthood intelligences operate in isolation. Indeed, except in abnormal individuals, intelligences always work in concert, and any sophisticated adult role will involve a melding of several of them. Following each biography is a survey of the various sources of data that support each candidate as an intelligence.

Musical Intelligence

When Yehudi Menuhin was three years old, his parents smuggled him into San Francisco Orchestra concerts. The sound of Louis Persinger's violin so entranced the young child that he insisted on a violin for his birthday and Louis Persinger as his teacher. He got both. By the time he was ten years old, Menuhin was an international performer (Menuhin, 1977).

Violinist Yehudi Menuhin's musical intelligence manifested itself even before he had touched a violin or received any musical training. His powerful reaction to that particular sound and his rapid progress on the instrument suggest that he was biologically prepared in some way for a life in music. Menuhin is one example of evidence from child prodigies that support the claim that there is a biological link to a particular intelligence. Other special populations, such as autistic children who can play a musical instrument beautifully but who cannot otherwise communicate, underscore the independence of musical intelligence.

A brief consideration of the evidence suggests that musical skill passes the other tests for an intelligence. For example, certain parts of the brain play important roles in the perception and production of music. These areas are characteristically located in the right hemisphere, although musical skill is not as clearly localized in the brain as natural language. Although the particular susceptibility of musical ability to brain damage depends on the degree of training and other individual characteristics, there is clear evidence that amusia, or a selective loss of musical ability, occurs.

Music apparently played an important unifying role in Stone Age (Paleolithic) societies. Birdsong provides a link to other species. Evidence from various cultures supports the notion that music is a universal faculty. Studies of infant development suggest that there is a "raw" computational ability in early childhood. Finally, musical notation provides an accessible and versatile symbol system. In short, evidence to support the interpretation of musical ability as an intelligence comes from many different sources. Even though musical skill is not typically considered an intellectual skill like mathematics, it qualifies under our criteria. By definition it deserves consideration; and in view of the data, its inclusion is empirically justified.

Bodily-Kinesthetic Intelligence

Fifteen-year-old Babe Ruth was playing catcher one game when his team was taking a "terrific beating." Ruth "burst out laughing" and criticized the pitcher loudly. Brother Mathias, the coach, called out, "All right, George, YOU pitch!" Ruth was stunned and nervous: "I never pitched in my life ... I can't pitch." The moment was transformative, as Ruth recalls in his autobiography: "Yet, as I took the position, I felt a strange relationship between myself and that pitcher's mound. I felt, somehow, as if I had been born out there and that this was a kind of home for me." As sports history shows, he went on to become a great major league pitcher (and, of course, attained legendary status as a hitter) (Ruth, 1948, p. 17).

Like Menuhin, Babe Ruth was a prodigy who recognized his "instrument" immediately on his first exposure to it, before receiving any formal training.

Control of bodily movement is localized in the motor cortex, with each hemisphere dominant or controlling bodily movements on the contralateral side. In right-handers, the dominance for bodily movement is ordinarily found in the left hemisphere. The ability to perform movements when directed to do so can be impaired even in individuals who can perform the same movements reflexively or on a nonvoluntary basis. The existence of apraxia constitutes one line of evidence for a bodily-kinesthetic intelligence.

The evolution of specialized body movements is of obvious advantage to the species, and in human beings this adaptation is extended through the use of tools. Body movement undergoes a clearly defined developmental schedule in children; there is little question of its universality across cultures. Thus, it appears that bodily-kinesthetic "knowledge" satisfies many of the criteria for an intelligence.

The consideration of bodily-kinesthetic knowledge as "problem solving" may be less intuitive. Certainly carrying out a mime sequence or hitting a tennis ball is not solving a mathematical equation. And yet, the ability to use one's body to express an emotion (as in a dance), to play a game (as in a sport), or to create a new product (as in devising an invention) is evidence of the cognitive features of body usage. The specific computations required to solve a particular bodily-kinesthetic problem, hitting a tennis ball, are summarized by Tim Gallwey:

> In order to anticipate how and where to move the feet and whether to take the racket back on the forehand or backhand side, the brain must calculate within a fraction of a second the moment the ball leaves the server's racket approximately where it is going to land, and where the racket will intercept it. Into this calculation must be computed the initial velocity of the ball, combined with an input for the progressive decrease in velocity and the effect of wind and of spin, to say nothing of the complicated trajectories involved. Then, each of these factors must be recalculated after the bounce of the ball to anticipate the point where contact will be made by the racket. Simultaneously, muscle orders must be given—not just once, but constantly refined on updated information. Finally, the muscles have to respond in cooperation with one another ... Contact is made at a precise point that depends on whether the order was given to hit down the line or cross-court, an order not given until after a split-second analysis of the movement and balance of the opponent. ... Even if you are returning the serve of an average player, you will have only about one second. Just to hit the ball is clearly a remarkable feat; to return it with consistency and accuracy is a mind-boggling achievement. Yet it is not uncommon. The truth is that everyone who inhabits a human body possesses a remarkable instrument (Gallwey, 1976, pp. 33–34).

Logical-Mathematical Intelligence

In 1983 Barbara McClintock won the Nobel Prize in Medicine or Physiology for her work in microbiology. Her intellectual powers of deduction and observation illustrate one form of logical-mathematical intelligence that is often labeled "scientific thinking." One incident is particularly illuminating. When she was a researcher at Cornell in the 1920s, McClintock was faced one day with a problem: while theory predicted 50 percent pollen sterility in corn, her research assistant (in the "field") was finding plants that were only 25 to 30 percent sterile. Disturbed by this discrepancy, McClintock left the cornfield and returned to her office where she sat for half an hour, thinking:

> Suddenly I jumped up and ran back to the (corn) field. At the top of the field (the others were still at the bottom) I shouted, "Eureka, I have it! I know what the 30% sterility is!" ... They asked me to prove it. I sat down with a

> paper bag and a pencil and I started from scratch, which I had not done at all in my laboratory. It had all been done so fast; the answer came and I ran. Now I worked it out step by step—it was an intricate series of steps—and I came out with [the same result]. [They] looked at the material and it was exactly as I'd said it was; it worked out exactly as I had diagrammed it. Now, why did I know, without having done it on paper? Why was I so sure? (Keller, 1983, p. 104).

This anecdote illustrates two essential facts of the logical-mathematical intelligence. First, in the gifted individual, the process of problem solving is often remarkably rapid—the successful scientist copes with many variables at once and creates numerous hypotheses that are each evaluated and then accepted or rejected in turn. The anecdote also underscores the nonverbal nature of the intelligence. A solution to a problem can be constructed before it is articulated. In fact, the solution process may be totally invisible, even to the problem solver. This phenomenon need not imply, however, that discoveries of this sort—the familiar "aha!"—are mysterious, intuitive, or unpredictable. The fact that it happens frequently to some people (e.g., Nobel Prize winners) suggests the opposite. We interpret this phenomenon as the work of the logical-mathematical intelligence.

Along with the companion skill of language, logical-mathematical reasoning provides the principal basis for IQ tests. This form of intelligence has been thoroughly investigated by traditional psychologists, and it is the archetype of "raw intelligence" or the problem-solving faculty that purportedly cuts across domains. It is perhaps ironic, then, that the actual mechanism by which one arrives at a solution to a logical-mathematical problem is not as yet completely understood—and the processes involved in leaps like those described by McClintock remain mysterious.

Logical-mathematical intelligence is supported as well by empirical criteria. Certain areas of the brain are more prominent in mathematical calculation than others; indeed, recent evidence suggests that the linguistic areas in the frontotemporal lobes are more important for logical deduction, and the visuospatial areas in the parietofrontal lobes for numerical calculation (Houdé & Tzourio-Mazoyer, 2003). There are savants who perform great feats of calculation even though they are tragically deficient in most other areas. Child prodigies in mathematics abound. The development of this intelligence in children has been carefully documented by Jean Piaget and other psychologists.

Linguistic Intelligence

At the age of ten, T. S. Eliot created a magazine called *Fireside*, to which he was the sole contributor. In a three-day period during his winter vacation, he created eight complete issues. Each one included poems, adventure stories, a gossip column, and humor. Some of this material survives, and it displays the talent of the poet (see Soldo, 1982).

As with the logical intelligence, calling linguistic skill an intelligence is consistent with the stance of traditional psychology. Linguistic intelligence also passes our empirical tests. For instance, a specific area of the brain, called Broca's area, is responsible for the production of grammatical sentences. A person with damage to this area can understand words and sentences quite well but has difficulty putting words together in anything other than the simplest of sentences. Other thought processes may be entirely unaffected.

The gift of language is universal, and its rapid and unproblematic development in most children is strikingly constant across cultures. Even in deaf populations where a manual sign language is not explicitly taught, children will often invent their own manual language and use it surreptitiously. We thus see how an intelligence may operate independently of a specific input modality or output channel.

Spatial Intelligence

Navigation around the Caroline Islands in the South Seas is accomplished by native sailors without instruments. The position of the stars, as viewed from various islands, the weather patterns, and water color are the principal signposts. Each journey is broken into a series of segments, and the navigator learns the position of the stars within each of these segments. During the actual trip the navigator must mentally picture a reference island as it passes under a particular star. From that envisioning exercise, he computes the number of segments completed, the proportion of the trip remaining, and any corrections in heading that are required. The navigator cannot see the islands as he sails along; instead he maps their locations in his mental picture of the journey (see Gladwin, 1970).

Spatial problem solving is required for navigation and for the use of the notational system of maps. Other kinds of spatial problem solving are brought to bear in visualizing an object from different angles and in playing chess. The visual arts also employ this intelligence in the use of space.

Evidence from brain research is clear and persuasive. Just as the middle regions of the left cerebral cortex have, over the course of evolution, been selected as the site of linguistic processing in right-handed persons, the posterior regions of the right cerebral cortex prove most crucial for spatial processing. Damage to these regions causes impairment of the ability to find one's way around a site, to recognize faces or scenes, or to notice fine details.

Blind populations provide an illustration of the distinction between the spatial intelligence and visual perception. A blind person can recognize shapes by a nonvisual method: running a hand along the contours of an object translates into length of time of movement, which in turn is translated into the size and shape of the object. For the blind person, the perceptual system of the tactile modality parallels the visual modality in the seeing person. The analogy between the spatial reasoning of the blind and the linguistic reasoning of the deaf is notable.

There are few child prodigies among visual artists, but there are savants like Nadia (Selfe, 1977), a preschool child who, despite a condition of severe autism, made drawings of the most remarkable representational accuracy and finesse.

Interpersonal Intelligence

With little formal training in special education and nearly blind herself, Anne Sullivan began the formidable task of instructing a blind and deaf seven-year-old, Helen Keller. Sullivan's efforts at communication were complicated by the child's emotional struggle with the world around her. At their first meal together, this scene occurred:

> Annie did not allow Helen to put her hand into Annie's plate and take what she wanted, as she had been accustomed to do with her family. It became a test of wills—hand thrust into plate, hand firmly put aside. The family, much upset, left the dining room. Annie locked the door and proceeded to eat her breakfast while Helen lay on the floor kicking and screaming, pushing and pulling at Annie's chair. [After half an hour] Helen went around the table looking for her family. She discovered no one else was there and that bewildered her. Finally, she sat down and began to eat her breakfast, but with her hands. Annie gave her a spoon. Down on the floor it clattered, and the contest of wills began anew (Lash, 1980, p. 52).

Anne Sullivan sensitively responded to the child's behavior. She wrote home: "The greatest problem I shall have to solve is how to discipline and control her without breaking her spirit. I shall go rather slowly at first and try to win her love." In fact, the first "miracle" occurred two weeks later, well before the famous incident at the pump house. Annie had taken Helen to a small cottage near the family's house, where they could live alone. After seven days together, Helen's personality suddenly underwent a change—the therapy had worked: "My heart is singing with joy this morning. A miracle has happened! The wild little creature of two weeks ago has been transformed into a gentle child" (Lash, 1980, p. 54).

It was just two weeks after this that the first breakthrough in Helen's grasp of language occurred; and from that point on, she progressed with incredible speed. The key to the miracle of language was Anne Sullivan's insight into the person of Helen Keller.

Interpersonal intelligence builds on a core capacity to notice distinctions among others—in particular, contrasts in their moods, temperaments, motivations, and intentions. In more advanced forms, this intelligence permits a skilled adult to read the intentions and desires of others, even when they have been hidden. This skill appears in a highly sophisticated form in religious or political leaders, salespersons, marketers, teachers, therapists, and parents. The Helen Keller–Anne Sullivan story suggests that this interpersonal intelligence does not depend on language. All indices in brain research suggest that the frontal lobes play a prominent role in interpersonal knowledge. Damage in this area can cause profound personality changes while leaving other forms of problem solving unharmed—after such an injury, a person is often not the "same person."

Alzheimer's disease, a form of dementia, appears to attack posterior brain zones with a special ferocity, leaving spatial, logical, and linguistic computations severely impaired. Yet people with Alzheimer's often remain well groomed, socially proper, and continually apologetic for their errors. In contrast, Pick's disease, a variety of dementia that is localized in more frontal regions of the cortex, entails a rapid loss of social graces.

Biological evidence for interpersonal intelligence encompasses two additional factors often cited as unique to humans. One factor is the prolonged childhood of primates, including the close attachment to the mother. In cases where the mother (or a substitute figure) is not available and engaged, normal interpersonal development is in serious jeopardy. The second factor is the relative importance in humans of social interaction. Skills such as hunting, tracking, and killing in prehistoric societies required the participation and cooperation of large numbers of people. The need for group cohesion, leadership, organization, and solidarity follows naturally from this.

Intrapersonal Intelligence

In an essay called "A Sketch of the Past," written almost as a diary entry, Virginia Woolf discusses the "cotton wool of existence"—the various mundane events of life. She contrasts this cotton wool with three specific and poignant memories from her childhood: a fight with her brother, seeing a particular flower in the garden, and hearing of the suicide of a past visitor:

> These are three instances of exceptional moments. I often tell them over, or rather they come to the surface unexpectedly. But now for the first time I have written them down, and I realize something that I have never realized before. Two of these moments ended in a state of despair. The other ended, on the contrary, in a state of satisfaction. ... The sense of horror [in hearing of the suicide] held me powerless. But in the case of the flower, I found a reason; and was thus able to deal with the sensation. I was not powerless. ... Though I still have the peculiarity that I receive these sudden shocks, they are now always welcome; after the first surprise, I always feel instantly that they are particularly valuable. And so I go on to suppose that the shock-receiving capacity is what makes me a writer. I hazard the explanation that a shock is at once in my case followed by the desire to explain it. I feel that I have had a blow; but it is not, as I thought as a child, simply a blow from an enemy hidden behind the cotton wool of daily life; it is or will become a revelation of some order; it is a token of some real thing behind appearances; and I make it real by putting it into words (Woolf, 1976, pp. 69–70).

This quotation vividly illustrates the intrapersonal intelligence—knowledge of the internal aspects of a person: access to one's own feeling life, one's range of emotions, the capacity to make discriminations among these emotions and eventually to label them and to draw on them as a means of understanding and guiding one's own behavior. A person with good intrapersonal intelligence has a viable and effective model of him- or herself—one consistent with a description constructed by careful observers who know that person intimately. Since this intelligence is the most private, evidence from language, music, or some other more expressive form of intelligence is required if the observer is to detect it at work. In the above quotation, for example, linguistic intelligence serves as a medium in which to observe intrapersonal knowledge in operation.

We see the familiar criteria at work in the intrapersonal intelligence. As with the interpersonal intelligence, the frontal lobes play a central role in personality change. Injury to the lower area of the frontal lobes is likely to produce irritability or euphoria, whereas injury to the higher regions is more likely to produce indifference, listlessness, slowness, and apathy—a kind of depressive personality. In persons with frontal lobe injury, the other cognitive functions often remain preserved. In contrast, among aphasics who have recovered sufficiently to describe their experiences, we find consistent testimony: while there may have been a diminution of general alertness and considerable depression about the condition, the individual in no way felt himself to be a different person. He recognized his own needs, wants, and desires and tried as best he could to achieve them.

The autistic child is a prototypical example of an individual with impaired intrapersonal intelligence; indeed, the child may not even be able to refer to himself. At the same time, such children may exhibit remarkable abilities in the musical, computational, spatial, mechanical, and other non-personal realms.

Evolutionary evidence for an intrapersonal faculty is more difficult to come by, but we might speculate that the capacity to transcend the satisfaction of instinctual drives is relevant. This potential becomes increasingly important in a species not perennially involved in the struggle for survival. The neural structures that permit consciousness probably form the basis on which self-consciousness is constructed.

In sum, then, both interpersonal and intrapersonal faculties pass the tests of an intelligence. They both feature problem-solving capacities that have significance for the individual and the species. Interpersonal intelligence allows one to understand and work with others. Intrapersonal intelligence allows one to understand and work with oneself. In the individual's sense of self, one encounters a melding of interpersonal and intrapersonal components. Indeed, the sense of self emerges as one of the most marvelous of human inventions—a symbol that represents all kinds of information about a person and that is at the same time an invention that all individuals construct for themselves.

Newly Identified Intelligences

For the first ten years after I proposed the theory of multiple intelligences, I resisted any temptation to alter the theory. Many individuals proposed candidate intelligences—humor intelligence, cooking intelligence, sexual intelligence. One of my students quipped that I would never recognize those intelligences, because I lacked them myself.

Two factors led me to consider additional intelligences. Once I spoke about the theory to a group of historians of science. After my talk, a short, elderly man approached and said, "You will never explain Charles Darwin with the set of intelligences that you proposed." The commentator was none other than Ernst Mayr, probably the most important twentieth-century authority on evolution.

The other factor was the frequent assertion that there was a spiritual intelligence, and the occasional assertion that I had identified a spiritual intelligence. In fact, neither statement was true. But these experiences motivated me to consider whether there is evidence for either a naturalist or a spiritual intelligence.

This inquiry led to very different conclusions. In the first case, the evidence for the existence of a naturalist intelligence is surprisingly persuasive. Biologists like Charles Darwin and E. O. Wilson and ornithologists like John James Audubon and Roger Tory Peterson excel at identifying and distinguishing one species from another. Persons with a high degree of naturalist intelligence are keenly aware of how to distinguish the diverse plants, animals, mountains, or cloud configurations in their ecological niche. These capacities are not exclusively visual; the recognition of birdsong or whale calls entails auditory perception. The Dutch naturalist Geermat Vermij, who is blind, depends on his sense of touch.

On the eight criteria for an intelligence, the naturalist intelligence scores well. In this type of intelligence, there is the core capacity to recognize instances as members of a species. There is also the evolutionary history of survival often depending on recognizing conspecifics and on avoiding predators. Young children easily make distinctions in the naturalist world—indeed, some five-year-olds are better than their parents or grandparents at distinguishing among dinosaur species.

Examining the naturalist intelligence through the cultural or brain lenses brings some interesting phenomena into focus. Today few people in the developed world are directly dependent on naturalist intelligence. We simply go to the grocery store or order groceries on the phone or the Internet. And yet, I suggest, our entire consumer culture is based on the naturalist intelligence. It includes the capacities we deploy when we are drawn to one car rather than another, or when we select one pair of sneakers or gloves rather than another.

The study of brain damage provides intriguing evidence of individuals who are able to recognize and name inanimate objects but who lose the capacity to identify living things; less often, one encounters the opposite pattern, where individuals are able to recognize and name animate entities but fail with artificial (man-made) objects. These capacities probably entail different perceptual mechanisms (Euclidean geometry operates in the world of artifacts but not in the world of nature) and different experiential bases (we interact with inanimate objects and tools very differently than with living beings).

My review of the evidence on spirituality proved less straightforward. People have very strong views on religion and spirituality. For many (particularly in the contemporary United States), experiences of the spirit are the most important ones; and many assume that a spiritual intelligence not only exists but actually represents the highest achievement of human beings. Others, particularly those of a scientific bent, cannot take seriously any discussion of the spirit or the soul; it smacks of mysticism. And they may be deeply skeptical about God and religion—especially so in the academy. Asked why I had not endorsed a spiritual or religious intelligence, I once quipped, "If I did so, it would please my friends—but it would please my enemies even more!"

Quips are no substitute for scholarship. I devoted the better part of a year to reviewing the evidence for and against a spiritual intelligence. I concluded that at least two facets of spirituality were quite remote from my conception of an intelligence. First, I do not believe that an intelligence should be confounded with an individual's phenomenological experience. For most observers, spirituality entails a certain set of visceral reactions—for example, a feeling that one is in touch with a higher being or "at one" with the world. Such feelings may be fine, but I do not see them as valid indicators of an intelligence. A person with a high degree of mathematical intelligence may undergo feelings of "flow" in the course of solving a difficult problem, but the person is equally mathematically intelligent even if he or she has no such phenomenological reaction.

Second, for many individuals, spirituality is indissociable from a belief in religion and God generally, or even from allegiance to a particular faith or sect: "Only a real Jew/Catholic/Muslim/Protestant is a spiritual being" is the explicit or implicit message. This requirement makes me uncomfortable and takes us far from the initial set of criteria for an intelligence.

But although a spiritual intelligence does not qualify on my criteria, one facet of spirituality seems a promising candidate. I call it the existential intelligence—sometimes described as "the intelligence of big questions." This candidate intelligence is based on the human proclivity to ponder the most fundamental questions of existence. Why do we live? Why do we die? Where do we come from? What is going to happen to us? What is love? Why do we make war? I sometimes say that these are questions that transcend perception; they concern issues that are too big or too small to be perceived by our five principal sensory systems.

Somewhat surprisingly, the existential intelligence does reasonably well in terms of our criteria. Certainly, there are individuals—philosophers, religious leaders, the most impressive statesman—who come to mind as high-end embodiments of existential intelligence. Existential issues arise in every culture—in religion, philosophy, art, and the more mundane stories, gossip, and media presentations of everyday life. In any society where questioning is tolerated, children raise these existential questions from an early age—though they do not always listen closely to the answers. Moreover, the myths and fairy tales that they gobble up speak to their fascination with existential questions.

My hesitation in declaring a full-blown existential intelligence comes from the dearth, so far, of evidence that parts of the brain are concerned particularly with these deep issues of existence. It could be that there are regions—for example, in the inferotemporal lobe—that are particularly crucial for dealing with the Big Questions. However, it is also possible that existential questions are just part of a broader philosophical mind—or that they are simply the more emotionally laden of the questions that individuals routinely pose. In the latter instances, my conservative nature dictates caution in giving the ninth place of honor to existential intelligence. I do mention this candidate intelligence in passing, but, in homage to a famous film by Federico Fellini, I shall continue for the time being to speak of "8½ Intelligences."

The Unique Contributions of the Theory

As human beings, we all have a repertoire of skills for solving different kinds of problems. My investigation began, therefore, with a consideration of these problems, the contexts in which they are found, and the culturally significant products that are the outcome. I did not approach "intelligence" as a reified human faculty that is brought to bear in literally any problem setting; rather, I began with the problems that human beings solve and the products that they cherish. In a sense I then worked back to the intelligences that must be responsible.

Evidence from brain research, human development, evolution, and cross-cultural comparisons was brought to bear in the search for the relevant human intelligences: a candidate was included only if reasonable evidence to support its membership was found across these diverse fields. Again, this tack differs from the traditional one: since no candidate faculty is necessarily an intelligence, I could make an up-or-down decision on a motivated basis. In the traditional approach to intelligence, there is no opportunity for this type of empirical decision.

My belief is that these multiple human faculties, the intelligences, are to a significant extent independent of one another. Research with brain-damaged adults repeatedly demonstrates that particular faculties can be lost while others are spared. This independence of intelligences implies that a particularly high level of ability in one intelligence, say mathematics, does not require a similarly high level in another, like language or music. This independence of intelligences contrasts sharply with traditional measures of IQ that find high correlations among test scores. I speculate that the usual correlations among subtests of IQ tests come about because all of these tasks in fact measure the ability to respond rapidly to items of a logical-mathematical or linguistic sort; these correlations might be substantially reduced if one were to survey in a contextually appropriate way—what I call "intelligence-fair assessment"—the full range of human problem-solving skills.

Until now, my discussion may appear to suggest that adult roles depend largely on the flowering of a single intelligence. In fact, however, nearly every cultural role of any degree of sophistication requires a combination of intelligences. Thus, even an apparently straightforward role, like playing the violin, transcends a reliance on musical intelligence. To become a successful violinist requires bodily-kinesthetic dexterity and the interpersonal skills of relating to an audience and, in a different way, of choosing a manager; quite possibly it involves an intrapersonal intelligence as well. Dance requires skills in bodily-kinesthetic, musical, interpersonal, and spatial intelligences in varying degrees. Politics requires an interpersonal skill, a linguistic facility, and perhaps some logical aptitude.

Inasmuch as nearly every cultural role requires several intelligences, it becomes important to consider individuals as a collection of aptitudes rather than as having a singular problem-solving faculty that can be measured directly through pencil-and-paper tests. Even given a relatively small number of such intelligences, the diversity of human ability is created through the differences in these profiles. In fact, it may well be that the total is greater than the sum of the parts. An individual may not be particularly gifted in any intelligence, and yet, because of a particular combination or blend of skills, he or she may be able to fill some niche uniquely well. Thus, it is of paramount importance to assess the particular combination of skills that may earmark an individual for a certain vocational or avocational niche.

In brief, MI theory leads to three conclusions:

1. All of us have the full range of intelligences; that is what makes us human beings, cognitively speaking.
2. No two individuals—not even identical twins—have exactly the same intellectual profile because, even when the genetic material is identical, individuals have different experiences (and identical twins are often highly motivated to distinguish themselves from one another).
3. Having a strong intelligence does not mean that one necessarily acts intelligently. A person with high mathematical intelligence might use her abilities to carry out important experiments in physics or create powerful new geometric proofs; but she might waste these abilities in playing the lottery all day or multiplying ten-digit numbers in her head.

All of these statements are about the psychology of human intelligence—to which MI theory seeks to make a contribution. But of course they raise powerful educational, political, and cultural questions. Those questions will engage us in later parts of the book.

Conclusion

I believe that in our society we suffer from three biases, which I have nicknamed "Westist," "Testist," and "Bestist." "Westist" involves putting certain Western cultural values, which date back to Socrates, on a pedestal. Logical thinking, for example, is important; rationality is important; but they are not the only virtues. "Testist" suggests a bias towards focusing on those human abilities or approaches that are readily testable. If it can't be tested, it sometimes seems, it is not worth paying attention to. My feeling is that assessment can be much broader, much more humane than it is now and that psychologists should spend less time ranking people and more time trying to help them.

"Bestist" is a thinly veiled reference to David Halberstam's 1972 book *The Best and the Brightest*. Halberstam's title referred ironically to the figures, among them Harvard faculty members, who were brought to Washington to help President John F. Kennedy and in the process launched the Vietnam War. I think any belief that all the answers to a given problem lie in one certain approach, such as logical-mathematical thinking, can be very dangerous. Current views of intellect need to be leavened with other, more comprehensive points of view.

It is of the utmost importance that we recognize and nurture all of the varied human intelligences and all of the combinations of intelligences. We are all so different largely because we have different combinations of intelligences. If we recognize this, I think we will have at least a better chance of dealing appropriately with the many problems that we face in the world. If we can mobilize the spectrum of human abilities, not only will people feel better about themselves and more competent; it is even possible that they will also feel more engaged and better able to join the rest of the world community in working for the broader good. Perhaps if we can mobilize the full range of human intelligences and ally them to an ethical sense, we can help increase the likelihood of our survival on this planet, and perhaps even contribute to our thriving.

References

Gallwey, T. (1976). *Inner tennis*. New York: Random House.

Gardner, H. (1983b). *Frames of mind: The theory of multiple intelligences*. New York: Basic Books.

Gardner, H. (1999a). *Intelligence reframed: Multiple intelligences for the 2lst century*. New York: Basic Books.

Gladwin, T. (1970). *East is a big bird: Navigation and logic on a Puluway atoll*. Cambridge, MA: Harvard University Press.

Halberstam, D. (1972). *The best and the brightest*. Greenwich, CT: Fawcett Publications.

Houdé, O., & Tzourio-Mazoyer, N. (2003). Neural foundations of logical and mathematical cognition. *Nature Reviews Neuroscience, 4* (6), 507–515.

Keller, E. (1983). *A feeling for the organism*. San Francisco: Freeman.

Lash, J. (1980). *Helen and teacher: The story of Helen Keller and Anne Sullivan Macy*. New York: Delacorte.

Menuhin, Y. (1977). *Unfinished journey*. New York: Knopf.

Ruth, B. (1948). *The Babe Ruth story as told to Bob Considine*. New York: American Books-Stratford Press.

Selfe, L. (1977). *Nadia: A case of extraordinary drawing ability in an autistic child*. New York: Academic Press.

Soldo, J. (1982). Jovial juvenilia: T.S. Eliot's first magazine: *Biography, 5*, 25–37.

Woolf, V. (1976). *Moments of being*. Sussex, England: University Press.

Green Fear and Green Courage

Underlying all human behavior is the unconscious and conscious experience of personal mortality.

—Ernest Becker

Introduction

Objectivity, reason, logic, and comprehensive judgment and decision making are faculties of human cognition. Depending on the context, and duration and type of stimulus, fear has been found to alter and even inhibition these faculties. The greatest fear is that of our own mortality (Chandler, 2014). Terror management theorists are social psychologists that study the effect of "mortality salience" or the potency of the fear of death (Pyszczynski, Greenberg, & Solomon, 2000; Pyszczynski, Greenberg, Solomon, & Maxfield, 2006) on human behavior. They have determined that the unconscious experience of our mortality can facilitate the worst forms of human behavior. These behaviors have been collectively referred to as "immortality projects" (Becker, 1971; Wilbur, 1981) and include but are not limited to war, imperialism, slavery, racism, bigotry, human trafficking, unilateralism, and environmental destruction (e.g., poaching and sprawl development). In the context of the psychology of sustainability I conceptualize immortality projects as manifestations of *green fear*, the negative denial and often violent response to reminders that nature ultimately holds sway on all life, we are all subject to the same laws of nature, and we must depend on diversity to survive.

Researchers in the human experience of Climate Change (Dickinson, 2009; Dyson, 2006) and of sustainability (Chandler, 2014) proffer that awareness of mortality likely stimulates conscious and unconscious experience of our dependency on nature, as well as increases existential threat arising from the destruction of the natural world. Drawing from this research it seems that how we experience (i.e., consciously or unconsciously) our mortality affects our sustainability inclination (Chapter 2 of this book). This is to say that conscious awareness of our mortality might facilitate simple and even remarkable acts of sustainability or what I refer to as *practical immortality projects* for example altruism, tolerance, nonviolence, collectivism, humanitarian and environmental charity and activism, and becoming a prosocial/sustainability change agent, all of which are products *green courag*e. Green courage is the type of fear of death that motivates us to design and implement practical immortality projects. Green fear is the deliberate employment of the fear energy that arises from the conscious experience of mortality and the acceptance that our only hope for a sustainable human ecology is to live cooperatively and in continuity with nature, and to appreciate diversity as a form of strength.

Theories and Concepts in Context of Sustainability

The Fertile Crescent: Beginning of Anthropogenic Climate Change?

For decades philosophers, and social and environmental scientists have wondered when did *Homo sapiens* start down the path of global destruction and why. One plausible answer to "when" is proffered by philosopher Ken Wilber (1981) and also suggests the general location to have been the Fertile Crescent also known as the Cradle of Civilization. The Fertile Crescent is the region formed by the confluence of the Tigris and Euphrates rivers. In the heart of what is now referred to as the Middle East the Fertile Crescent was once among the most biodiverse regions in the world and was characterized by abundant fauna and flora, fertile soils, and plentiful freshwater. The Fertile Crescent is also considered to be the birthplace of incipient permanent agriculture evidenced from archeological findings dating back over 8,000 years.

Within a relatively short time and as more nomadic gather-hunters began to settle and farm in the region the once verdant landscape was rendered mostly barren, hot, and parched due to deforestation, water diversion, draining of marshes, and unsustainable irrigation practices. For a time, though, before the rivers periodically ran dry and when the soil was still fertile, food production was abundant. Families grew and so did the need for more food and more land. With this expansion property boundary disputes developed and with those came acquisitiveness and even murder (Wilbur, 1981).

Terror management theory (e.g., Pyszczynski et al., 2000) would indicate that fear had a hand in the decision to become placed-based farmers and to store and hoard rather than hunt-gather, and to act violently toward neighbors in response to existential threat, for example the prospect of less food in the upcoming season than was had in the previous season(s). If this generalization is representative, then the Fertile Crescent was also the birthplace of our immortality projects and by extension it was then and there that we began to implement anthropogenic Climate Change.

Since the dawn of civilization societies have repeated the severe socially and ecologically discontinuous behavior first observed in the Fertile Crescent 8,000–9,000 years ago. This is why

I refer to this destructive pattern of behavior as the "Fertile Crescent phenomenon." We have yet to, on any significant level, treat a landscape and its residents any differently. It seems clear that until we recognize the Fertile Crescent phenomenon and take action guided by the psychology of sustainability we will not be able to avert the worst of environmental and social outcomes due to Climate Change.

Terror Management Theory in Context of Sustainability Inclination

Otto Rank (1884–1939), one of the world's great psychologists, was likely the first to holistically investigate why as individuals and as a society we behave as we do within a wide range of conditions or scenarios. He is credited with framing research in "the psychology of the human condition" and developed the concept "humanity's ever-present tension" (ca. 1926). In short, Rank found that each human experience is inextricably linked with all human experience, and contended that these linkages form a dynamic system characterized by an ever-present tension between essential polar opposites of perception for example scarcity and abundance, and isolation and unity. Furthermore, Rank theorized that our perception of our situation was influenced by sociocultural and socioecological factors, and that this influence on our perception was constant and ever-present (Chandler, 2010).

Cultural anthropologist, Ernest Becker (1973, 1975) sought to understand what energized Rank's ever-present tension and why this tension characterized the psychology of the human condition? Through years of research Becker determined that the driving force of this tension, for example the push and pull between a sense of scarcity or abundance, love or hate, and safety and danger is the level or salience of our experience of mortality. If mortality salience is high, Becker theorized, experience of scarcity, isolation, defensiveness, and so on would be elevated in an unconscious attempt to buffer the inevitability of our personal extinction. With this discovery Becker (1973) concluded that "[t]he problem with death is how to make sense of it" (p. 13).

To make sense of something is to bring it to the fore of our consciousness in an attempt to understand. Recall the sixth tenet of the psychology of sustainability (Chapter 1), *At the heart of all human behavior (the worst, the best, and all points between) is the unconscious or conscious experience of personal mortality.* From a holistic sustainability perspective, the importance of this tenet cannot be overstated. Early research guided by terror management theory identified examples of the worst of human behavior motivated by the unconscious experience or salience of mortality. In more recent research, terror management theorists (Pyszczynski, Rothschild, & Abdollahi, 2008), as well as existential theorists (Cozzolino, Sheldon, Schachtman, & Meyers, 2009), revealed that when individuals are asked to contemplate personal mortality and to imagine their lives from the present until their inevitable demise they tended to be more prosocial, specifically more generous, more tolerant of another's worldview, to work cooperatively rather than competitively, and were more patient (Cozzolino, et al., 2009; Niemiec et al., 2010; Vail et al., 2012). Therefore, if acceptance of personal mortality results in increased prosocial behavior it will likely increase an individual's sustainability inclination.

Before you read the feature article, reflect on what you have learned thus far and especially review Chapter 2 and the likely role of attachment style and social value orientation to sustainability inclination. Now think about what you have learned in this chapter. Consider the effect of fear and especially of mortality salience on human behavior throughout history as well as the likely effect this might have on your personal sustainability inclination. Finally, ask yourself how you would employ what you have learned thus far to bolster your green courage or motivate you to engage in practical immortality projects.

About the Feature

As you read the feature article for this chapter, *Raising the Specter of Death: What Terror Management Theory Brings to the Study of Fear Appeals*, think about how fear is employed toward convincing people to adopt one point of view over another. Also, consider how you could use terror management theory to more frequently "catch" fear messaging in what you are reading or hearing.

References

Becker, E. (1973). *The denial of death.* New York, NY: The Free Press.

Becker, E. (1975). Escape from evil. New York, NY: Free Press.

Chandler, R. (2014). *I am the paradigm shift: A grounded theory of learners' sustainability outcome comprehension experience.* Ann Arbor, MI: ProQuest.

Chandler, R. (2010). Overview of terror management theory and general implications for sustainability. Unpublished

Cozzolino, P. J., Sheldon, K. M., Schachtman, T. R., & Meyers, L. S. (2009). Limited time perspective, values, and greed: Imagining a limited future reduces avarice in extrinsic people. *Journal of Research in Personality, 43*(3), 399–408. doi:10.1016/j.jrp.2009.01.008

Dickinson, J. L. (2009). The people paradox: Self-esteem striving, immortality ideologies, and human response to climate change. *Ecology and Society, 14*(1), 34.

Dyson, T. (2006). On development, demography and climate change: The end of the world as we know it? *Population and Environment, 27*(2), 274–321.

Niemiec, C., Brown, K., Kashdan, T., Cozzolino, P., Breen, W., & Levesque-Bristol, C. (2010). Being present in the face of existential threat: The role of trait mindfulness in reducing defensive responses to mortality salience. *Journal of Personality and Social Psychology, 99*(2), 344–365. doi:10.1037/a0019388

Pyszczynski, T., Greenberg, J., & Solomon, S. (2000). Proximal and distal defense: A new perspective on unconscious motivation. *Current Directions in Psychological Science, 9*(5), 156–160. doi:10.1111/1467-8721.00083

Pyszczynski, T., Greenberg, J., Solomon, S., & Maxfield, M. (2006). COMMENTARY: On the unique psychological import of the human awareness of mortality: Theme and variations. *Psychological Inquiry*, *17*(4), 328–356.

Pyszczynski, T., Rothschild, Z., & Abdollahi, A. (2008). Terrorism, violence, and hope for peace: A terror management perspective. *Current Directions in Psychological Science, 17*(5), 318–322. Retrieved from http://www.jstor.org/stable/20183311

Vail, K., Juhl, J., Arndt, J., Vess, M., Routledge, C., & Rutjens, B. T. (2012). When death is good for life considering the positive trajectories of terror management. *Personality and Social Psychology Review*, *16(4)*, 303–329. doi:10.1177/1088868312440046

Wilbur, K. (1981). *Up from Eden: A transpersonal view of human evolution.* Boston, MA: Shambhala.

READING 7

Raising the Specter of Death

What Terror Management Theory Brings to the Study of Fear Appeals

Susanna Dilliplane
University of Pennsylvania

How do people respond to persuasive appeals that invoke the threat of death? This chapter calls attention to Terror Management Theory (TMT), a theoretical framework that considers the unique effects of raising the salience of one's mortality and yet has remained largely outside the focus of inquiry into the effects of fear appeals. The distinct conceptual and predictive features of TMT, as well as their relevance to health and political communication research, are discussed and then juxtaposed with those found in the dominant strains of the fear appeal literature. The analysis articulates the theoretical and empirical implications of these conceptual differences and offers a set of testable predictive contrasts, with the goal of stimulating and facilitating new lines of fear appeal scholarship.

Imagine you are watching television and an ad comes on the screen.[1] A video of the twin towers on September 11th zooms in on the gaping, burning holes from the hijacked planes, bringing to mind the horrific fates of those on the planes and trapped in the World Trade Center buildings. Warning that the threat of terrorist attacks still looms large, the narrator urges you to support a particular political candidate. Or your TV screen is filled by the pained face of a man who has been hospitalized with throat and lung cancer, and yet doggedly expresses his intent to be alive for his daughter's upcoming visit. This scene is followed by the stark message that the man died before his daughter arrived, as well as an appeal for viewers to quit smoking.[2]

Susanna Dilliplane, "Raising the Specter of Death: What Terror Management Theory Brings to the Study of Fear Appeals," *Communication Yearbook 34, ed. Charles T. Salmon*, pp. 93-131. Copyright © 2010 by Taylor & Francis Group. Reprinted with permission.

How do people react to such appeals that invoke the threat of death? One class of answers to this question may be found in the literature on fear appeals. A number of existing theoretical frameworks from the health and political arenas, well known to communication researchers, could readily classify the above examples as high-fear appeals and derive predictions about likely message responses. However, different answers are emerging from research that specifically focuses on fear of death, rather than fear generally. The purpose of this chapter is to call attention to Terror Management Theory (TMT), a theoretical framework that has remained largely outside the focus of communication research, and to juxtapose its distinct conceptual and predictive features with those found in the dominant strains of the literature on fear and persuasion.

I begin with an explication of Terror Management Theory and its relevance to research on fear appeals. I then discuss major constructs within the existing fear appeal research, with a particular emphasis on two prominent theoretical frameworks that exemplify how these constructs and their interrelationships are conceptualized in the health and political arenas. These highlighted models are then used to consider conceptual comparisons and contrasts with TMT, along with the implications of these differences for understanding responses to persuasive appeals invoking the threat of death. Based on the key conceptual distinctions among the frameworks, the analysis concludes with a series of testable predictive contrasts, which is offered as a first step toward productively incorporating TMT into future scholarship in health and political communication.

This chapter is not about presenting an original theoretical model. TMT is a well-established theory in psychology, and various TMT studies have either hinted at or articulated some of the same points that I make here, particularly in the health context, where the theory's authors have offered a model of health behavior decisions that integrates TMT with more traditional approaches to health psychology (see Goldenberg & Arndt, 2008). Nonetheless, prior TMT scholarship has very rarely been explicitly situated in a persuasive communications context. Thus, my central aim here is to discuss TMT's potential contributions from a communication perspective, with a particular emphasis on comparing and contrasting TMT's core constructs, their interrelationships, and corresponding predictions with those of existing theoretical frameworks in the fear communication literature.

By focusing on theoretical comparison, this chapter is oriented toward understanding how to leverage the unique features of TMT in relation to prior research on fear appeals—a body of work that is concerned not only with predicting attitudes and behaviors, but also with communication and persuasion processes involved in the use of emotional appeals and with questions of message design. In addition, this comparison brings to light a number of intriguing questions about how to understand responses to fear appeals invoking the threat of death, such as the possibility of a two-part sequential response that is not mediated by fear arousal. In positioning TMT relative to important themes in the health and political literature on persuasion and fear appeals, this chapter seeks to bring terror management more squarely into the focus of communication scholars.

Terror Management Theory: An Overview

Terror Management Theory seeks to explain the motivational underpinnings of human behavior, positing that concerns about the inevitability of death affect a broad array of attitudes and behaviors that have no logical or semantic relationship with mortality (Greenberg, Pyszczynski, & Solomon, 1986; Solomon, Greenberg, & Pyszczynski, 1991; see also Pyszczynski, Solomon, & Greenberg, 2003). Although TMT has generated a vast number of studies, it appears to have been almost entirely neglected in communication research, including the fear appeal literature.[3] Given the theory's focus on terror—generally defined as intense or overwhelming fear—its potential contributions to the study of fear appeals deserve consideration. In this section, I provide an overview of the theory and its relevance to health and political communication.

Based on insights derived from Ernest Becker's work (1962, 1973, 1975), TMT begins with an existential dilemma facing humans: as animals, we possess a general orientation toward continued life or self-preservation, but our unique mental ability of consciousness and self-consciousness, which enables reflection on the past and anticipation of the future, unfortunately renders us conscious of the disturbing inevitability of our own deaths (Goldenberg, Pyszczynski, Greenberg, & Solomon, 2000; Pyszczynski, Greenberg, Solo-mon, & Maxfield, 2006). It is human awareness of the inevitability of death and the possibility of total annihilation of one's being upon death that creates the potential for existential terror. TMT's conception of fear of death, which has roots in evolutionary theorizing, thus generally encompasses all humans; put simply, humans fear death (Pyszczynski, Greenberg, et al., 2006).

According to TMT, cultural beliefs systems save us by mitigating the horror and dread caused by awareness of our own mortality.[4] Terror is managed via a "dual-component cultural anxiety-buffer" consisting of a cultural worldview and self-esteem (Arndt, Greenberg, Pyszczynski, & Solomon, 1997, p. 379). A cultural worldview provides an explanation for one's existence, standards through which individuals can attain a sense of personal value, and the potential for literal or symbolic immortality if one lives up to those standards. An individual acquires and maintains self-esteem by believing in the cultural worldview and living up to the standards it sets.

Although cultural worldviews—which provide order, permanence, and meaning to reality and one's existence in it—obviously differ from culture to culture (and from individual to individual), their *purpose* is the same: "cultural worldviews set up the path to immortality, to transcendence of one's own death. By being valued contributors to such a meaningful world, we become permanent constituents of an eternal symbolic reality, instead of just corporeal beings in a wholly material reality" (Pyszczynski et al., 2003, p. 19). Thus, existential terror is managed through belief systems that deny that death is the end of one's existence, either by promising literal immortality (e.g., heaven, reincarnation) or by enabling a person to feel that he or she is an important part of a significant and enduring reality (Pyszczynski, Greenberg, et al., 2006).

In the context of this chapter, it is important to note that the death-denying function of worldviews is not simply about controlling fear of an immediate physical threat; the problem of mortality represents an existential threat that also operates on a more abstract level. When one thinks about what happens to oneself when one dies, it is not necessarily the imminent threat of death that drives existential terror, but rather knowledge of the inevitability of one's own death, which may be non-imminent but nonetheless terrifying due to its potential finality (for consideration of the physical versus abstract components of existential threat, see Pyszczynski, Greenberg, et al., 2006; Hirschberger, Pyszczynski, & Ein-Dor, 2009).

Given the vast diversity in cultural worldviews and standards by which self-esteem is obtained, TMT views the two components of the cultural anxiety buffer as relatively fragile social constructions requiring continual consensual validation; hence, many behaviors focus on attaining this validation (Pyszczynski, Greenberg, & Solomon, 1999). To the extent that cultural worldviews protect against deep-rooted fears of death, reminders of mortality are hypothesized to lead to an increased need for these beliefs and, by extension, more positive responses to things that validate it and more negative responses to things that threaten it (Pyszczynski et al., 1999). More specifically, TMT posits that a two-stage defense process kicks in when one's mortality becomes salient (Greenberg, Arndt, Simon, Pyszczynski, & Solomon, 2000). First, a person puts conscious thoughts of death out of his or her mind by engaging in threat-focused cognitive maneuvers such as distraction strategies, alteration of beliefs to deny vulnerability, or reassuring thoughts about one's health and the remoteness of the threat (Pyszczynski et al., 2003). These proximal defenses are the direct, rational (though not necessarily unbiased) psychological defenses that are activated to cope with conscious awareness of death—i.e., active suppression.

Once thoughts of death are out of focal attention, but are still accessible, distal defenses are activated. At this stage, people bolster faith in their cultural worldviews and their self-esteem to defend against unconscious thoughts of death. For example, individuals may derogate those who violate or challenge their beliefs, increase regard for those who validate or praise their beliefs, subscribe more strongly to group stereotypes, or exhibit greater in-group favoritism and out-group hostility or prejudice (e.g., Das, Bushman, Bezemer, Kerkhof, & Vermeulen, 2009; Greenberg et al., 1990; Hoyt, Simon, & Reid, 2009; Schimel et al., 1999; Halloran & Kashima, 2004). Such worldview bolstering reduces the accessibility of thoughts of mortality (Arndt, Greenberg, Solomon, et al., 1997). Given that the physical reality of the inevitability of death cannot, in the end, be rationally denied, it is posited that these distal defenses enable the individual to attack the problem at a more abstract level. The confirmation of culturally constructed conceptions of reality and a corresponding sense of self-esteem functions to symbolically control the problem of inevitable death and protect against the potential terror it engenders (Pyszczynski et al., 2003).

The latent accessibility of thoughts of mortality is critical to the theory's predictions. Defensive distortions caused by suppression should occur immediately after mortality is made salient, while worldview and self-esteem bolstering should be greatest once thoughts of mortality are no longer in focal consciousness. Experimental manipulations have provided support for the temporal sequence of this dual process (Greenberg, Arndt, Simon, Pyszczynski, & Solomon, 2000). Active suppression occurs directly after mortality salience is induced, pushing thoughts of death from conscious awareness. Following a delay and distraction, the death concerns that are accessible—but beneath one's conscious radar—provoke distal terror management defenses (see Arndt, Cook, & Routledge, 2004, for a model of the cognitive architecture of terror management). Unlike the individual's conscious suppression of mortality-related thoughts (proximal defenses), distal defenses occur without the individual's awareness of the connection between the threat of death and worldview defense (or the motivation that underlies this response) (Pyszczynski et al., 1999).

A typical TMT experiment manipulates mortality salience (MS) by asking people to respond to two open-ended questions: "Please briefly describe the emotions that the thought of your own death arouses in you" and "Jot down, as specifically as you can, what you think will happen to *you* as you physically die" (Solomon, Greenberg, & Pyszczynski, 2004). Other operationalizations of MS induction, also relevant to a communication context, include subliminal death primes (e.g., flashing the word "death," as in Arndt, Greenberg, Pyszczynski, et al., 1997, or flashing the words "9/11" and "WTC," as in Landau et al., 2004), gory footage of a fatal automobile accident (Nelson, Moore, Olivetti, & Scott, 1997), news reports about terrorist attacks (Das et al., 2009), and even insurance brand logos (Fransen, Fennis, Pruyn, & Das, 2008).[5] Control groups either receive an innocuous version of this treatment (e.g., asking open-ended questions about television use, or subliminally flashing a neutral word like "field") or a non-death-related treatment with a negative valence (e.g., asking people to think about intense physical pain, social exclusion, general anxieties, or dental pain), neither of which appears to produce the same distal defense effects as an MS induction (Pyszczynski et al., 2003).

Following the MS treatment, a delay is introduced, typically in the form of a distracter task or an opportunity to engage in proximal defenses, in order to allow for death thoughts to recede from focal attention. No delay is required if subliminal priming is used because death-related thoughts are not brought to conscious awareness. Next, latent accessibility of death-thoughts is assessed through a word fragment completion task, asking respondents to fill in a series of words, some of which may be completed into death-related words. For example, "coff _ _" could be *coffin* or *coffee*, and "gra _ _" could be *grave* or *grape*. Alternative measures of death thought accessibility, such as reaction times, have been used to provide validation of this word fragment completion task (Arndt, Cook, Greenberg, & Cox, 2007). According to TMT, accessibility should be *higher* among those whose mortality is primed prior to the delay. (Note, however, that accessibility measured directly after mortality salience is raised, as opposed to after a delay, is expected to be *lower* due to active suppression involved in proximal defenses.)

Defense of cultural worldviews (distal defenses) is then assessed through attitudinal and behavioral measures, with the expectation that defense will be greater among people whose mortality was made accessible. For example, thinking about death led respondents to evaluate a source of pro-American views more positively and a source of anti-American views more negatively compared to a control group, demonstrating how MS influences responses to those who support or oppose important aspects of cultural worldviews (Green-berg et al., 1990, Study 3). A similar pro-American bias was found when people's personal mortality was made salient by a video of a fatal car accident, as opposed to a neutral driving video (Nelson et al., 1997).

This overview of TMT has aimed to provide a broad understanding of the theory's core concepts and propositions. More in-depth treatments of the theory's nuances and the kinds of research questions they have inspired may be found elsewhere. In addition, while theoretical critiques of TMT are certainly important to recognize and consider (e.g., Baron, 1997; Buss, 1997; Mikulincer & Florian, 1997; Wicklund, 1997; McGregor, 2006; Proulx & Heine, 2006; Kirkpatrick & Navarrete, 2006; see Pyszczynski, Greenberg, et al., 2006, for a response), as are ethical and philosophical questions regarding the use of fear appeals (e.g., Pfau, 2007), these issues lie somewhat beyond the immediate objective of this chapter. The focus here is on laying out TMT's basic tenets in order to facilitate a discussion of its relevance to the study of fear appeals and its conceptual comparison to other frameworks.

Intuitively, TMT's conceptualization of how people respond when their mortality is made salient seems directly relevant to fear appeal research. Based on the theory's propositions, a fear appeal that raises the salience of personal mortality will elicit an initial suppression response to remove thoughts of death from focal awareness. In addition, if the appeal advocates views that challenge a person's worldview as a relevant source of self-esteem, it will encourage message rejection once thoughts of death are accessible but latent, while an appeal that validates the person's beliefs should receive an especially positive evaluation, enhancing the likelihood of message acceptance. TMT thus has the potential to provide new insights for understanding and predicting responses to fear appeals.

Further, this framework is applicable to both health and political contexts—indeed, to any context in which death and fear appeals are employed. For example, reminders of death in conjunction with health-related behaviors are quite commonplace in health persuasion campaigns, as well as experimental manipulations in which death-related appeals serve as a "high" fear condition (Henley & Donovan, 2003). In recognition of this fact, Goldenberg and Arndt (2008) have recently integrated terror management into a model for predicting health decisions, which revolves around the impact of conscious versus unconscious death thoughts on health behaviors. Their model posits that either defensive avoidance or health-promoting behavior may serve the same function of removing conscious thoughts of death by reducing a perceived health-related threat (i.e., proximal defenses), and that distal defenses activated by nonconscious thoughts of death can motivate behavior that is either beneficial or antithetical to physical health, depending not on the implications for health but on the implications of the behavior for worldview and self-esteem.[6] This work represents an important contribution toward making TMT a useful tool in health promotion campaigns and illustrates the need for further consideration of terror management's relevance to research on fear communications in the health domain.

Death-related themes also arise in the context of political persuasion. Although political studies have largely focused on non-death-related appeals (or do not differentiate among specific types of fear appeals), reminders of death are not unfamiliar features of political persuasive appeals. Among the examples that readily come to mind are post-9/11 speeches made by President Bush that sounded themes of death (see Merskin, 2004) and campaign appeals containing reminders of 9/11, which have appeared in a number of political contests. However, references to death have certainly been used in war-related contexts prior to 9/11, both in presidential rhetoric (see, e.g., Ivie, 1999) and in campaign appeals (e.g., the famous "Daisy Girl" TV ad). They also appear in non-war policy contexts; for example, in the recent U.S. debate over health care reform, an ad by the conservative Independent Women's Forum warned that 300,000 American women could have died if the United States had a "government-run" health insurance plan similar to that of England.[7]

Given that mortality salience has been found to produce greater nationalistic bias, enhanced endorsement of values associated with a salient social identity, greater out-group hostility or prejudice, increased ingroup bias, and greater support for extreme military force or violence (Das et al., 2009; Greenberg et al., 1990, 2000; Halloran & Kashima, 2004; Hoyt et al., 2009; Pyszczynski, Abdollahi, et al., 2006; see also Pyszczynski, Rothschild, & Abdollahi, 2008), the potential ramifications of political appeals containing reminders of death could be significant for outcomes such as policy support, candidate support, and other political attitudes or actions. Indeed, in the context of politics—an arena often associated with the use of tactics intended to subtly manipulate the public—it is worth noting that persuasive messages need not hammer people over the head with an MS treatment in order to produce worldview defense. More subtle treatments, including some outside of conscious awareness, show stronger effects than when people are made to ponder death extensively (Pyszczynski et al., 2003, p. 56). In addition, reminders of the 9/11 terrorist attacks have been found to raise mortality salience and provoke worldview defense among American students in a manner akin to standard MS inductions (Landau et al., 2004; Pyszczynski, Abdollahi, et al., 2006; see also Das et al., 2009, for a non-American example). Real-world messages whose text, imagery, or audio provide reminders of death thus seem well equipped to produce terror management responses.

Major Constructs in Fear Appeal Research

A number of theoretical frameworks have been developed to account for the impact of fear—and persuasive appeals that seek to elicit fear—on attitudes and behaviors in both health and political contexts. Although there is variation among these models, they have in common an interest in delineating the role of key constructs such as environmental (message) threat, threat appraisal, fear arousal, and cognition in shaping outcomes such as information seeking and processing, attitudes, and behaviors. The following discussion provides an overview of the major constructs within prior fear communication research, drawing particular attention to two dominant frameworks in the health and political science literatures—the Extended Parallel Process Model (Witte, 1992, 1994, 1998) and the Theory of Affective Intelligence (Marcus, Neuman, & MacKuen, 2000)—in order to more fully illustrate the concepts and their theoretical relationships.

Theorizing in a Health Context

In the health communication context, fear appeals have inspired a wealth of studies, along with a number of theoretical frameworks for explaining the effects of these appeals. Examples include the drive models proposed by Janis (1967; Hovland, Janis, & Kelly, 1953) and McGuire (1968, 1969), which were followed by Leventhal's (1970, 1971) parallel response model and subjective expected utility approaches such as Rogers' (1975, 1983) protection motivation theory (PMT) and Sutton's (1982) subjective expected utility (SEU) model. Each of these theoretical perspectives placed varying degrees of emphasis on the cognitive versus emotional processes involved in people's reactions to fear appeals. The drive models focused on fear, positing a curvilinear (inverted U-shaped) relationship between fear and attitude change. Leventhal's parallel response model (later called the parallel process model) took theorizing in a new direction by separating the emotional and cognitive processes involved in responses to fear appeals. Subjective expected utility approaches largely ignored fear in favor of the cognitive side of fear appeals, focusing on the perceived utility of the threat and subjective probabilities of its occurrence (Sutton's SEU model) and perceptions of threat and efficacy (Rogers' PMT).

Witte (1992, 1994) advanced these earlier approaches with her proposal for the Extended Parallel Process Model (EPPM). Drawing on Leventhal's parallel process model, Witte's EPPM differentiates between danger control processes, which lead to message acceptance, and fear control processes, which lead to message rejection. The EPPM also builds on PMT in its use of the key concepts of perceived threat (the additive effects of perceived susceptibility to the threat and perceived severity of the threat) and perceived efficacy (self-efficacy and response efficacy). According to the model, a rapid sequential appraisal process takes place: threat appraisal comes first, followed by an appraisal of efficacy, provided that the threat meets a certain threshold (Witte, 1998). Thus, a fear appeal may produce one of three responses: (a) no response if perceived threat is low; (b) message acceptance, produced by a high threat/high efficacy interaction; or (c) message rejection, produced by a high threat/low efficacy interaction. The combination of high perceived threat and efficacy is hypothesized to lead to cognitions about the threat and ways to avoid it, which leads to behavior change (i.e., message acceptance). This response represents a deliberate effort to control the danger. By contrast, high perceived threat coupled with low perceived efficacy is hypothesized to produce message rejection and even boomerang responses, as people deal with the overwhelming fear of a danger they think they cannot control by engaging in defensive avoidance, message minimization, or reactance. This is a potentially unconscious response to control the emotion of fear.

The EPPM posits that the role of fear is contingent on perceived efficacy. Fear directly causes message rejection when efficacy is low; message threat leads to greater perceived threat, which leads to fear that then causes message rejection. Put simply, as perceived threat increases when perceived efficacy is low, people will do the opposite of what the message advocates (Witte, 1998, p. 439). As a result, persuasion or message acceptance should be *lowest* among those in high threat/low efficacy conditions relative to all other conditions (suggesting a boomerang effect), or at the very least message acceptance should not be significantly different from low threat conditions (which is more akin to a null effect). Fear also can indirectly influence message acceptance when efficacy is high; the fear produced by perceived threat is cognitively appraised, causing a further increase in perceived threat that then increases message acceptance. Thus, a person may experience a great deal of fear in a high threat/high efficacy situation, but the "critical point" at which fear outweighs cognitions has not been reached. Overall, affect drives the fear control responses characterizing message rejection, while cognitions (beliefs about severity, susceptibility, self-efficacy, and response efficacy, as well as cognitive appraisals of fear) characterize the danger control processes associated with message acceptance. Moreover, danger control and fear control responses are treated as competing: "if one is defensively responding to a fear appeal and rejecting it, one is not making attitude, intention, or behavior changes" (Witte & Allen, 2000, p. 601).

More recently, further modifications to these theoretical approaches were proposed in the stage model of the processing of fear-arousing communications (Das, de Wit, & Stroebe, 2003; de Hoog, Stroebe, & de Wit, 2005, 2007). The stage model bears some similarities to the EPPM, but distinguishes itself by incorporating aspects of dual process theories of persuasion (e.g., Chaiken, 1980; Chaiken, Liberman, & Eagly, 1989; Petty & Cacioppo, 1986), building on the proposition that fear arousal can both act as a motivator to encourage systematic (in-depth) processing and induce defense motivation (information processing that is positively or negatively biased in order to support one's own beliefs or preferences). Further, the stage model hypothesizes different effects of defense motivation on primary appraisal of the threat (Stage 1) and secondary appraisal of the action recommendation (Stage 2).[8] While this and other frameworks represent important streams of theorizing about fear appeals, I focus on the EPPM because it is an elegant model that incorporates major constructs in the health-related fear appeal literature and concisely maps out their relationships. As a result, it not only provides a useful model with which to set up a theoretical comparison with TMT, but it has fostered a great deal of research and continues to be influential in the fear appeal domain.

For example, in a meta-analysis of studies in the health context, Witte and Allen (2000) found a positive linear function for all independent variables; messages with stronger fear appeals, stronger severity and susceptibility, and stronger response efficacy and self-efficacy produced a greater persuasive impact on attitude, intention, and behavior (danger control responses). High threat/high efficacy appeals produced the greatest persuasive impact, as predicted by the EPPM (as well as the SEU model). Further, this meta-analysis was the first to examine fear control responses, or the defensive tactics used to resist a message. The authors found that (a) the stronger the fear appeal (i.e., the greater the threat), the greater the defensive response; (b) the weaker the efficacy message, the greater the defensive response; and (c) fear control responses were negatively correlated with danger control responses.

However, not all of the EPPM's predictions have garnered empirical support. For example, the EPPM predicts that high threat/low efficacy appeals should produce the strongest fear control responses (i.e., the least persuasion, the most message rejection), but Witte and Allen's meta-analysis (2000) revealed no difference between high threat/low efficacy and low threat/high efficacy messages—both types were less persuasive than high threat/high efficacy messages but more persuasive than low threat/low efficacy messages. Other empirical research based on the EPPM has found a similar pattern of consistent support for the persuasiveness of high threat/high efficacy messages (although see Muthusamy, Levine, & Weber's 2009 study in Namibia for an interesting exception), but greater ambiguity regarding other propositions of the model. For example, people who perceived high threat and efficacy showed greater cognition about cardiovascular disease (indicative of danger control response) compared to people who perceived high threat and low efficacy, but the latter group exhibited greater cognition as well as greater health media use and discussion than those with low perceived threat (Rimal, 2001).[9]

Similarly, a recent study of anti-smoking appeals found partial support for the superior persuasiveness of high threat/high efficacy messages, but no boomerang effect (message rejection) in response in the high threat/low efficacy conditions relative to the low threat conditions (which would be hypothesized to have a null effect) (Wong & Cappella, 2009). Interestingly, respondents with low readiness to quit, who would be expected to be the least open to an appeal advocating smoking cessation, showed the greatest intention to quit in the high threat/high efficacy condition and the lowest intention to quit in the low threat conditions, with the high threat/low efficacy condition squarely in the *middle*—a pattern that does not reflect the fear control response to high threat/low efficacy appeals predicted by the EPPM. In addition, Witte's initial test of the EPPM (1994) produced some unexpected results, including a *negative* relationship between fear and message minimization and defensive avoidance (rather than a positive relationship between fear and message rejection) and a non-significant relationship between perceived threat and attitude and behavior (only behavioral intent showed the predicted significant positive relationship).

These patterns in the empirical research suggest room for speculation about whether terror management processes may enhance explanations of fear appeal responses in cases where mortality salience is raised. For example, *lower* fear may be related to *higher* fear control responses such as message minimization or defensive avoidance (as found by Witte, 1994) if people are engaging in proximal defenses aimed at immediately reducing mortality salience. Further, message acceptance in the form of information searching or behavioral modification may be observed after exposure to a high threat/low efficacy message that raises the salience of death if such responses serve to validate cultural beliefs and symbolically reduce the threat of death. On the flip side, perceived threat may sometimes fail to be related to message acceptance if worldview defense manifests in message rejection.

Theorizing in a Political Context

Theorizing about the impact of fear appeals on political attitudes and behaviors has been somewhat limited compared to the health context. In part, the relative dearth of models that specifically focus on fear communications is reflective of the fact that a significant stream of political science research has employed a bipolar valence approach to modeling affect, which lumps together positively valenced emotions (e.g., enthusiasm, hope, pride) and negatively valenced emotions (e.g., anger, guilt, fear, sadness). For example, research on campaign advertising effects has tended to use this positive/negative model of affect (e.g., Ansolabehere & Iyengar, 1995; Lau, Sigelman, Heldman, & Bab-bit, 1999; Brooks, 2006). The "hot cognition hypothesis" of Lodge and Taber's dual-process model of motivated political reasoning similarly seems to map onto a bipolar valence approach (Lodge & Taber, 2000, 2005). This hypothesis suggests that all sociopolitical concepts (e.g., political leaders, issues, groups) have an affective charge (positive or negative), an evaluative tally that automatically comes to mind upon exposure to the associated object and thus influences the judgment process (Lodge & Taber, 2005). Other theories of emotion and politics include Affect Transfer, which posits that a stimulus that provokes negative emotion causes more negative evaluations of that stimulus and vice versa for a stimulus that elicits positive emotion, and Endogenous Affect, which predicts the reverse causal direction so that preexisting candidate evaluations induce corresponding emotional reactions (Ladd & Lenz, 2008).

A significant departure from this approach to modeling the role of affect in political judgments is found in the Theory of Affective Intelligence (Marcus et al., 2000). Drawing on the circumplex model of affect, which represents affective states as a circle in a two-dimensional bipolar space (Russell, 1980; Neuman, Marcus, MacKuen, & Crigler, 2007), Affective Intelligence (AI) models emotional variation along two axes (a dual unipolar model). The theory also departs from a dominant view of affect in politics that equates emotion with irrationality. AI envisions a marriage of emotion and reason in which affective and cognitive processes are intertwined, not mutually exclusive.

The theory predicts political behavior as a function of two physiological subsystems in the brain—the preconscious emotional systems of disposition and surveillance.[10] The disposition system provides feedback on whether an ongoing sequence of habitual actions is successfully advancing one's plans or failing to do so. Emotional assessments (enthusiasm or frustration/despair) control the execution of habits, which can be relied upon in a safe, familiar, and rewarding environment. The surveillance system scans the environment for novel or threatening stimuli. If no threat is detected, a person's affective reaction is a sense of calm or tranquility. If a threat is detected, the person experiences anxiety, which has a notable impact on attention: current activity is suspended and attention is oriented to the threat in order to facilitate learning. Key to AI's conceptualization of threat is its novelty, or the uncertainty involved in the nature or consequences of the threat. Anxiety thus revolves around uncertainty about an unknown, rather than aversion to a known negative entity.

Emotions—which are generated by affective appraisal processes that precede conscious awareness—serve as key mediators of political judgment and behavior. The disposition system's signal of enthusiasm leads to reliance on enduring political habits, while the surveillance system's signal of fear leads to less reliance on habits as well as greater motivation to gather contemporary information about issues and candidates' positions on those issues.[11] According to AI, anxiety creates the conditions for rational reconsideration of one's "normal" vote choice, thus leaving the door open for "candidates of all political stripes to have a plausible shot at persuasion"—i.e., possible defection (Marcus et al., 2000, p. 61). In sum, contrary to the notion that a calm mind is best equipped for reasoned, thoughtful judgment, the central tenet of AI is that anxiety produces a more "rational" voter—one who sets aside habit and carefully considers the options to decide on the best course of action (Marcus et al., 2000, p. 58).

Support for the theory has been provided by survey data on vote choice in U.S. elections: anxiety (about the candidate of one's party) appeared to reduce reliance on partisanship and ideology and increase the impact of specific and contemporary information about candidate qualities and issue positions on vote choice (Marcus et al., 2000; MacKuen, Marcus, Neuman, & Keele, 2007). Moreover, while anxiety alone was not found to motivate greater defection, it interacted with voters' assessments of candidates' issue distances and qualities, thereby influencing the probability of defection (MacKuen et al., 2007). Other research found that anxiety was positively associated with greater willingness to learn more about specific issue debates and to learn more about the perspectives of opponents, even regarding a contentious issue like affirmative action (Wolak, Marcus, & Neuman, 2003). The experimental findings of Redlawsk, Civettini, and Lau (2007) also provided some support for the idea that anxiety affects information processing and learning in a campaign context. Exposure to a significant amount of negative information about one's preferred candidate (i.e., a high-threat environment) was found to increase anxiety, resulting in more careful information processing, greater efforts to learn about that candidate, and greater accuracy in issue placement of that candidate. Though this study did not examine subsequent changes in vote preference, AI points to the possibility that such behaviors—driven by anxiety—could lead to defection from one's original candidate choice.

Studies with a stronger communications bent have provided more specific links between Affective Intelligence and the fear appeal literature. For example, messages that included a high-anxiety prime, as opposed to a low-anxiety prime, were found to increase the influence of contemporary information (the message's argument), and decrease the influence of predispositions, on attitudes regarding tolerance toward racist groups (Marcus et al., 2005). Though not presented as a specific test of AI, another study found that anxiety produced by a threatening news article increased attention to a campaign, online information seeking, and learning (Valentino, Hutchings, Banks, & Davis, 2008). Supportive of AI's conceptualization of the role of anxiety, the authors found that anxiety functioned as a mediator between the high-threat message and behavioral outcomes.

Expanding Affective Intelligence to a campaign advertising context, Brader (2006) manipulated television ads involving candidates in a real election in order to examine the effects of emotionally evocative (i.e., high) fear appeals and enthusiasm appeals. In expressing subsequent candidate assessments and preferences, people exposed to a high fear appeal tended to rely less on their predispositions or prior candidate preferences and more on recent information or contemporary evaluations, as shaped by the ad. The high fear appeal produced a greater shift toward the ad's sponsor, particularly among those initially opposed or indifferent toward that candidate. It also led to greater interest in relevant information such as political news, suggesting support for the predicted impact of fear on information seeking and learning processes.

More recently, Brader, Valentino, and Suhay (2008) tested the theory's propositions in a policy-oriented communications context. They found that a negative news story on immigration that incorporated a cue for a stigmatized immigrant group (Latinos) increased anxiety compared to the same story with a cue for a European immigrant group, particularly when Latinos were depicted in a stereotypic manner (low-skill). Elevated anxiety in turn affected policy opinions, information seeking, and political action. Mediation analyses suggested that anxiety mediated the relationship between message threat and outcomes, while perceived threat to the self or the nation did not. Though this study focused on a news article rather than a persuasive appeal, its finding that anxiety facilitated attitudinal and behavioral change in the direction of the currently available information points to the potential impact of persuasive fear appeals in a policy debate.

It should be noted that Affective Intelligence is not specifically a communication theory, though it has been adapted to this area of research. Additionally, AI is not the only theory that speaks to the role of anxiety in a political persuasion context. For example, Nabi's Cognitive-Functional Model (Nabi, 1999, 2002), which integrates a discrete emotions approach and dual process cognitive response models of persuasion, considers the impact of fear on persuasion. Straddling the health and political contexts, Nabi specifically highlights differences between the CFM and the EPPM, yet also tests the model by studying responses to manipulations of a news article on domestic terrorism and related proposed legislation (Nabi, 2002).

That being said, this chapter focuses on Affective Intelligence because it is a dominant framework for understanding the role of anxiety in the political science literature. Unlike the health context, the literature on politics and affect contains few if any direct inquiries into the effects of fear appeals that incorporate the threat of death. Prior research in this area therefore provides less guidance for isolating a significant block of studies or empirical patterns that may gain explanatory clarity through the application of a TMT perspective. The relative influence of Affective Intelligence in the field thus served as a dominant criterion in its selection as an appropriate model to compare with TMT in a political context. Moreover, similar to the EPPM, Affective Intelligence presents a clear conceptualization of major constructs that are central to fear appeal research—such as environmental (message) threat, threat perception, anxiety, and cognition—as well as their interrelationships and effects on attitudinal and behavioral outcomes, which makes the theory a useful representative framework against which to compare TMT.

Comparing and Contrasting Theoretical Frameworks

How does the conceptual framework provided by TMT compare to how major constructs in the fear appeal research are defined and interconnected in the EPPM and Affective Intelligence? Four important areas of conceptual contrast distinguish terror management from the other theoretical frameworks: (a) the conceptualization of threat and fear, (b) the temporal sequence of fear appeal response, (c) the role of rationality and consciousness, and (d) the impact of individual differences.

The Conceptualization of Threat and Fear

Threat and fear are core constructs in the fear appeal literature, providing for the communication processes that link the environment (which produces a threat) and an individual (who perceives threat, feels fear, and responds accordingly). Stripped down to the simplest of terms, a persuasive message communicates a threat to an individual, who, upon perception of the threat, experiences fear as a result, and that arousal of fear then shapes attitudes and behaviors in a manner that is either congruent or incongruent with the message advocacy. TMT's conceptualization of the roles of threat and fear in producing responses serves to distinguish it from the EPPM and AI, but also points to how this theory may be integrated into prior fear appeal scholarship.

As discussed earlier, the EPPM conceptualizes perceived threat as an additive construct consisting of perceived susceptibility and perceived severity—perceptions that respond to the threat embedded in the message. In addition to this communication of threat, the EPPM also views efficacy as an important message component, which affects individuals' perceptions of self-efficacy and response efficacy. Greater perceived threat leads to greater fear arousal, which is followed by either fear or danger control responses depending on the level of perceived efficacy. In Affective Intelligence, perception of threat occurs initially as a preconscious affective response to a novel or unsettling stimulus in the environment, such as messages communicating alarming information about one's preferred candidate or frightening imagery and sounds. Greater anxiety triggered by the perception of threat functions as a mediator that strengthens responsiveness to contemporary information, including the immediate message, and potential persuasion in a direction congruent with that information. Generally speaking, in both AI and the EPPM, message threat, perceived threat, and fear arousal work in tandem, such that as the information in the message becomes progressively more threatening, threat perception and fear arousal should increase correspondingly (allowing for moderation by individual differences).

Also important is the manner in which emotional variation is modeled by AI and the EPPM. As noted earlier, AI models emotional variation along two axes, each of which ranges from absence of emotion to greater emotionality (i.e., from calm to increasing levels of anxiety, and from depression to increasing levels of enthusiasm). The EPPM similarly models fear arousal along a low-to-high continuum, from absence of fear to high fear.[12] This approach to modeling emotional variation has important implications for the classification of fear appeals. For example, in the EPPM, a message that invokes the threat of severe pain and a message that invokes the threat of death would be similarly classified as high threat messages, or "high fear" appeals because of their intended effect on emotional arousal, and to the extent that fear arousal was comparable for these two messages, predicted outcomes would be expected to be similar. Although Affective Intelligence does not directly address the threat of death, it seems reasonable to extrapolate that predictions about the effects of death-related fear appeals would be similar as those for other frightening appeals. To the extent that a death-related appeal generates uncertainty due to the novelty of the threatening information—for example, information that a repeat of 9/11 will happen if the Democratic candidate is elected makes a Democratic voter uncertain about his usual vote choice (see also the example described in Marcus et al., 2000, p. 43)—the message should be expected, within an AI framework, to influence anxiety arousal and subsequent behavioral outcomes in a manner similar to other highly threatening appeals.

Interpreted within a TMT framework, the constructs of threat and fear are imbued with new meaning and give rise to a different set of implications. To begin with, given that awareness of the inevitability of death is a human ability, perceived susceptibility to the threat is universal (though perhaps moderated by individual differences, as discussed in a later section). Humans perceive more than risk or degree of vulnerability to that outcome; they perceive the inevitability of their own deaths. Thus, a message that contains the threat of death may be internalized not only in terms of level of risk that this negative consequence will be experienced (as in the EPPM) or as uncertainty about the negative consequences of the threat (as in AI), but as an eventual outcome that is inescapably inevitable and a physical certainty.[13] In addition, threat severity may be understood differently. Given that death signals the end to physical existence, threat severity encompasses both the (maximal) physical threat as well as a more abstract threat to symbolic constructs. That is, existential threat represents more than the prospect of a negative (albeit more extreme) physical outcome; it represents concerns about what happens to a person when he or she inevitably dies.

Thus, TMT suggests that the threat of death is not the same as the threat of any other negative outcome, just in the extreme; there is something qualitatively different about death that makes it more than just a question of degree. By extension, fear of death, as conceptualized in TMT, uniquely pertains to existential anxieties about the inevitability and potential finality of physical death: "Whereas fears of clear and present dangers or possible future threats are adaptive because they motivate action to avert the threat, or at least reduce the chances of it happening, fear of the inevitability of death is uniquely problematic, and qualitatively different from fears of not finding a mate or virtually any other aversive event, because there is nothing one can do to reduce the probability of death to less than 100% certain" (Pyszczynski, Greenberg et al., 2006, p. 342). Of course, just because a message contains reference to death does not mean that it will raise the salience of mortality (see Nelson et al., 1997; Ullrich & Cohrs, 2007). However, to the extent that a message communicating the threat of death is internalized as implicating personal mortality (i.e., raises thoughts of one's own death), a terror management perspective suggests that it may belong in a separate class of appeals rather than at the extreme end of a low-to-high continuum.

TMT also speaks to the concept of efficacy and its relationship with threat, a central fulcrum for the EPPM's predictions. While some theorizing has proposed that response efficacy could function as a moderator of proximal defenses (Goldenberg & Arndt, 2008), the concept of efficacy may also be conceived as playing a symbolic role in distal defenses. If TMT's perspective is articulated within the language of the EPPM, individuals are faced with a situation in which perceived threat is maximized, but perceived efficacy cannot fully make up for the fact that death is ultimately inevitable. That is, to the extent that thoughts of one's eventual demise are made salient, efficacy revolving around behavioral modification may address the delay of death but cannot prevent its inevitable arrival. In that sense, TMT would suggest the need for something akin to *symbolic* efficacy through validation of cultural worldviews, which allows people to control the threat posed by awareness of mortality. If an appeal focuses on values that are relevant to the target audience, this message component could be understood as providing symbolic efficacy, encouraging people to bolster those values in order to reduce the accessibility of death-related thoughts. However, although it may function as a mechanism for threat control, such worldview defense will not necessarily lead to message acceptance (e.g., if the message attacks one's beliefs).

In terms of the theoretical linkages between perceived threat, fear, and outcomes, TMT contrasts with the EPPM and Affective Intelligence in that it does *not* assume fear arousal to be at the heart of the relationship between mortality salience and subsequent behaviors. Recall that in the EPPM, fear aroused by a threatening appeal is a direct cause of message rejection, as well as an indirect cause of message acceptance, while in AI, predicted effects on political decision-making (i.e., greater reliance on contemporary information) are driven by the arousal of anxiety, which mediates the relationship between message threat and outcomes. This prescribed role for fear arousal is consistent with an interest in issues of message reception in the persuasion and communication literature; fear-arousing content is a tool used to grab a receiver's attention and motivate him or her to process the message. Within the EPPM and AI, the arousal of fear is understood to be an important influence on the receiver's attention to and processing of the message, stages in the persuasion process that help determine the ultimate message response (null effect, message-congruent response, or message-incongruent response).

By contrast, TMT specifically rejects the proposition that fear arousal mediates the relationship between MS induced by the threat of death and worldview defense. The theory's proponents argue that the theory is about "how we cope with our knowledge of mortality *without* perpetual anxiety," drawing on Erdelyi's argument (1974) that the brain is a multistage processing system involving conscious and unconscious monitoring of stimuli, which allows defensive reactions to be triggered by the "informational value of stimuli" prior to affect arousal (Solomon et al., 2004, p. 25, emphasis added). It is not suggested that thoughts of death never produce affect, but rather that subjective affect is not necessary for terror management effects to occur. TMT posits that mortality salience can intensify worldview defense without arousing higher levels of anxiety because the defensive reactions control the threat posed by the stimulus, thereby averting the experience of affect. It is the *potential* for experiencing fear (or terror inspired by awareness of death's inevitability) that mediates MS effects rather than the actual subjective experience of affect.

TMT research has provided support for the contention that fear arousal does not mediate the relationship between MS and worldview defense, primarily by showing that raising MS does not arouse significantly greater levels of negative affect (using scales such as the PANAS as well as physiological measures) (see Pyszczynski et al., 2003, p. 55). The effects of an MS treatment are compared to those of treatments that raise the salience of other severe threats or sources of fear, such as intense physical pain, paralysis, failure, worries about life after college, and intense uncertain future bouts of pain. While terror management defenses are found to occur only in response to the MS treatments, not in response to other serious threats, fear arousal is not found to differ significantly across conditions (see, e.g., Shehryar & Hunt, 2005). Such studies that compare an MS treatment and a non-death treatment that is associated with strong negative affect (such as intense pain) have also helped to demonstrate that MS specifically, rather than negative affect more generally, explains the observed effects (Arndt et al., 2007).

TMT thus suggests a new way of thinking about the role of fear in persuasive appeals. If greater fear arousal is not what motivates the distinct terror management responses, as proposed by TMT, then death-related fear appeals and responses to such messages may not fit into a classification system that conceptualizes threat and fear in terms of levels. Rather, persuasive appeals that raise the salience of mortality may involve a modified set of communication and psychological variables, such as priming of cultural values relevant for maintaining a symbolic buffer against existential anxiety. The theory therefore provides reason for caution in assuming that fear appeals that raise the salience of death have the same persuasive outcomes as other fear appeals, including "high fear" messages that invoke other serious negative outcomes such as physical harm, arrest, or economic hardship.

The Temporal Sequence of Responses to Fear Appeals

The three theoretical frameworks may also be compared in terms of how they conceptualize the temporal nature of fear appeal responses. As noted earlier, the EPPM treats the two responses to fear appeals—fear control processes and danger control processes—as competing. The more one is engaged in defensive avoidance or message minimization (message rejection), the less one is thinking about attitude or behavior changes to address the threat (message acceptance). This posited inverse relationship assumes simultaneity of responses; the impact on attitude or behavior outcomes—whatever the degree of message acceptance or rejection—is understood to be measurable at one time. AI's predictions are similarly oriented toward a single measurable response, by which I mean that people are assumed to have one reaction to a given fear appeal, rather than two entirely different responses depending on a temporal sequence (the latter of which is not the same as allowing for deterioration of effects over time). The EPPM also hypothesizes an appraisal process involving a rapid two-step sequence: threat appraisal, followed by efficacy appraisal (Witte, 1998). For Affective Intelligence, the preconscious processes of threat appraisal and anxiety arousal—and their impact on attention—may be understood to be similarly immediate.

By contrast, TMT proposes a sequential response consisting of proximal defenses (active suppression) followed by distal defenses (worldview and self-esteem bolstering). Proximal defenses involve people's conscious and rational efforts to defend against the threat of mortality by removing death-thoughts from focal attention. Distal defenses involve an unconscious response that bears no logical relationship to the threat of mortality and only occurs once thoughts of death have drifted from conscious focus. When mortality salience is raised by a fear appeal, responses measured immediately after exposure to the appeal would be expected to be different from responses measured after a delay and distraction.

A number of studies provide support for this sequential response. For example, to test the temporal sequence of proximal and distal defenses, Greenberg and colleagues (2000) assessed proximal defenses by giving respondents a chance to bias their responses in order to indicate that they were not the type of person with a short life expectancy (rational minimization); distal defenses were assessed by respondents' evaluations of pro- and anti-American essays. Greater vulnerability-denying bias was found among those assessed immediately after mortality salience was induced, compared to those assessed after a distraction or delay. Further, those respondents who were distracted or engaged in proximal defenses between MS induction and essay evaluation showed greater pro-American bias (worldview defense) than those who evaluated the essays directly after MS. In fact, the latter participants, who evaluated the essays directly after thinking about death, showed no more worldview defense than those who were in a control condition. These findings suggest that proximal defenses are the immediate response to mortality salience, while symbolic terror management does not occur until conscious thoughts of death have been removed from focal awareness by proximal defenses or distraction. Other research has similarly found worldview defense to occur only after a delay, but not before (e.g., Shehryar & Hunt, 2005).

In a study examining the effects of priming thoughts of cancer, Arndt and colleagues (2007) provided further insight into the proximal-distal sequential response. They found that respondents who were under low cognitive load exhibited lower accessibility of death-related thoughts directly after cancer was primed (indicative of active suppression), compared to respondents under high cognitive load (simultaneously mentally rehearsing a 10-digit number). From a TMT perspective, this makes sense because proximal defenses are conscious cognitive efforts to push thoughts of death from focal attention; people with a low cognitive load were better able to focus on suppressing thoughts of death than those with a high cognitive load. Providing an intriguing linkage to the EPPM, the authors also manipulated perceived vulnerability and measured perceived threat. They found that increased vulnerability led respondents to perceive an article on cancer as more threatening, which then led to greater immediate suppression. Interestingly, the fear control responses that the EPPM would predict in a situation where perceived threat exceeds perceived efficacy, particularly defensive avoidance and message minimization, are similar to the psychological suppression maneuvers posited to serve as proximal defenses. A terror management perspective thus suggests that death-related appeals may produce EPPM-predicted effects in the initial stage of proximal defense, while leaving open the possibility of other message effects as part of distal defenses.

The sequential nature of the responses predicted by TMT has important repercussions for the measurement of responses to fear appeals and expectations about when message acceptance or rejection will be most likely. Notably, neither proximal defense nor distal defense is synonymous with message acceptance or rejection. For example, suppression of death-related thoughts was related to greater intention to engage in cancer-preventive behavior, which suggests that initial proximal defense can have *positive* effects if it enables people to engage in healthy behaviors more than when they are not able to suppress these thoughts (Arndt et al., 2007; see also Goldenberg & Arndt, 2008). With regard to distal defenses, a source who validated important cultural views was evaluated more positively after a delay, suggesting the potential for message acceptance as a consequence of distal defenses (Greenberg et al., 2000). On the other hand, message acceptance of a drunk-driving fear appeal that invoked the threat of death was found to be *lower* among a target population (those who value drinking alcohol) after a delay, which suggests that distal defenses produced greater message rejection (Shehryar & Hunt, 2005).

The Role of Rationality and Consciousness

Comparisons and contrasts may also be drawn between TMT and the other frameworks in their conceptualization of the role of "rationality" and consciousness in the emotional and cognitive processes underlying responses to fear appeals. The EPPM portrays danger control processes as a largely cognitive effort geared toward appraisal of the threat and how best to avoid it through behavioral modification. In contrast to this more conscious, rational process, efforts to control one's fear may be more unconscious. Further, while fear control processes are dependent on fear arousal, danger control processes are more cognition-oriented and do not depend on fear, though fear can indirectly affect danger control responses. As Witte has argued (1994), "fear must be present for fear control processes to occur, while danger control processes can occur with or without the production of fear" (p. 118). Affective Intelligence envisions a somewhat different role for consciousness and rationality. Anxiety arousal affects attention as part of a preconscious response to environmental stimuli. It also directly increases the rationality of predicted attitude and behavior outcomes insofar as the person becomes more responsive to relevant current information in the environment that will help to alleviate the threat.

TMT distinguishes between a rational mode of thinking and a more "experiential" mode of thinking, the latter being characterized as neither conscious nor logical. The theory argues that fear of death is an "unconscious, primal concern," so distal defenses occur when a person is in an experiential mode of processing rather than a rational mode (Pyszczynski et al., 2003, p. 65). The individual therefore does not make a conscious connection between worldview defense and the thoughts of death raised by the stimulus. It is the proximal defenses that deal directly and logically with the problem of mortality through active suppression of conscious thoughts of death.

In some ways, this cognitive and rational approach to dealing with the threat of death is reminiscent of the EPPM's danger control responses. Indeed, Goldenberg and Arndt (2008) specifically allow for the possibility that health-promoting behavior could serve as a form of proximal defense (e.g., eating healthier to reduce conscious vulnerability to death), which would represent a conscious message-congruent response akin to danger control. However, as noted earlier, psychological defensive maneuvers such as distraction and denial are also posited to serve as proximal defenses, and this type of response bears greater similarity to the EPPM's conceptualization of fear control processes. Moreover, it is possible that expressing an intent to engage in healthy behavior after exposure to a fear appeal is sufficient to remove thoughts of death from consciousness, allowing for subsequent actual behavior to be unconsciously shaped by distal defenses. Thus, there is somewhat of a mismatch between the two theories in terms of how cognitive reasoning is thought to interact with threat to produce responses. For TMT, conscious cognitive efforts may be directed toward a message response that the EPPM would classify as potentially unconscious fear control caused by fear arousal (a direct role for affect that TMT denies), and a response that TMT views as *un*consciously occurring as part of distal defenses could be categorized by the EPPM as deliberate cognitive danger control.

Meanwhile, Affective Intelligence and TMT share a common focus on unconscious responses. However, AI sees the actual experience of anxiety as integrated in unconscious responses, rather than the potential for anxiety. Moreover, while Affective Intelligence portrays anxiety's effects on behavior as a rational adjustment of attention and information seeking in response to threat, the worldview defense responses predicted by TMT are produced by an essentially irrational process with no conscious connection to the source of fear (death). Indeed, subliminal priming of mortality has been found to lead to worldview defense, despite the fact that respondents are not consciously aware of the increased accessibility of death-related thoughts (Arndt, Greenberg, Pyszczynski, et al., 1997).

The Impact of Individual Differences

The final area of conceptual comparison among the theoretical frameworks concerns the impact of individual differences. All three theories provide accommodation for factors that distinguish individuals, including direction and strength of predispositions (e.g., political views, personal relevance of message components) and characteristics like gender, age, and cultural or ethnic group identity. Comparing the frameworks is a challenge, given the range of individual differences that may be integrated into any given model's predictions. In the interests of clarity and relative brevity, the present discussion is limited to a selection of differences that suggest linkages among the theories.

A few broad contrasts may be noted upfront in how the models conceptualize the role of individual differences. The EPPM sees individual differences as having an indirect effect on outcomes such that they affect perceived threat and efficacy, which in turn affect message response (Witte, 1998). For example, differences in readiness to quit smoking were found to moderate some of a fear appeal's effects on message acceptance in a three-way interaction with threat and efficacy (Wong & Cappella, 2009), though trait anxiety (Witte & Morrison, 2000) and cultural orientation (Murray-Johnson, Witte, Wen-Ying, & Hubbell, 2001) did not moderate the relationships as predicted. Affective Intelligence incorporates individual differences such as political predispositions as moderators of the effects of a fear appeal. For example, increased information searching was contingent on hearing threatening information about one's favored candidate (a predisposition) (Redlawsk et al., 2007), while message acceptance was increased among people exposed to a fear appeal sponsored by a candidate whom they were predisposed to oppose (Brader, 2006).

TMT strives for universality and breadth of explanation, but also acknowledges the importance of individual differences in culturally shaped beliefs and their relevance to maintaining self-esteem. As stated earlier, self-esteem derived from living up to the standards of one's cultural worldviews buffers against death-related anxiety. It follows, then, that individuals with higher self-esteem will be less defensive after mortality salience is raised—a proposition that initially seems straightforward. The role of individual differences is more complicated than this, however, in part because cultural values made salient by a message interact with individual differences in value relevance and self-esteem (see, e.g., Das et al., 2009; Arndt et al., 2009). For example, Arndt and Greenberg (1999) showed that a self-esteem boost can reduce worldview defense in response to MS, but suggested that the protective capacity of self-esteem to reduce worldview defense depends on the type of threat and the individual's source of self-esteem: "When the source of value on which self-esteem is predicated is undermined, self-esteem is diluted of its anxiety-buffering capacity and is unable to provide protection"—hence, the need for worldview defense (p. 1339; see also Schmeichel et al., 2009, on explicit versus implicit self-esteem, and Landau et al., 2009, on situations where self-esteem enhancement and worldview bolstering are in conflict).

The role of individual differences within a TMT framework is also complicated by the two-part sequential response. For example, worldview defense in the form of message rejection is expected if the source attacks a belief that is relevant to the individual. Shehryar and Hunt (2005) found this pattern in their study of reactions to drunk-driving fear appeals. Only those with a strong prior commitment to drinking alcohol (compared to those who did not view alcohol as relevant to self-esteem) exhibited worldview defense in the form of significantly lower message acceptance. On the surface, the obvious response to that finding is, so what? It is unsurprising that a person who is highly committed to a behavior will be more likely to reject a message attacking that behavior. However, what is distinct about this finding is that it *only* occurred after exposure to a fear appeal that invoked the threat of death, not after exposure to fear appeals invoking other severe threats such as arrest or serious injury. Moreover, worldview defense among those committed to drinking alcohol was observed only after a delay between message exposure and assessment of message acceptance (for a comparable finding for smoking behavior, see Hansen, Winzeler, & Topolinski, in press, especially note 2). This is a potentially important insight from the standpoint of message effects and persuasion, suggesting a three-way interaction between mortality salience, time of measurement, and individual differences in the personal relevance to self-esteem of values primed by an appeal.

The role that TMT prescribes for individual differences in value relevance may have implications for two important individual-level moderators in health communication research: gender and age. For example, one area of inquiry has focused on testing a common belief that young people, particularly young men, are especially prone to engage in risky behaviors because they believe in their own invulnerability. Henley and Donovan (2003), for instance, compared responses of two age groups (ages 16–25 and 40–50) to fear appeals about emphysema that either included death as a consequence or did not. The authors interpreted the null difference between young people's responses to death and non-death appeals, even among men, as evidence that feelings of invulnerability do not drive risky behavior in youth. Another study of alcohol use among adolescents suggested that young people are not simply irrationally engaging in risky behavior (i.e., illegal alcohol consumption) because they believe they are invulnerable; rather, they *rationally* perceive the benefits of performing risky behaviors as outweighing the risks (Goldberg, Halpern-Felsher, & Millstein, 2002).

TMT may offer new insights for this area of research by suggesting how defense against thoughts of death may paradoxically lead to greater risky behavior. In a twist on the explanation offered in the above-mentioned study by Goldberg and colleagues (2002), some TMT research has suggested that symbolic benefits to self-esteem, as a buffer against mortality-related anxiety, may *irrationally* drive risky behaviors due to *sensitivity* to vulnerability to death, rather than a sense of invulnerability (Hirschberger, Florian, Mikulincer, Goldenberg, & Pyszczynski, 2002). For example, Hirschberger and colleagues (2002) found that U.S. male students exhibited significantly greater intention to engage in a range of risky behaviors after mortality salience compared to a control condition, even controlling for sensation-seeking. Their follow-up study revealed that Israeli male students were more willing to try illicit drugs in three hypothetical scenarios after MS compared to a control condition, controlling for baseline attitudes toward drug use. The authors suggested that the cultural values relevant to men's self-esteem (e.g., courage, valor, thumbing one's nose at danger) are more oriented toward risk-taking compared to women, who did not exhibit these effects after MS. This interpretation is consistent with other work suggesting that cultural emphasis on different values for men versus women (e.g., the ideal of thinness for women) may contribute to gender differences in responses when mortality is salient (Goldenberg, Arndt, Hart, & Brown, 2005), as well as research linking MS to increased engagement in risky behaviors (Arndt et al., 2009).

TMT's conceptualization of the role of individual differences is also relevant to a number of key political variables. For example, consider the potential implications of an interaction between mortality salience and age, which is an important predictor of political participation. If more youthful feelings of invulnerability do tend to attenuate with age, then older people may respond differently to a political appeal invoking the threat of death. This may be particularly true if the message content relates most directly to the personal mortality of older people—an illustration of which is aptly provided by the rhetoric of "death panels" in the recent debate over end of life issues and health care insurance reform in the United States. Moreover, given that older people tend to participate in politics more, their responses to appeals raising the salience of mortality may have a disproportionately strong impact on policy and electoral outcomes.

TMT also speaks strongly to the relationship between mortality salience and individual differences in national, ethnic, cultural, and ideological orientation—all of which play central roles in domestic as well as international politics. A number of studies have shown how values attached to membership or identification with various groups may interact with MS to produce responses with important political implications. For example, as noted earlier, mortality salience increased pro-American bias in evaluations of a person who voiced negative views of the United States and a person who voiced positive views of the United States, producing significantly more negative and positive evaluations, respectively (Greenberg et al., 1990). That study also found that MS increased in-group favoritism and out-group hostility based on religious affiliation. Similarly, news reports on terrorist attacks were found to raise MS and to increase out-group prejudice—not only prejudice against Arabs among non-Muslims, but prejudice against Europeans among Muslims (Das et al., 2009). Priming mortality along with different in-group identities (e.g., Australian, Aboriginal) led to corresponding out-group value rejection and in-group value endorsement (Halloran & Kashima, 2004). Worldview defense can also come in the form of bolstering faith in one's political ideology. A study of American conservatives and liberals found that both groups showed greater aggression against and derogation of critics of their political orientation after reminders of mortality (McGregor et al., 1998). Further, recent research has shown that that MS can enhance evaluations of charismatic political candidates, but only if their rhetoric bolsters one's pre-existing ideological values, while evaluations of candidates espousing the opposing ideology can be diminished by MS (Kosloff, Greenberg, Weise, & Solomon, in press).[14]

Given that a great deal of politics revolves around conflicts between groups, it is important to emphasize the ramifications of TMT's propositions about the role of belief systems in shaping people's responses to reminders of mortality. As noted earlier, cultural worldviews differ widely across individuals and cultures, and yet they may serve the same purpose insofar as confirmation of one's belief system can serve as a buffer against existential terror engendered by awareness of mortality. Thus, TMT's predictions for worldview bolstering after mortality salience has been raised apply as much to a Western nation such as the United States as they do to an Islamic country such as Iran (see Pyszczynski, Abdollahi et al., 2006; Pyszczynski et al., 2008). Indeed, Pyszczynski, Abdollahi, and colleagues (2006) found that, when MS was raised, Iranian students preferred a student expressing pro-martyrdom (attacking the U.S.) views over an anti-martyrdom student and showed greater interest in joining the pro-martyrdom cause than the anti-martyrdom cause; these patterns were reversed in the control condition (dental pain). These authors also examined American students' support for extreme military force as an appropriate tactic in the war on terrorism, and found that support was significantly higher after reminders of mortality and 9/11 compared to the dental pain condition, though this pattern only occurred among conservatives. These findings not only suggest the cross-cultural explanatory potential of TMT, but also highlight how terror management responses can revolve around intergroup value differences; in the face of reminders of mortality, hostility toward out-groups who threaten one's cultural worldviews and enhanced regard for in-group members who validate one's views provide symbolic protection against fear of death. (Note, though, that priming values such as tolerance or compassion may mitigate out-group hostility in response to MS; see Pyszczynski et al., 2008.)

Together, these patterns found in TMT research suggest that mortality salience will *increase* the influence of people's preexisting political values and beliefs on their attitudes and behaviors. This proposition stands in contrast to the predictions of Affective Intelligence that a fear appeal arousing anxiety will decrease reliance on predispositions and increase the influence of contemporary information, opening the door for message acceptance by those with oppositional preexisting views (Brader, 2006; Wolak et al., 2003). In this way, AI allows for fear appeals to encourage greater crossover among groups with conflicting standing decisions (e.g., policy positions), while TMT suggests that appeals invoking fear of death may lead to reinforced subscription to preexisting beliefs and polarization along group lines.

Toward New Directions in Fear Communication Research

This chapter's discussion of TMT and its conceptual contrasts with dominant frameworks in existing fear communication scholarship is intended to stimulate new directions in fear appeal research. To that end, I have constructed a summary table that depicts the major constructs and their relationships as conceptualized by TMT, the EPPM, and Affective Intelligence (Table 6.1). A summary cannot capture all of the theoretical nuances unique to each model, but the virtue of a simplified and easily comprehendible comparative overview is its utility in suggesting new empirical research questions.

Table 6.1 Conceptual Summary of the EPPM, Affective Intelligence, and TMT

EPPM	AFFECTIVE INTELLIGENCE	TMT
Message: Threat and efficacy.	*Message:* Threat (novel).	*Message:* Threat.
Appraisal: Individual appraises threat and, if perceived threat is high enough, appraises efficacy.	*Appraisal:* Individual experiences preconscious affective response (fear).	*Appraisal:* Individual perceives threat of own death, raising the salience of mortality.
Affect: Greater perceived threat leads to greater fear, which has direct and indirect effects on subsequent response.	*Affect:* Greater perceived threat leads to greater fear, which mediates subsequent response.	*Affect:* Death-related threat does not arouse greater fear than non-death-related threat.
Response: If perceived threat and perceived efficacy are high, cognitions about the threat and recommendations for behavioral modification dominate, leading to message acceptance. If perceived threat is high and efficacy is low, fear dominates, leading to message rejection. Low threat leads to a null response.	*Response:* Attention is oriented toward contemporary information, lessening reliance on predispositions and increasing the likelihood of attitude and behavioral change in the direction of the message.	*Response (proximal defense):* Individual suppresses thoughts of death, which may initially affect message acceptance. *Response (distal defense):* Individual bolsters self-esteem by engaging in worldview defense, which may increase message acceptance or rejection depending on which cultural values are made salient by the message.
Individual differences: Perceived threat and perceived efficacy are affected by individual differences.	*Individual differences:* What is considered threatening information is affected by individual differences (e.g., threatening information diverges from expectations based on preexisting beliefs).	*Individual differences:* Mortality salience and worldview defense are affected by individual differences (e.g., relevance of cultural values and valence of arguments made in message).

Taking some initial steps toward generating such questions, I suggest two sets of predictive contrasts derived from the theoretical comparison (Table 6.2). TMT is juxtaposed against the EPPM and Affective Intelligence in a health context and a political context, respectively. Given that TMT is more of a new kid on the block from a communications perspective, testing its predictive contrasts with existing models is an appropriate first step in a research agenda integrating TMT into the study of fear appeals. Indeed, because there has been so little research specifically attempting to study the potential for fear appeals to produce terror management responses, it makes sense to test the predictions of TMT against the predictions of other theories, where contrasts arise, rather than moving directly to the development of hybrid models.

A number of competing predictions are embedded in Table 6.2, which could be tested in an experimental context. For example, TMT predicts effects for a death-related appeal that are distinct from the effects of a non-death-related fear appeal, yet are not driven by greater fear arousal. Both the EPPM and Affective Intelligence do not specifically predict distinct effects for a death-related fear appeal unless it produces greater threat perception and thus

Table 6.2 Contrasting Predictions by the EPPM, Affective Intelligence, and TMT

HEALTH CONTEXT	
EPPM	TMT
Death versus neutral (non-fear) appeals: Exposure to a death appeal will increase perceived threat, leading to message acceptance if perceived efficacy is high and message rejection if perceived efficacy is low. Personal relevance of the message qualifies these responses such that greater personal relevance leads to stronger effects.	*Death versus neutral appeals:* Exposure to a death appeal will significantly increase worldview defense, regardless of efficacy level, leading to message acceptance if the advocacy is congruous with validation of cued cultural values and message rejection if the advocacy is incongruous with validation. Personal relevance of the message qualifies the responses such that greater personal relevance leads to stronger worldview defense.
Fear (non-death) versus death appeals: Exposure to a fear appeal will produce the same effects as a death appeal.	*Fear versus death appeals:* Exposure to a fear appeal will *not* produce the same effects as exposure to a death appeal.
The role of fear arousal: Greater fear will be directly related to message rejection and indirectly related to message acceptance. Only to the extent that a death appeal arouses greater fear will that appeal produce different effects from a fear appeal.	*The role of fear arousal*: The distinct effects of a death appeal will *not* be mediated by a significantly greater arousal of fear compared to the fear appeal.
Time of response measurement: The hypothesized effects will not change if assessed before or after a delay.	*Time of response measurement:* The worldview defense effects of a death appeal will only obtain if measured after a delay.* Suppression effects akin to fear control may emerge if response is measured immediately after exposure to a death appeal.
POLITICAL CONTEXT	
AFFECTIVE INTELLIGENCE	**TMT**
Death versus neutral appeals: Exposure to a death appeal will significantly increase favorable attitudes toward the advocated candidate or policy position, particularly among people who were predisposed against that preference or who had no strong predisposition.	*Death versus neutral appeals:* Exposure to a death appeal will significantly increase favorable attitudes toward the advocated candidate or policy position among those who were predisposed toward that preference (message validates values), while exposure to a death appeal will significantly decrease favorable attitudes toward the advocated candidate or policy position among those who were predisposed against that preference (message challenges values).
Fear versus death appeals: Exposure to a fear appeal will produce the same effects as a death appeal.	*Fear versus death appeals:* Exposure to a fear appeal will *not* produce the same effects as exposure to a death appeal.
The role of fear arousal: The effects of exposure to death and fear appeals will be mediated by elevated levels of fear. Only to the extent that a death appeal arouses greater anxiety will that appeal create stronger effects than a fear appeal.	*The role of fear arousal*: The distinct effects of a death appeal will *not* be mediated by a significantly greater arousal of fear compared to the fear appeal.
Time of response measurement: The hypothesized effects will not change if assessed before or after a delay.	*Time of response measurement:* The distinct effects of a death appeal will only obtain if measured after a delay.*

**Provided* that death-related thoughts are brought to focal attention; a delay is not needed if thoughts of death are primed but not brought to conscious awareness.

Note: In this table, a "death" appeal is one that raises the salience of personal mortality, a "fear" appeal is one that primes non-death-related fears, and a "neutral" appeal is one that does not arouse fear. Note that while Affective Intelligence does not directly address death as a threat, its predictions for a death-related fear appeal may be reasonably extrapolated as similar to those for other highly threatening fear appeals. Also, in a political context, a "predisposition" is not necessarily limited to party identification or ideological orientation; in either AI or TMT, it could theoretically refer to other group-based identification or values (e.g., associated with one's race/ethnicity, nationality, religion).

fear arousal. Timing of measurement also points to predictive contrasts, with TMT proposing different responses to a death-related appeal depending on whether outcomes are assessed immediately after message exposure or following a delay, and the EPPM and AI proposing no difference. More specifically, in response to an appeal invoking the threat of death, TMT allows for delayed message rejection when personally relevant values are attacked, even if efficacy is high, and delayed message acceptance when relevant values are validated, even if efficacy is low; by contrast, the EPPM predicts message acceptance in the former case and rejection in the latter case. TMT's predictions of delayed message acceptance among those whose beliefs are validated and delayed rejection among those whose beliefs are attacked also contrast with expectations based on Affective Intelligence—i.e., greater message acceptance among those who were predisposed *against* the views articulated in a message and relatively little effect on those who already agreed with the message.[15]

Differentiation of fear appeals by quality of consequence (i.e., death versus some other fear-inducing consequence) and differentiation of response by temporal sequence have not been part of prior fear appeal theorizing. TMT thus offers strong hypotheses about this class of appeals and a new set of considerations for evaluating the persuasive value of the threat of death. At the same time, great care must be taken in integrating this theory into the fear appeal literature and testing it against other frameworks. Attentiveness to detail is essential in the design of studies that test contrasting predictions derived from separate theories, including a systematic approach to measurement timing and careful pretesting and manipulation checks (e.g., mortality salience, fear arousal, and salience of relevant values cued by the messages). Sensitivity to cued values is important because worldview defense will reflect validation of whichever values provide the greatest protection against death-related anxiety in a given context (Weise et al., 2008; Halloran & Kashima, 2004). For example, a persuasive appeal priming mortality and national identity may be expected to increase support for a counterterrorism policy if the source validates important national values, while an appeal priming mortality and political orientation may decrease support for the same policy among those who feel their ideological values have been attacked and increase support among those whose ideological beliefs have been validated.

From a message design perspective, drawing on TMT may help researchers determine what types of appeals work best in different circumstances. Identifying message design principles that do not rely on audience evaluation as a proxy (e.g., what makes a "strong" versus "weak" argument, what makes a message emotionally evocative) is notoriously difficult (Cappella, 2006). Conceptualizing death as a qualitatively different threatening consequence, distinct from the more nebulous continuum of low to high fear-arousing content, may contribute to efforts to define message factors that produce reliable responses. That said, further investigation is needed regarding whether, when, and how messages that communicate the threat of death raise the salience of mortality. For example, do some reminders of mortality, such as images embedded in an appeal, make death-related thoughts accessible at an unconscious level, rather than bringing them to focal attention? Recall that, as conceptualized by TMT, fear of death may not revolve solely around the threat of its imminence, but also around the more abstract threat that its inevitability poses. The persuasive influence of reminders of death communicated in messages therefore may not be limited to increasing perceptions of risk, but may also be exerted by triggering more abstract-level thinking about what happens when one dies. That is, reminders of death, even relatively subtle message features, could produce worldview defense and thus affect message acceptance without necessarily convincing people that death is lurking around the corner.

At the same time, it is not a given that any reminder of death will lead people to think about their own mortality. Indeed, priming mortality more generally, as opposed to personal mortality, does not appear to bring about terror management responses (Nelson et al., 1997; Ullrich & Cohrs, 2007). Further, reminders of death may be more likely to raise the salience of personal mortality among some populations compared to others, depending on individual-level and contextual factors. This limitation is not particularly troublesome from a persuasive communications perspective. Appeals are almost never expected to be universally persuasive; in fact, the trend is toward greater microtargeting based on audience characteristics likely to maximize message reception.[16] The fact that worldview defense is predicated on raising mortality salience does not limit TMT's contribution to fear appeal research; it simply defines the parameters of terror management's potential influence on message response.

In sum, terror management theory represents a promising yet underused source of theoretical predictions in fear appeals research. Its integration into the communication research agenda would provide a complement to, not a replacement of, existing theoretical frameworks for analyzing people's responses to fear appeals. Obviously, in terms of appeals that employ threats other than death, TMT does not necessarily pose a challenge to frameworks such as the EPPM or Affective Intelligence. It is when the salience of mortality is raised that TMT provides a distinct perspective that parts ways with other theoretical frameworks. Its potential contribution lies with its recognition of human fears of death and the way that these fears might uniquely affect reactions to messages.

The communications context encompasses a wealth of message features through which mortality may be primed, from text to imagery to audio, and situations in which mortality salience may be raised in the service of persuasive appeals are abundant, both within and outside the United States. Indeed, given the theory's emphasis on cultural values and their relevance to self-esteem and symbolic immortality, using a TMT framework to explore cross-cultural and cross-national differences in responses to fear appeals priming mortality may prove particularly fruitful. Though its application to fear appeal research requires sensitivity to the specific factors involved in the prediction of different types of attitudes and behaviors among different populations, TMT offers a rich and versatile framework whose integration into communication research may make unique empirical and conceptual contributions to the study of fear communications and persuasion.

Notes

1. The author is indebted to Joseph N. Cappella for his many insightful comments and continual encouragement throughout the writing of this paper. Special thanks also to Russell Neuman, the editor, and the anonymous reviewers for their very thoughtful and constructive feedback.
2. These ad descriptions are only partly hypothetical. In the 2008 U.S. presidential election, the National Republican Trust PAC aired an attack ad against Barack Obama that incorporated images invoking 9/11; the ad may be viewed at http://www.npr.org/blogs/secretmoney/2008/10/pac_ties_obamas_policies_to_se.html (accessed Aug. 28, 2009). The anti-smoking example is taken directly from an ad developed by the Department of Health United Kingdom in 2004. The ad may be downloaded from the Cancer Institute NWS website, at http://www.cancerinstitute.org.au/cancer_inst/campaigns/anthony.html (accessed Aug. 28, 2009).
3. Exceptions include studies by Shehryar and Hunt (2005) and Ben-Ari, Florian, and Mikulincer (2000) in the health context, Miller and Hansen (2007) in the political context, and Solomon et al. (1995) in a college campus context. These studies specifically tested TMT propositions using fear appeals. Other theoretical (e.g., Miller & Landau, 2005, 2008; Pfau, 2007) and empirical (Goldenberg et al., 1999, 2007; Magee & Kalyanaraman, 2009; Das et al., 2009) work has drawn on TMT in a communication context, but not with a specific focus on either fear appeals or conceptual comparisons between TMT and existing fear appeal models.
4. The theory's authors recognize that cultural worldviews can serve purposes other than terror management (see Pyszczynski, Greenberg, et al., 2006).
5. As Fransen et al. (2008) emphasize, MS effects induced by messages may be unintentional, such as with brands whose associations with death (in their study, insurance) induce MS and then affect consumer behaviors (e.g., preference for domestic products over foreign products).
6. Note that this model brings a more specific focus to health-promoting behaviors as a form of proximal defenses, in addition to the psychological defensive maneuvers (e.g., denial of vulnerability, distraction) emphasized in other TMT research (e.g., Pyszczynski et al., 2003; Greenberg et al., 2000).
7. This ad may be viewed at the FactCheck.org website: http://www.factcheck.org/2009/09/a-false-appeal-to-womens-fears/(accessed Sept. 4, 2009).
8. The authors of the stage model emphasize a number of differences from earlier models. For example, severity and vulnerability are seen as having separate effects (as well as interaction effects) on persuasion outcomes, as well as main and interaction effects on information processing. The model also predicts that any recommendation, so long as the action is somewhat plausible and not impossible to carry out, will be seen as effective when vulnerability and severity are high due to biased processing. Thus, defensive reactions such as minimization of threat do not necessarily impede message acceptance (as found by Witte & Allen, 2000), but can actually enhance message acceptance.

9 Because this study used the terminology of perceived risk (internalization of a threat) and self-efficacy and did not include threat severity or response efficacy, it does not map perfectly onto the EPPM. However, perceived risk is conceptually closely related to perceived susceptibility, and the author drew on the EPPM as a theoretical framework for the study (see also Rimal & Real, 2003, for a discussion of the risk perception attitude (RPA) framework, which is derived from the predictions of the EPPM).

10 The authors do not suggest that all behaviors are driven by affective systems; some may be influenced more by conscious considerations (Marcus et al., 2000, pp. 51–52).

11 Although AI focuses on anxiety and enthusiasm, it should not be confused with discrete emotion models, which represent another established approach to modeling affect in the political science literature (Neuman et al., 2007). Discrete emotion models view various affects as associated with distinct signal values and functions (Dillard & Meijnders, 2002; Dillard & Peck, 2000; Dillard, Plotnick, Godbold, Freimuth, & Edgar, 1996).

12 With some minor variations, fear arousal has been operationalized in similar ways by studies based on Affective Intelligence and the EPPM. Marcus and colleagues (2000, Appendix B) recommended drawing on affect items in the PANAS (Positive and Negative Affect Schedule; Watson, Clark, & Tellegen, 1988) to measure anxiety, including how much respondents feel afraid, scared, anxious, upset, distressed, nervous, frightened, and uneasy. Witte and colleagues (Witte, 1994; Witte & Morrison, 2000) have incorporated similar items in assessments of fear arousal.

13 In TMT research, the theoretical role of perceived vulnerability is open to debate (see, e.g., Goldenberg & Arndt, 2008, who viewed it as a moderator of proximal defenses, and Hirschberger, Pyszczynski, & Ein-Dor, 2009, who examined its role as a moderator of distal defenses).

14 By "charismatic," the authors refer to leadership characteristics such as self-confidence, a visionary outlook, readiness for risk-taking, and an emphasis on a collective identity (Kosloff et al., in press). In addition, some studies have examined the effects of MS and reminders of 9/11 on attitudes toward President George W. Bush and other political figures (e.g., Landau et al., 2004; Cohen, Ogilvie, Solomon, Greenberg, & Pyszczynski, 2005; Miller & Hansen, 2007; Weise et al., 2008). While the results seem to replicate other findings of pro-American bias after MS—increasing regard for Bush as a symbolic protector of the American value system, particularly among liberals—a TMT interpretation is vulnerable to alternative explanations due to the specific circumstances involved in this case. Further research in this vein that moves beyond a focus on Bush is needed (see, e.g., Kosloff et al., in press).

15 From AI's perspective, it would make sense if those who were initially supportive of the advocacy showed no movement, given that the information provided by the anxiety-producing ad was congruent with predispositions and thus posed no novel threat.

16 At the same time, the Internet has created new opportunities for reaching a greater portion of the target audience, easing some of the traditional constraints of time, money, and space. Consider, for example, a recent PSA produced by a local police department in South Wales. The 4-minute video, which depicts in detail the fatal consequences of texting and driving, went viral on the Internet, attracting millions of viewers as well as news coverage in the United States. (See S. Morris, "Made in Gwent with £10,000: the road safety video taking YouTube by storm," *The Guardian*, Sept. 3, 2009, http://www.guardian.co.uk/uk/2009/sep/03/gwent-road-safety-film.)

References

Ansolabehere, S., & Iyengar, S. (1995). *Going negative: How political advertisements shrink and polarize the electorate.* New York: Free Press.

Arndt, J., Cook, A., & Routledge, C. (2004). The blueprint of terror management: Understanding the cognitive architecture of psychological defense against the awareness of death. In J. Greenberg, S. L. Koole, & T. Pyszczynski (Eds.), *Handbook of experimental existential psychology* (pp. 35–53). New York: Guilford Press.

Arndt, J., Cook, A., Greenberg, J. L., & Cox, C. R. (2007). Cancer and the threat of death: The cognitive dynamics of death-thought suppression and it impact on behavioral health intentions. *Journal of Personality and Social Psychology, 92*(1), 12–29.

Arndt, J., Cox, C. R., Goldenberg, J. L., Vess, M., Routledge, C., Cooper, D. P., & Cohen, F. (2009). Blowing in the (social) wind: Implications of extrinsic esteem contingencies for terror management and health. *Journal of Personality and Social Psychology, 96*(6), 1191–1205.

Arndt, J., & Greenberg, J. (1999). The effects of a self-esteem boost and mortality salience on responses to boost relevant and irrelevant worldview threats. *Personality and Social Psychology Bulletin, 25,* 1331–1341.

Arndt, J., Greenberg, J., Pyszczynski, T., & Solomon, S. (1997). Subliminal exposure to death-related stimuli increase defense of the cultural worldview. *Psychological Science, 8*(5), 379–385.

Arndt, J., Greenberg, J., Solomon, S., Pyszczynski, T., & Simon, L. (1997). Suppression, accessibility of death-related thoughts, and cultural worldview defense: Exploring the psychodynamics of terror management. *Journal of Personality and Social Psychology, 73,* 5–18.

Baron, R.M. (1997). On making terror management theory less motivational and more social. *Psychological Inquiry, 8*(1), 21–58.

Becker, E. (1962). *The birth and death of meaning.* New York: Free Press.

Becker, E. (1973). *The denial of death.* New York: Free Press.

Becker, E. (1975). *Escape from evil.* New York: Free Press.

Ben-Ari, O. T., Florian, V., & Mikulincer, M. (2000). Does a threat appeal moderate reckless driving? A terror management theory perspective. *Accident Analysis and Prevention, 32,* 1–10.

Brader, T. (2006). *Campaigning for hearts and minds: How emotional appeals in political ads work.* Chicago: University of Chicago Press.

Brader, T., Valentino, N. A., & Suhay, E. (2008). What triggers public opposition to immigration? Anxiety, group cuts, and immigration threat. *American Journal of Political Science, 52*(4), 959–978.

Brooks, D. J. (2006). The resilient voter: Moving toward closure in the debate over negative campaigning and turnout. *Journal of Politics, 68*(3), 684–696.

Buss, D. M. (1997). Human social motivation in evolutionary perspective: Grounding terror management theory. *Psychological Inquiry, 8*(1), 22–26.

Cappella, J. N. (2006). Integrating message effects and behavior change theories: Organizing comments and unanswered questions. *Journal of Communication, 56,* S265–S279.

Chaiken, S. (1980). Heuristic versus systematic information processing and the use of source versus message cues in persuasion. *Journal of Personality and Social Psychology, 39,* 752–766.

Chaiken, S., Liberman, A., & Eagly, A. H. (1989). Heuristic and systematic information processing within and beyond the persuasion context. In J. S. Uleman & J. A. Bargh (Eds.), *Unintended thought* (pp. 212–252). New York: Guildford Press.

Cohen, F., Ogilvie, D.M., Solomon, S., Greenberg, J., & Pyszczynski, T. (2005). American roulette: The effect of reminders of death on support for George W. Bush in the 2004 presidential election. *Analyses of Social Issues and Public Policy, 5*(1), 177–187.

Das, E. H. H. J., Bushman, B. J., Bezemer, M.D., Kerkhof, P., & Vermeulen, I. E. (2009). How terrorism news reports increase prejudice against outgroups: A terror management account. *Journal of Experimental Social Psychology, 45*, 452–459.

Das, E. H. H. J., de Wit, J. B. F., & Stroebe, W. (2003). Fear appeals motivate acceptance of action recommendations: Evidence for a positive bias in the processing of persuasive messages. *Personality and Social Psychology Bulletin, 29*, 650–663.

De Hoog, N., Stroebe, W., & de Wit, J. B. F. (2005). The impact of fear appeals on processing and acceptance of action recommendations. *Personality and Social Psychology Bulletin, 31*, 24–33.

De Hoog, N., Stroebe, W., & de Wit, J. B. F. (2007). The impact of vulnerability to and severity of a health risk on processing and acceptance of fear-arousing communications: A meta-analysis. *Review of General Psychology, 11*(3), 258–285.

Dillard, J. P., & Meijnders, A. (2002). Persuasion and the structure of affect. In J. P. Dillard & M. Pfau (Eds.), *The persuasion handbook* (pp. 309–327). Thousand Oaks, CA: Sage.

Dillard, J. P., & Peck, E. (2000). Affect and persuasion: Emotional responses to public service announcements. *Communication Research, 27*(4), 461–495.

Dillard, J. P., Plotnick, C. A., Godbold, L. C., Freimuth, V. S., & Edgar, T. (1996). The multiple affective outcomes of AIDS PSAs: Fear appeals do more than scare people. *Communication Research, 23*(1), 44–72.

Erdelyi, M. H (1974). A new look at the new look: Perceptual defense and vigilance. *Psychological Review, 81*, 1–25.

Fransen, M. L., Fennis, B. M., Pruyn, A. T. H., & Das, E. (2008). Rest in peace? Brand-induced mortality salience and consumer behavior. *Journal of Business Research, 61*, 1053–1061.

Goldberg, J. H., Halpern-Felsher, B. L., & Millstein, S. G. (2002). Beyond invulnerability: The importance of benefits in adolescents' decision to drink alcohol. *Health Psychology, 21*(5), 477–484.

Goldenberg, J. L., & Arndt, J. (2008). The implications of death for health: A terror management health model for behavioral health promotion. *Psychological Review, 115*(4), 1032–1053.

Goldenberg, J. L., Arndt, J., Hart, J., & Brown, M. (2005). Dying to be thin: The effects of mortality salience and body mass index on restricted eating among women. *Personality and Social Psychology Bulletin, 31*(10), 1400–1412.

Goldenberg, J. L., Pyszczynski, T., Johnson, K. D., Greenberg, J., & Solomon, S. (1999). The appeal of tragedy: A terror management perspective. *Media Psychology, 1*, 313–329.

Goldenberg, J. L., Pyszczynski, T., Greenberg, J., Solomon, S. (2000). Fleeing the body: A terror management perspective on the problem of human corporeality. *Personality and Social Psychology Review, 4*(3), 200–218.

Goldenberg, J. L., Goplen, J., Cox, C. R., & Arndt, J. (2007). "Viewing" pregnancy as an existential threat: The effects of creatureliness on reactions to media depictions of the pregnant body. *Media Psychology, 10*, 211–230.

Greenberg, J., Arndt, J., Simon, L., Pyszczynski, T., & Solomon, S. (2000). Proximal and distal defenses in response to reminders of one's mortality: Evidence of a temporal sequence. *Personality and Social Psychology Bulletin, 26*, 91–99.

Greenberg, J., Pyszczynski, T., & Solomon, S. (1986). The causes and consequences of a need for self-esteem: A terror management theory. In R. F. Baumeister (Ed.), *Public self and private self* (pp. 189–212). New York: Springer-Verlag.

Greenberg, J., Pyszczynski, T., Solomon, S., Rosenblatt, A., Veeder, M., Kirkland, S., et al. (1990). Evidence for terror management theory II: The effects of morality salience on reactions to those who threaten or bolster the cultural worldview. *Journal of Personality and Social Psychology, 58*(2), 308–318.

Halloran, M. J., & Kashima, E. S. (2004). Social identity and worldview validation: The effects of ingroup identity primes and mortality salience on value endorsement. *Personality and Social Psychology Bulletin, 20*, 915–925.

Hansen, J., Winzeler, S., & Topolinski, S. (In press). When the death makes you smoke: A terror management perspective on the effectiveness of cigarette on-pack warnings. *Journal of Experimental Social Psychology.*

Henley, N., & Donovan, R. J. (2003). Young people's response to death threat appeals: Do they really feel immortal? *Health Education Research, 18*(1), 1–14.

Hirschberger, G., Florian, V., Mikulincer, M., Goldenberg, J. L., & Pyszczynski, T. (2002). Gender differences in the willingness to engage in risky behavior: A terror management perspective. *Death Studies, 26*, 117–141.

Hirschberger, G., Pyszczynski, T., & Ein-Dor, T. (2009). Vulnerability and vigilance: Threat awareness and perceived adversary intent moderate the impact of mortality salience on intergroup violence. *Personality and Social Psychology Bulletin, 35*(5), 595–607.

Hovland, C., Janis, I., & Kelly, H. (1953). *Communication and persuasion.* New Haven, CT: Yale University Press.

Hoyt, C. L., Simon, S., & Reid, L. (2009). Choosing the best (wo)man for the job: The effects of mortality salience, sex, and gender stereotypes on leader evaluations. *Leadership Quarterly, 20*, 233–246.

Ivie, R. L. (1999). Fire, flood, and red fever: Motivating metaphors of global emergency in the Truman doctrine speech. *Presidential Studies Quarterly, 29*(3), 570–591.

Janis, I. L. (1967). Effects of fear arousal on attitude change: Recent developments in theory and experimental research. In L. Berkowitz (Ed.), *Advances in experimental social psychology* (Vol. 3, pp. 166–225). New York: Academic Press.

Kirkpatrick, L. A., & Navarrete, C. D. (2006). Reports of my death anxiety have been greatly exaggerated: A critique of terror management theory from an evolutionary perspective. *Psychological Inquiry, 17*(4), 288–298.

Kosloff, S., Greenberg, J., Weise, D., & Solomon, S. (In press). The effects of mortality salience on political preferences: The roles of charisma and political orientation. *Journal of Experimental Social Psychology.*

Ladd, J. M., & Lenz, G. S. (2008). Reassessing the role of anxiety in vote choice. *Political Psychology, 29*(2), 275–296.

Landau, M. J., Greenberg, J., & Sullivan, D. (2009). Managing terror when self-worth and worldviews collide: Evidence that mortality salience increases reluctance to self-enhance beyond authorities. *Journal of Experimental Social Psychology, 45*, 68–79.

Landau, M. J., Solomon, S., Greenberg, J., Cohen, F., Pyszczynski, T., Arndt, J., et al. (2004). Deliver us from evil: The effects of mortality salience and reminds of 9/11 on support for President George W. Bush. *Personality and Social Psychology Bulletin, 30*, 1136–1150.

Lau, R. R., Sigelman, L., Heldman, C., & Babbit, P. (1999). The effects of negative political advertisements: A meta-analytic assessments. *American Political Science Review, 93*(4), 851–875.

Leventhal, H. (1970). Findings and theory in the study of fear communications. In L. Berkowitz (Ed.), *Advances in experimental social psychology* (Vol. 5, pp. 119–186). New York: Academic Press.

Leventhal, H. (1971). Fear appeals and persuasion: The differentiation of a motivational construct. *American Journal of Public Health, 61*, 1208–1224.

Lodge, M., & Taber, C. (2000). Three steps toward a theory of motivated political reasoning. In A. Lupia, M. McCubbins, & S. Popkin (Eds.), *Elements of reason: Cognition, choice, and the bounds of rationality* (pp. 183–213). Cambridge, UK: Cambridge University Press.

Lodge, M., & Taber, C. (2005). The automaticity of affect for political leaders, groups, and issues: An experimental test of the hot cognition hypothesis. *Political Psychology, 26*(3), 455–481.

MacKuen, M., Marcus, G. E., Neuman, W. R., & Keele, L. (2007). The third way: The theory of affective intelligence and American democracy. In W. R. Neuman, G. E., Marcus, A. N. Crigler, & M. MacKuen (Eds.), *The affect effect: Dynamics of emotion in political thinking and behavior* (pp. 124–151). Chicago: University of Chicago Press.

Magee, R. G., & Kalyanaraman, S. (2009). Effects of worldview and mortality salience in persuasion processes. *Media Psychology, 12*(2), 171–194.

Marcus, G. E., Neuman, W. R., & MacKuen, M. (2000). *Affective intelligence and political judgment*. Chicago: University of Chicago Press.

Marcus, G. E., Sullivan, J. L., Theiss-Morse, E., & Stevens, D. (2005). The emotional foundation of political cognition: The impact of extrinsic anxiety on the formation of political tolerance judgments. *Political Psychology, 26*(6), 949–963.

McGregor, I. (2006). Offensive defensiveness: Toward an integrative neuroscience of compensatory zeal after mortality salience, personal uncertainty, and other poignant self-threats. *Psychological Inquiry, 17*(4), 299–308.

McGregor, H., Lieberman, J., Greenberg, J., Solomon, S., Arndt, J., Simon, L., et al. (1998). Terror management and aggression: Evidence that mortality salience promotes aggression toward worldview-threatening individuals. *Journal of Personality and Social Psychology, 74*, 590–605.

McGuire, WJ. (1968). Personality and susceptibility to social influence. In E. Borgatta & W. Lambert (Eds.), *Handbook of personality theory and research* (pp. 1130–1187). Chicago: Rand McNally.

McGuire, WJ. (1969). The nature of attitudes and attitude change. In G. Lindzey & E. Aronson (Eds.), *The handbook of social psychology* (Vol. 3, pp. 136–314). Reading, MA: Addison-Wesley.

Merskin, D. (2004). The construction of Arabs as enemies: Post-September 11 discourse of George W. Bush. *Mass Communication & Society, 7*(2), 157–175.

Mikulincer, M., & Florian, V. (1997). Do we really know what we need? A commentary on Pyszczynski, Greenberg, and Solomon. *Psychological Inquiry, 8*(1), 33–36.

Miller, C., & Hansen, G. (2007). *The effects of mortality salience on response to presidential campaign ads: An application of terror management theory.* Paper presented at the annual meeting of the NCA 93rd Annual Convention, November 15. Chicago, IL.

Miller, C., & Landau, M. J. (2005). Communication and terrorism: A terror management theory perspective. *Communication Research Reports, 22*, 79–88.

Miller, C., & Landau, M.J. (2008). Communication and the causes and costs of terrorism: A terror management theory perspective. In H. D. O'Hair, R. L. Heath, K. J. Ayotte, & G. R. Ledlow (Eds.), *Terrorism: Communication and rhetorical perspectives* (pp. 93–128). Cresskill, NJ: Hampton Press.

Murray-Johnson, L., Witte, K., Wen-Ying, L., & Hubbell, A. P. (2001). Addressing cultural orientations in fear appeals: Promoting AIDS-protective behaviors among Mexican immigrant and African American adolescents and American and Taiwan-ese college students. *Journal of Health Communication, 6*, 335–358.

Muthusamy, N., Levine, T. R., & Weber, R. (2009). Scaring the already scared: Some problems with HIV/AIDS fear appeals in Namibia. *Journal of Communication, 59*, 317–344.

Nabi, R. L. (1999). A cognitive-functional model for the effects of discrete negative emotions on information processing, attitude change, and recall. *Communication Theory, 9*(3), 292–320.

Nabi, R. L. (2002). Anger, fear, uncertainty, and attitudes: A test of the cognitive-functional model. *Communication Monographs, 69*(3), 204–216.

Nelson, L. J., Moore, D. L., Olivetti, J., & Scott, T. (1997). General and personal mortality salience and nationalistic bias. *Personality and Social Psychology Bulletin, 23*, 884–892.

Neuman, W. R., Marcus, G. E., MacKuen, M., & Crigler, A. N. (2007). Theorizing affect's effects. In W. R. Neuman, G. E., Marcus, A. N. Crigler, & M. MacKuen (Eds.), *The affect effect: Dynamics of emotion in political thinking and behavior* (pp. 1–20). Chicago: University of Chicago Press.

Petty, R. E., & Cacioppo, J. T. (1986). The elaboration likelihood of persuasion. *Advances in Experimental Social Psychology, 19*, 193–205.

Pfau, M. W. (2007). Who's afraid of fear appeals? Contingency, courage, and deliberation in rhetorical theory and practice. *Philosophy and Rhetoric, 40*(2), 216–237.

Proulx, T., & Heine, S. J. (2006). Death and black diamonds: Meaning, mortality, and the meaning maintenance model. *Psychological Inquiry, 17*(4), 309–318.

Pyszczynski, T., Abdollahi, A., Solomon, S., Greenberg, J., Cohen, F., & Weise, D. (2006). Mortality salience, martyrdom, and military might: The great Satan versus the axis of evil. *Personality and Social Psychology Bulletin, 32*, 525–537.

Pyszczynski, T., Greenberg, J., & Solomon, S. (1999). A dual-process model of defense against conscious and unconscious death-related thoughts: An extension of terror management theory. *Psychological Review, 106*(4), 835–845.

Pyszczynski, T., Greenberg, J., Solomon, S., & Maxfield, M. A. (2006). On the unique psychological import of death: Theme and variations. *Psychological Inquiry, 17*(4), 328–356.

Pyszczynski, T., Rothschild, Z., & Abdollahi, A. (2008). Terrorism, violence, and hope for peace. *Current Directions in Psychological Science, 17*(5), 318–322.

Pyszczynski, T., Solomon, S., & Greenberg, J. (2003). *In the wake of 9/11: The psychology of terror*. Washington, DC: American Psychological Association.

Redlawsk, D. P., Civettini, A. J. W., & Lau, R. R. (2007). Affective intelligence and voting: Information processing and learning in a campaign. In W. R. Neuman, G. E. Marcus, A. N. Crigler, & M. MacKuen (Eds.), *The affect effect: Dynamics of emotion in political thinking and behavior* (pp. 152–179). Chicago: University of Chicago Press.

Rimal, R. N. (2001). Perceived risk and self-efficacy as motivators: Understanding individuals' long-term use of health information. *Journal of Communication, 51*(4), 633–654.

Rimal, R. N., & Real, K. (2003). Perceived risk and efficacy beliefs as motivators of change: Use of the risk perception attitude (RPA) framework to understand health behaviors. *Human Communication Research, 29*(3), 370–399.

Rogers, R.W. (1975). A protection motivation theory of fear appeals and attitude change. *Journal of Psychology, 91*, 93–114.

Rogers, R.W. (1983). Cognitive and physiological processes in fear appeals and attitude change: A revised theory of protection motivation. In J. Cacioppo & R. Petty (Eds.), *Social psychophysiology* (pp. 153–176). New York: Guildford Press.

Russell, J. A. (1980). A circumplex model of affect. *Journal of Personality and Social Psychology, 39*(6), 1161–1178.

Schimel, J., Simon, L., Greenberg, J., Pyszczynski, T., Solomon S., Waxmonski, J., et al. (1999). Support for a functional perspective on stereotypes: Evidence that mortality salience enhances stereotypic thinking and preferences. *Journal of Personality and Social Psychology, 77*(5), 905–926.

Schmeichel, B. J., Gailliot, M. T., Filardo, E., McGregor, I., Gitter, S., & Baumeister, R. F. (2009). Terror management theory and self-esteem revisited: The roles of implicit and explicit self-esteem in mortality salience effects. *Journal of Personality and Social Psychology, 96*(5), 1077–1087.

Shehryar, O., & Hunt, D. M. (2005). A terror management perspective on the persuasiveness of fear appeals. *Journal of consumer psychology, 15*(4), 275–287.

Solomon, S., Greenberg, J., & Pyszczynski, T. (1991). A terror management theory of social behavior: The psychological functions of self-esteem and cultural worldviews. In M. Zanna (Ed.), *Advances in experimental social psychology* (Vol. 24, pp. 91–159). Orlando, FL: Academic Press.

Solomon, S., Greenberg, J., & Pyszczynski, T. (2004). The cultural animal: Twenty years of terror management theory and research. In J. Greenberg, S. L. Koole, & T. Pyszczynski (Eds.), *Handbook of experimental existential psychology* (pp. 13–34). New York: Guilford Press.

Solomon, S., Greenberg, J., Pyszczynski, T., & Pryzbylinski, J. (1995). The effects of mortality salience on personally-relevant persuasive appeals. *Social Behavior and Personality, 23*(2), 177–190.

Sutton, S. R. (1982). Fear-arousing communications: A critical examination of theory and research. In J. R. Eiser (Ed.), *Social psychology and behavioral medicine* (pp. 303–337). London: Wiley.

Ullrich, J., & Cohrs, J. C. (2007). Terrorism salience increases system justification: Experimental evidence. *Social Justice Research, 20*(2), 117–139.

Valentino, N. A., Hutchings, V. L., Banks, A. J., & Davis, A. K. (2008). Is a worried citizen a good citizen? Emotions, political information seeking, and learning via the Internet. *Political Psychology, 29*(2), 247–273.

Watson, D., Clark, L. A., & Tellegen, A. (1988). Development and validation of brief measures of positive and negative affect: The PANAS scales. *Journal of Personality and Social Psychology, 54*(6), 1063–1070.

Weise, D. R., Pyszczynski, T., Cox, C. R., Arndt, J., Greenberg, J., Solomon, S., & Kosloff, S. (2008). Interpersonal politics: The role of terror management and attachment processes in shaping political preferences. *Psychological Science, 19*(5), 448–455.

Wicklund, R. A. (1997). Terror management accounts of other theories: Questions for the cultural worldview concept. *Psychological Inquiry, 8*(1), 54–58.

Witte, K. (1992). Putting the fear back into fear appeals: The extended parallel process model. *Communication Monographs, 59*, 329–349.

Witte, K. (1994). Fear control and danger control: A test of the extended parallel process model (EPPM). *Communication Monographs, 61*, 113–133.

Witte, K. (1998). Fear as motivator, fear as inhibitor: Using the extended parallel process model to explain fear appeal successes and failures. In P. A. Andersen & L. K. Guerrero (Eds.), *Handbook of communication and emotion* (pp. 423–451). San Diego, CA: Academic Press.

Witte, K., & Allen, M. (2000). A meta-analysis of fear appeals: Implications for effective public health campaigns. *Health Education & Behavior, 27*(5), 591–615.

Witte, K., & Morrison, K. (2000). Examining the influence of trait anxiety/repression-sensitization on individuals' reactions to fear appeals. *Western Journal of Communication, 64*(1), 1–27.

Wolak, J., Marcus, G. E., & Neuman, W. R. (2003). *How the emotions of public policy affect citizen engagement, public deliberation, and the quality of electoral choice.* Paper presented at the Annual Meeting of the American Political Science Association, Philadelphia, PA.

Wong, N. C. H., & Cappella, J. N. (2009). Antismoking threat and efficacy appeals: Effects on smoking cessation intentions for smokers with low and high readiness to quit. *Journal of Applied Communication Research, 37*(1), 1–20.

COPYRIGHTED MATERIAL — DO NOT DUPLICATE, DISTRIBUTE, OR POST

Becoming the Paradigm Shift

The Psychosocial Development of the Effective Sustainability Agent

I am not waiting for a paradigm shift, I am the paradigm shift!

—Anonymous

Introduction

As I mentioned in an earlier chapter, my doctoral program provided me with the opportunity and resources to piece together a way of thinking about sustainability that I would later refer to as the psychology of sustainability. That psychology must inform every effort to establish and maintain a sustainable human ecology has become an indelible perspective. It also became increasingly clear that psychology must inform all sustainability pedagogy. With this in mind I began research for and development of sustainability psychology, an approach to sustainability education and research that would improve the experience of sustainability students and that would also attract students in other degree programs to sustainability. Fortunately, just a few years before I began development of this field, groundbreaking insight pertaining to the efficacy of educational approaches had been developed and provided the essential framework with which to structure my research.

Theories and Concepts in Context of Sustainability

Characteristics of the Effective Sustainability Agent

Researchers in the areas of education, human development, and psychology (King, Brown, Lindsey, & VanHecke, 2007; Pascarella, Wolniak, Seifert, Cruce, & Blaich, 2005; Wabash College, 2006) revealed that liberal arts education in general is the most effective at providing students with the training necessary to work effectively in their professional lives. Drawing from this research Seifert and colleagues (2008) identified and described six outcomes (Table 7.1) that are distinctive to liberal arts education. Systematic review by Chandler (2014) of research in social value orientation (SVO) (Bogaert, Boone, & Declerck, 2008; Van Lange, 1999), prosocialness (Caprara, Zelli, Setca, & Capana, 2005; Cuadrado, Tabernero, García, Luque, & Seibert, 2017; Van Lange, Otten, De Bruin, & Joireman, 1997), and effective sustainability leadership (Orr, 2002, 2011) revealed striking similarities between Seifert and colleagues' (2008) six outcomes and the characteristics of individuals with cooperative SVO, high in prosocialness and effective in sustainability leadership. Consequently, Chandler (2014, 2017) adopted Seifert and colleagues' (2008) outcomes and referred to these as the "six characteristics of the effective sustainability agent." Following is a brief description of each characteristic. Unless otherwise stated these descriptions are taken from Seifert and colleagues (2008) and modified by Chandler (2014) in context of sustainability.

Intercultural effectiveness (IcE): This concerns individual ability to synthesize information and problem solve in sociocultural and socioecological contexts. With respect to sustainability, IcE facilitates interest in and the capability to understand how those experiencing a sustainability problem perceive the problem and solutions to it.

Inclination to inquire and lifelong learning (IiLL): Refers to the enjoyment of engaging in varied and challenging learning activities and an interest in sharing knowledge gained from these activities. IiLL facilitates the sustainability agent's ability to understand situational changes, work with others to modify sustainability solutions, and educate others as to the reason for and nature of those changes.

Leadership: This is experienced and practiced both individually and socially. An individual high in leadership will first be effective with self-management (balanced and focused attention to values and goals) as well as guide others effectively. Leadership has five components: consciousness of self, congruence, commitment, collaboration, and common purpose. Leadership enables the sustainability agent to be self-motivated as well as cooperative.

Post-conventional moral reasoning (PCMR): Along with reflective reasoning PCMR is likely the most important in that it facilitates the sustainability agent's ability to consider problems and solutions not only in typical ways but especially in novel, creative ways that are likely to be more effective and resilient, especially concerning more complex and dynamic sociocultural and socioecological situations.

Reflective reasoning (RR): Refers to the capability to take stock in past experiences, lessons, decisions, and positions, and to consider these in the context of current issues toward problem solving. RR is of particular importance given that many sustainability solutions of the past continue to be applied in the present even though those solutions have proven marginally effective. An individual who is high RR employs cause and effect, that is learns from past successes and mistakes toward understanding effective ways to approach a sustainability problem.

Well-being: Closely aligned with leadership, well-being is a holistic ability to cultivate an experience of esteem, efficacy, and agency for oneself as well as for others. It has five components: autonomy, positive relationship with others, environmental mastery, personal growth, and life purpose. To be an effective, resilient sustainability agent one must first attend to his or her well-being and in so doing can better facilitate well-being with/among others.

I Am the Paradigm Shift Theory: Describing the Development Experience of an Effective Sustainability Agent

Once Seifert and colleagues' (2008) outcomes were identified as accurate descriptors for the characteristics that are essential to efficacy in action for sustainability, the question then became "What is the individual's experience of developing these outcomes?" Put another way, in order to improve sustainability education, the factors that affect development of these characteristics needed to be identified and described in context of learners' experiences. A study employing constructivist grounded theory (Charmaz, 2006) was conducted for this purpose.

Results of the study revealed that learners' development experience of the aforementioned characteristics occurred through a sequential as well as reciprocal relationship between four phenomena. Drawing from narratives collected during this study these phenomena were labeled in order of relative occurrence as *nature as resolve*, *fear mastery*, *paradigm shift*, and *new normal* (Figure 7.1). It is important to understand that development of these characteristics is not only

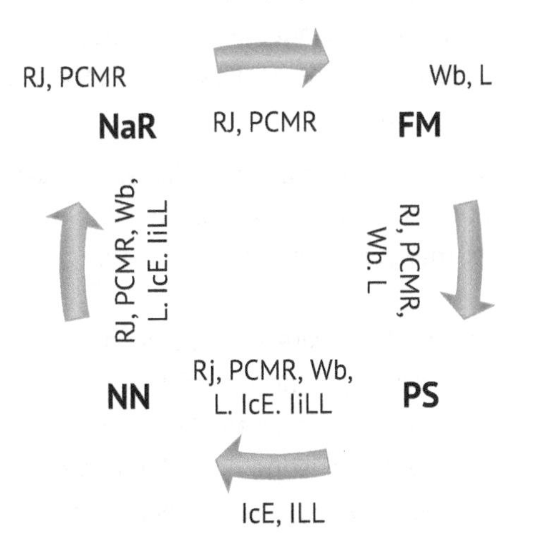

Figure 7.1 I am the paradigm shift theory. Image illustrates relationship of four phenomena nature as resolve, fear mastery, paradigm shift, and new normal in context of development of the six essential characteristics of the effective sustainability agent. PCMR = Post-conventional moral reasoning; RJ = Reflective judgment; L = Leadership; Wb = Well-being; IcE = Intercultural effectiveness; IiLL = Interest in lifelong learning.

dependent on this sequential-reciprocal relationship but also on the spatial and temporal relationship of the phenomena. Put another way, it appears not only that it is critical that the individual experience these phenomena in sequence but also in a relatively short length of time. The description of individuals' experience of development of the six essential characteristics of the effective sustainability agent was named *I am the Paradigm Shift Theory.*

Brief Description of I am the Paradigm Shift Theory Phenomena

The phenomena of I am the paradigm shift theory are listed in order of relative experience along with the characteristics that were observed to develop with or through each phenomenon.

> Nature as resolve: Characteristics include post-conventional moral reasoning and reflective judgment. For most students "nature" is understood as wilderness and non-human aspects of life. However, for some individuals, nature also included humanity and especially marginalized members of society. Their experience of nature motivated them to begin their program of study. The experience of nature as resolve serves as a validating, positive, and reflexive experience.
>
> Fear mastery: Characteristics include leadership and well-being. Students experience fear mastery as one of facing challenges straight on and of recognizing their strengths and weaknesses. This experience facilitates a desire to be effective leaders on their own behalf as well as on behalf of others. Fear mastery is a recurring experience.
>
> Paradigm shift: Characteristics include intercultural effectiveness and interest in lifelong learning. Paradigm shift in the context of development of the essential characteristics is not an outcome; instead it is the engagement in a personal process. Moreover, when the individual serves as a paradigm shift he or she catalyzes the action necessary to create and maintain sustainable human ecology.
>
> New normal: All six of the essential characteristics are present. Students experience new normal as a positive but not rosy image of a sustainable human ecology, and one that is also ever-evolving rather than a fixed point or outcome.

Nature as resolve and fear mastery were considered by participants to be foundational phenomena and essential to the development of healthier society. However, without the catalyzing effect of paradigm shift, nature as resolve and fear mastery would remain unorganized as nothing more than improvements of the existing norm. Paradigm shift was considered essential to raise society to the highest level of ever-evolving organization: new normal.

Importance of I Am the Paradigm Shift Theory

Myers and Beringer (2010) observed that substantive theory was necessary to guide development of sustainability education. I am the paradigm shift theory describes individuals' development of the six essential characteristics of the effective sustainability agent. Students' experience of this development is described in the following narrative from Chandler (2014):

> We learn through the passion for and potency of an anticipatory experience of a sustainable human ecology. Through nature as resolve and fear mastery we become healthier individuals, thus these are essential phenomena. However, without paradigm shift, the individual assumption of responsibility for and engagement with collective action, Nature, and fear mastery remain unorganized improvements of the existing norm. Prosocial change is a creation of a new normal society, a sustainable human ecology manifested along a continuum of improvement toward just treatment of Earth and all her inhabitants. Education for effective participation in this continuum of prosocial change is described by I am the paradigm shift theory. (p. 172)

About the Feature Article

As you read the feature article for this chapter *Moral Philosophy: An Adventure in Reasoning*, in addition to the four questions he presented at the end of the introduction, also compare "moral philosophy" with I am the paradigm shift theory (IPST) and make note of what your comparison reveals. In addition, think about how IPST might be employed toward developing reasoning that yields a stronger environmental ethic.

References

Caprara, G. V., Steca, P., Zelli, A., & Capanna, C. (2005). A new scale for measuring adults' prosocialness. *European Journal of Psychological Assessment, 21*(2), 77–89.

Chandler, R. (2014). *I am the paradigm shift: A grounded theory of learners' sustainability outcome comprehension experience.* Ann Arbor, MI: ProQuest.

Chandler, R. (2017). I am the paradigm shift theory: Explaining students' sustainability outcome comprehension experience. *Psychology and Psychological Research International Journal,* 2, 1–12.

Cuadrado, E., Tabernero, C., García, R., Luque, B., & Seibert, J. (2017). The role of prosocialness and trust in the consumption of water as a limited resource. *Frontiers in Psychology, 8*, 694.

King, P., Brown, M., Lindsay, N., & Van Hecke, J. (2007, September-October). Liberal arts student learning outcomes: An integrated approach. *About Campus, 12*(4), 2–9. doi:10.1002/abc.222

Myers, O. & Beringer, A. (2010). Sustainability in higher education: Psychological research for effective pedagogy. *Canadian Journal of Higher Education, 40*(2), 51–77.

Pascarella, E., Wolniak, G., Seifert, T., Cruce, T., & Blaich, C. (2005). *Liberal arts colleges and liberal arts education: New evidence on impacts.* San Francisco, CA: Jossey-Bass.

Seifert, T., Goodman, K., Lindsay, Jorgensen, J. D., Wolniak, G, Pascarella, E., & Blaich, C. (2008). The effects of liberal arts experiences on liberal arts outcomes. *Research in Higher Education*, *49*(2), 107–125. doi:10.1007/s11162-007-9070-7

Van Lange, P., Otten, W., De Bruin, E., & Joireman, J. (1997). Development of prosocial, individualistic, and competitive orientations: Theory and preliminary evidence. *Journal of Personality and Social Psychology, 21*(1), 273–292.

Wabash College: Center of Inquiry in the Liberal Arts. (2006). *Wabash national study of liberal arts education.* Crawfordsville, IN. Author.

READING 8

Moral Philosophy

An Adventure in Reasoning

Robert Traer

The word *ethics* comes from the Greek *ethos,* for custom, but ethics has long meant prescribing, and not simply describing, what our customs ought to be. Ethics answers the question, how should we live? Some philosophers distinguish *morality* from ethics by claiming that ethics necessarily involves critical reflection, whereas morality may simply refer to the moral rules and customs of a culture.[1] In everyday speech, however, the adjectives *ethical* and *moral* are interchangeable. Ethics is moral philosophy.[2]

Studying ethics, I suggest, is like hiking on a (conceptual) mountain, where the wider paths reflect the main traditions of ethical thought, and the narrower trails branching off these paths represent the arguments of individuals. As we have little time to explore this mountain (ethics), I will generally guide us along the paths (theories), but endnotes offer observations about some of the trails.

To illustrate what *doing ethics* means, consider how we might describe an actual mountain in diverse ways. We could emphasize its unusual rock formations, or point out a striking waterfall, or recall the sweep of the forest below the summit, or identify wildlife in the meadows. Each of these four descriptions would tell us about the mountain, but all four would be necessary to convey our impression of the whole mountain.

To offer an overview of moral philosophy, I will lead us along paths that reflect four patterns of thought, which I identify by the keywords *duty, character, relationships,* and *rights,* and a fifth path identified by the keyword *consequences*. Each keyword represents the crux of the debate within the pattern of thought it identifies. The first four patterns of ethical thought (concerning our duty, character, relationships,

Robert Traer, "Moral Philosophy: An Adventure in Reasoning," *Doing Environmental Ethics*, pp. 3-20, 315-316, 367-374.

and rights) assert that some actions or ways of being have *intrinsic worth.* The fifth pattern of thought (predicting consequences) rejects the notion of intrinsic worth and argues that actions and goods only have *extrinsic value* (derivative or use value) based on their utility (usefulness).[3]

To prepare for our ethical trek, we "stretch" our minds a bit by considering four questions. How are the words *right* and *good* used in moral philosophy? What is the role of reason in ethics? How is environmental ethics different from traditional ethics? Why rely on diverse patterns of moral reasoning instead of deciding which ethical theory is best?

Right and Good

Traditional ethics is about human life in societies. The natural world, which is center stage in environmental ethics, has for centuries been merely the backdrop for the drama of moral philosophy. Because ethics developed without any direct concern for the environment, the main patterns of thought were constructed without considering many of the issues we now face.

Our challenge, therefore, involves drawing on the traditions of moral philosophy to construct arguments that address our environmental crisis. We begin our trek on the mountain (of ethics) below the (environmental) slope, along the main paths that have been worn smooth by seeking to know what is "right" and "good."

What do we mean by taking the right action? We mean that we are acting "in accord with what is just, good, or proper."[4] We take a right action by correctly applying a principle (norm, premise, presupposition, rule, standard, or law).[5] We offer reasons to justify the principle and its application. We do our duty, or act to protect a person's rights. For instance, we might assert that not littering in a public park is right, because we have a duty to respect the rights of others who use the park.

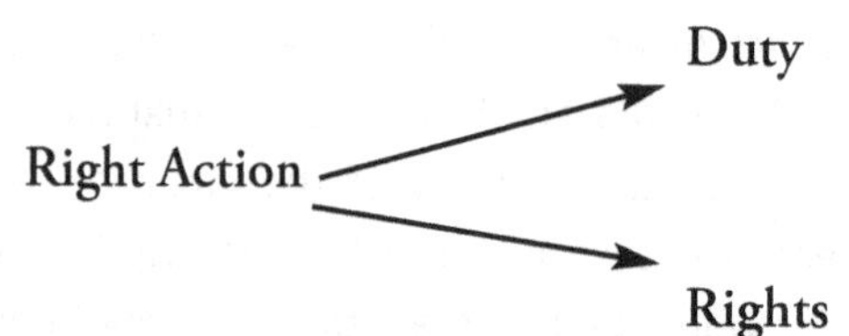

By *being a good person,* we mean that a person is "virtuous."[6] Being good involves having the character and personal qualities that we recognize as having moral worth. The traditional word for a good character trait is *virtue,* and chapter 5 gives reasons for the virtues of gratitude, integrity, and frugality. Would a person who is grateful for the beauty of the flowers in a park throw a candy wrapper in the flowerbed? Not if he has integrity.

Because a virtue identifies a way of being good, it has no plural. That is, a virtue is not an action, but a way of aspiring to be good. It is how we can be or not be. We can be grateful, so the virtue of being grateful is gratitude. There is no such word as "gratitudes." Similarly, an honest and trustworthy person has the virtue of integrity and a person who is frugal the virtue of frugality. It makes no sense to speak of "integrities" or "frugalities."

Examples of other character traits that are often said to be virtues are patience, generosity, compassion, humility, courage, and diligence. None of these nouns has a plural, but each has a related adjective that is used to describe a character trait, which is understood to reflect a good quality of how we may be as persons.

The adjectives *good* and *right* are related in meaning, but are not synonyms. It makes no sense to speak of a "right person" when we mean a "good person." Good has a broader range of meanings than right, and both words have meanings that do not involve ethics.

For example, we speak of the "good looks" of a person, or of a "good joke." Saying someone is the right person for a job means that we think the person will do a good job, but in this statement the adjectives right and good have nothing to do with moral philosophy. The phrase "good science," which appears in debates about climate change, does not refer to an ethical presumption, but to relying on proper procedures in scientific research.

Because ethics concerns how we ought to live together, our goal is "a good society." No one argues that our goal is "a right society" or "the right society." Also, we speak of "the common good" and "good relationships," rather than "right relationships," to identify the ethical goals of ensuring freedom, equality, and social justice for everyone. This sense of being good refers to the way a society is or to the hope shared by many of its members about how it should be.

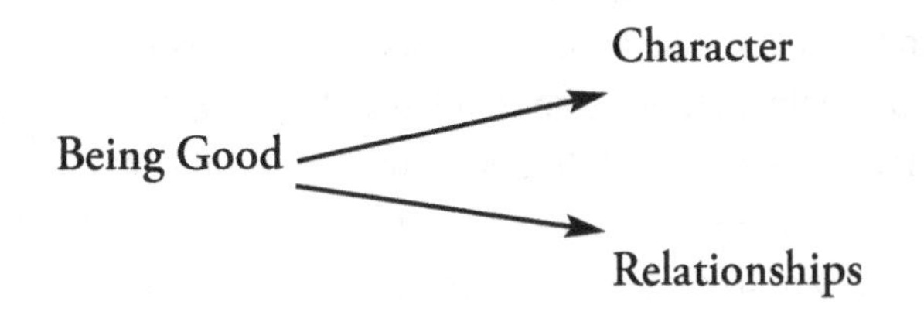

Both adjectives, *right* and *good*, have opposites that help define their meanings. If an action is morally wrong, it is not right. A good person is not a bad person, and a bad person is not a good person. Yet the opposition between what is good and bad is more complex than the dichotomy between what is right and wrong. For example, a good person may act badly. We may distinguish between the bad behavior of a child and the child herself. In caring for children, we are told, we should refrain from calling a child "bad" when she is behaving badly.

Another distinction between the adjectives right and good is that good has comparative and superlative forms (better and best), but right does not. Good refers to a way of being that has a range of possibilities or levels of aspiration. There is nothing comparable when speaking of what is right, because right and wrong are opposites. It makes sense to speak of a "lesser evil," or a "greater good." It makes no sense, however, to refer to a "lesser wrong" or a "greater right." What is good may not be as good as it could be, but if it is better than what is bad, it is good.

These distinctions usually become clear to us early in our moral development as children. Our actions are right when we follow the rules, or when we act responsibly by drawing an inference from the rules. Our actions are wrong when we violate a rule or behave in a manner that seems contrary to the intention of the rules.

In addition, we encourage children to act in a manner that involves being good with one another, and this means doing more than any set of rules requires. We want children to be more than obedient. We hope they will learn to be kind, fair, and forgiving in their relationships with one another.

These examples should help us see that good refers to a level of "goodness" and to "the quality or state of being good." No matter how good we are, we may aspire to be better. Right, however, does not identify a level of rightness, as an action is either right or wrong. Another difference is that right takes the form of a verb, for we may try "to right a wrong," but good does not have a similar verb. Being good is not an action, which may be right or wrong, but a way of being.

These differences in our everyday language are reflected in the diverse patterns of thought in moral philosophy. I suggest that the keywords *duty* and *rights* are largely concerned with right action, whereas the keywords *character* and *relationships* are primarily about being good persons. Right action and being good identify different paths on the mountain. Ethical theories emphasizing duty or rights branch off the "right action" path. Moral theories about character or relationships diverge from the "being good" path.

The words *right* and *good* are also nouns with distinctive meanings. A right refers to a moral claim that a person has against other persons. If backed by law, this moral right is a legal right. A good is a way of being (an end, a goal) that has moral worth in itself, not because it is a means to realizing some other value. Having respect for other persons, most moral philosophers argue, is a good not because we are likely to receive better treatment from those we respect, but because each person is capable of moral actions and so is worthy of respect.

When I use the plural noun *rights* I am referring to *legal rights*, some of which are *human rights* under international law. *Moral rights* are not necessarily legal rights, as ethics has a larger concern than the law. Yet making and enforcing law is an ethical responsibility. The plural noun

DECISION 7.1 Becoming More Responsible

BP's massive oil spill in 2010 has prompted residents of south Mississippi to take more responsibility for protecting wildlife and the wetlands. In the Pascagoula School District on "environmental day," sixth graders explore the wetlands in kayaks and canoes. "They see now that there are some things that they can lose that they value and cherish," ecologist Mark LaSalle says. "A lot of what these kids are learning today is to appreciate nature."

Analyze LaSalle's ethical reasoning. What other arguments do you think would persuade people to take better care of the environment?

Source: "Gautier Students Learn to Care for the Environment," *Your Daily Update,* October 28, 2010, http://yourdailyupdateblog.com/archives/9387.

goods is sometimes used by moral philosophers to speak of moral values, interests, or ends. In economic theory, however, goods are simply commodities.

Reasoning About Our Feelings

I agree with those who argue that ethics is "concerned with making sense of intuitions"[7] about what is right and good. We do this by reasoning about our feelings. Biologists verify that: "Emotion is never truly divorced from decision-making, even when it is channeled aside by an effort of will."[8] Physicists now confirm that seeing the world with complete objectivity is not possible, as our observations affect what we perceive.[9]

Moral philosopher Mary Midgley writes: "Sensitivity requires rationality to complete it, and vice versa. There is no siding onto which emotions can be shunted so as not to impinge on thought."[10] We rely on our reason to guard against feelings that may reflect a bias, or a sense of inadequacy, or a desire simply to win an argument. We also rely on reason to refine and explain a felt conviction that passes the test of critical reflection and discussion. We rely on feelings to move us to act morally and to ensure that our reasoning is not only consistent but also humane.

Empathy and Reason

Scientific evidence supports this approach to ethics. As children, we manifest empathy before developing our rational abilities, and there is evidence for the same order of development in the evolution of the human brain.[11] "Empathy is a unique form of intentionality in which we are directed toward the other's experience."[12] This involves feeling, at least to some extent, what another person is feeling. Empathy means experiencing another human being as a person, an intentional being whose actions express a state of mind.

Empathy enables us to identify with others and may generate in us a feeling that another person deserves concern and respect. This does not guarantee ethical conduct, but encourages it. "Aid to others in need would never be internalized as a duty without the fellow-feeling that drives people to take an interest in one another. Moral sentiments came first; moral principles second."[13]

We use the word *conscience* to refer to a person's integration of moral sentiments and principles. We should each test our conscience, however, by explaining to others the reasons for our moral presumptions, and we should listen carefully to concerns they may have. Peter Singer probably speaks for all moral philosophers when he asserts that an ethical argument should only appeal to "emotions where they can be supported by reason."[14]

Both our feelings and our reason reflect our *moral community*, which is made up of all those we care about (or should care about). As children, our moral community is our family, but this soon includes our friends and then is defined primarily by our school experience. As adults, our moral community may grow from our family and friends (at work, in our neighborhood or a support group, and perhaps in our religious community) to include our city, our country, and even all the people of the world, whose moral and legal rights are defined by international law. It may even, as we will see, also embrace nonhuman organisms, ecosystems, and the biosphere of our planet.

Critical Reasoning

A *reason* is a statement that expresses a rational motive and supports a conclusion or explains a fact. As a verb, to reason means to use the faculty of reason to arrive at conclusions. Reasoning is thinking. Being rational is the same as being reasonable, which means acting or being in accord with reason. In moral philosophy, *arguing* involves giving reasons for drawing a conclusion. Simply expressing contrary opinions or beliefs is not arguing. In ethics we are interested in the reasons for our opinions or beliefs. We argue not to "win," but to clarify our reasoning.

This means unmasking *rationalizations*. In some disciplines of thought, to rationalize means "to bring into accord with reason," but in ethics it means "to attribute (one's actions) to rational and creditable motives without analysis of true and especially unconscious motives."[15] In moral philosophy a reason is not a rationalization, because reasoning involves analyzing our motives. It is often difficult, however, to distinguish reasons from rationalizations.

For example, if I own land that I want to log to make a profit, but argue at a public hearing that logging should be allowed because it will bring jobs into the community, my public statement is a rationalization. If, however, I state publicly that I support logging because I will benefit from it *and* think the community will also benefit, I am giving two reasons for my position. Self-interest is rational and is not a rationalization, unless it is intentionally concealed or is the unconscious motivation for making an argument.

Reasoning by analogy explains one thing by comparing it to something else that is similar, although also different. In a good analogy, the similarity outweighs the dissimilarity and is clarifying. For example, (nonhuman) animals are both like and unlike humans (who are also animals). Is the similarity sufficiently strong to support the argument that we should ascribe rights to nonhuman animals as we do to humans? Chapter 7 reflects critically on this analogy.

Deductive reasoning applies a principle or general rule to a situation or person. For example, if every person has human rights, and you are a person, then by deductive reasoning you have human rights like every person. *Inductive reasoning* involves providing evidence to support a hypothesis. For example, the hypothesis that ingesting lead damages our bodies has been verified by extensive scientific research. The greater the evidence for a hypothesis, the more we may rely on it.

Chapter 15 notes that there is growing scientific evidence for the hypothesis that the burning of fossil fuels in power plants, factories, motor vehicles, and airplanes is contributing to global warming. This evidence substantiates the ethical argument that human communities have a duty to reduce carbon emissions to prevent the further degradation of the earth's biosphere.

Making an inference is *deductive* when it involves deriving logical conclusions from principles known or assumed to be true. Making an inference is *inductive* when we are reasoning from evidence of factual knowledge to argue for what is true.[16]

DECISION 7.2 What Should Government Do? Government's Duty To Protect the Public Welfare

"Health-related obesity costs are projected to reach $344 billion by 2018—with roughly 60 percent of that cost borne by the federal government. For a precedent in attacking this problem, look at the action government took in the case of tobacco. The historic 1998 tobacco settlement, in which the states settled health-related lawsuits against tobacco companies, and the companies agreed to curtail marketing and finance antismoking efforts, was far from perfect, but consider the results. More than half of all Americans who once smoked have quit and smoking rates are about half of what they were in the 1960s."

Evaluate the strengths and weaknesses of the analogy used in this argument. What sort of ethical reasoning is this?

Source: Mark Bittman, "Bad Food? Tax It, and Subsidize Vegetables," *New York Times*, July 23, 2011, http://www.nytimes.com/2011/07/24/opinion/sunday/24bittman.html.

The words *therefore* or *thus*, or *because* or *it follows*, or *given that* imply a conclusion is about to be stated. As critical readers, when we see these words we should begin raising questions. What principle is being asserted? Have the motives behind the argument been clarified, or is the conclusion a rationalization? If the argument relied on an analogy, was it strong and relevant? Are the inferences that have been made, either deductively or inductively, reasonable and convincing? Is the conclusion supported by the facts and reasons given in the argument?

Faith and Reason

For many people, morality and religious faith are inextricable, like a knot that cannot be untied. Moral philosophers, however, warn against relying on religious arguments in ethics. Some turn to Plato (ca. 428–327) for support, as his dialogue *Euthyphro* considers whether "right" can be understood as what the gods command or what is right in itself. Socrates reasoned that it would be contradictory to conclude that a god could make an action right by commanding it, if reasonable persons would otherwise judge the action to be wrong. Plato's resolution to the dilemma, which is expressed by Socrates, requires affirming that a god only commands what is right, which infers that we can know (and do) what is right without relying on any divine commands. This would mean religion is unnecessary for ethics.

Philosophers and theologians have debated this conclusion for centuries, but to do ethics we do not need to explain the issues that remain contentious. Instead, we proceed on the assumption that we need not agree on what God commands (or not) to apply various forms of ethical reasoning to environmental issues. In other words, we can rely on our reason, rather than on divine intervention, to reveal that human actions have created an environmental crisis requiring significant changes in our way of life.

This pragmatic approach, however, does not rule out considering religious arguments that draw reasonable inferences from divine commands for addressing ethical issues concerning our use of the natural environment. Therefore, in doing ethics I include religious arguments among the reasons given for living more responsibly within the earth's biosphere.

Plato assumed a dichotomy between divine commands and reasoning about the natural world that many today no longer find helpful. The history of moral philosophy is in large part a quest to create ways of reasoning that do not require choosing between an absolute form of knowledge of the good and a divinely ruled world that makes human ethical reasoning irrelevant.

In doing ethics we consider reasons for the limitations of our knowledge, as well as arguments for ascribing value to universal moral truths. We also take note of reasoning in the Jewish, Christian, and Islamic traditions that permits inferences about our duty to care for the earth. In addition, we draw on ethical arguments from cultures shaped largely by religious and philosophical traditions that revere a plurality of gods.

Moral philosophers are right to insist that ethical principles and decisions be justified by rational arguments, and this is why the study of ethics requires critical thinking. Relying on reason, however, does not mean that we should ignore all religious arguments, which have guided human reasoning for centuries and today inspire many persons of faith to live more sustainably.

Environmental Ethics

The discipline of environmental ethics took off in the 1970s, in response to the environmental movement protesting air and water pollution. Ethical arguments in support of laws to protect the environment initially emphasized the government's duty (moral and legal) to protect the public welfare. Scientific evidence that environmental pollution is a threat to human health was used to argue that taking action to clean up the environment was right.

A few activists, however, affirmed that reducing pollution and taking other actions to preserve the environment are justified simply because nature has moral worth, not because humans will benefit from conserving and preserving the environment. Blazing this trail meant diverging from the main path of moral philosophy, which has been characterized as anthropocentric (centered on humans). The dissidents relied on various adjectives (*biocentric, ecocentric,* and *holistic*) to distinguish their new nonanthropocentric ethics from traditional ethics.[17]

Those who defend anthropocentric ethics hold that only humans have value, so ethical decisions about nature only involve assessing human welfare. Our actions may adversely impact other organisms, but we have no duty to these organisms to mitigate these consequences. Proponents of nonanthropocentric ethics assert that nature has value for itself, which humans should recognize. In using natural resources for our own ends, therefore, we also have a duty to preserve the natural habitats of other organisms.[18]

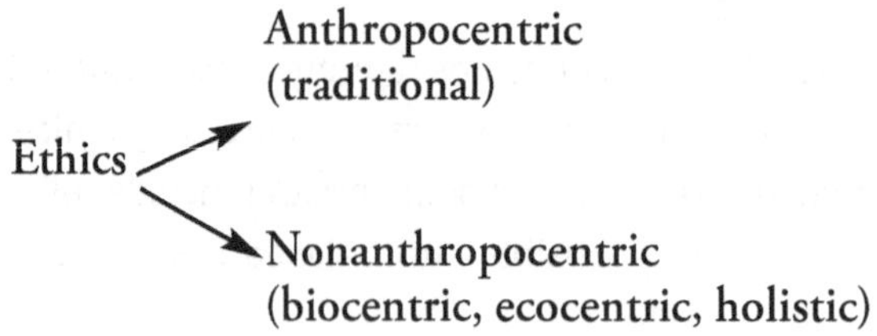

Anthropocentric
(traditional)

Ethics

Nonanthropocentric
(biocentric, ecocentric, holistic)

In traditional ethics our *moral community* consists only of persons. The argument for a duty of mutual respect, as well as the argument for the goal of personal and social happiness, presume a moral community that (at least potentially) includes all humans, but only humans. For example, the moral community for international human rights law includes every person, but only persons (as individuals, groups, and peoples).

In environmental ethics, however, nonanthropocentric advocates assert that our moral community also includes other organisms, endangered species, ecosystems, and even the entire biosphere. Chapter 2 considers this debate about the extent to which the rest of nature, in addition to human civilization, should be included in our *moral consideration*.

Environmental ethics is a hike you don't want to miss! Learning more about the paths (theories) of traditional ethics will help you appreciate this. So we do that next, to give you a sense of the terrain that lies ahead and a glimpse of the worldview that each path offers.

Learning from Diverse Theories

Conceiving of ethics as a mountain with many paths raises the question of which path to follow. In moral philosophy this is identified as the problem of *pluralism*. How are we to choose among ethical theories when each is supported by reasoning that makes sense to at least some moral philosophers? Three answers seem possible. First, one theory is right, and the others are wrong. Second, we can gain insights from every theory that has stood the test of time. Third, we have no way to know whether any of these ethical theories is right.

Continuing support for more than one theory is evidence that there is no way to prove to everyone's satisfaction that only one ethical theory is right. As long as reasonable people disagree, we should resist the temptation to defend one way of thinking against all the others. Therefore, I opt for the second answer and take a pluralist approach to ethics. I have learned from the varied traditions of moral philosophy and in part II will explain how we might draw on five patterns of moral reasoning to construct and test ethical presumptions.

Before doing this, however, I offer a brief argument about why we should reject the third answer, which is known as ethical relativism.

Ethical Relativism

If we are unable to know whether or not any view of ethics is right or wrong, it is difficult to avoid the conclusion that ethics is nothing but "different strokes for different folks." This would mean that what individuals think is right *is* right for them, and that this is true for every culture. Philosophers refer to these notions as *individual* and *cultural relativism*.

Many of us are relativists in the sense that we think people should be free to make their own moral choices as long as no one else is harmed. In law, this is reflected in property laws and the right of privacy. We may also argue, however, that some land use choices—such as watering your lawn when there is a drought, or clear-cutting forests on private land in a time when

DECISION 7.3 Learning by Doing

"Various philosophers have suggested ways in which our beliefs and standards could improve over time in spite of the fact that we are historically and culturally situated creatures. For example, John Dewey and others argue that our epistemic [knowledge] standards evolve in [the] trial-and-error process of inquiry itself. Others suggest that the criteria for rational change, even in science, sometimes involve things like problem-solving ability, rather than getting closer to the truth about some reality that is independent of our language and thought."

Explain how this statement affirms that our knowledge is limited but opposes "ethical relativism."

Source: Chris Swoyer, "Relativism," *The Stanford Encyclopedia of Philosophy* (Winter 2010), http://plato.stanford.edu/archives/win2010/entries/relativism/.

ecosystems need to be preserved to maintain the health and integrity of the biosphere—should be restrained by governments to protect the environment and promote the public good.

If you agree that your personal freedom should be limited in some way, even when your behavior poses no direct harm to others, you are not a moral relativist. You affirm that some actions are right or wrong, and that some ways of being are better than others.

Cultural relativism poses a more difficult question, as history and anthropology reveal that human cultures have evolved diverse ethical standards. Does this mean that ethical reasoning simply rationalizes the customs and values of a culture? To assess this claim, I suggest we assume that the answer is yes, and then consider the implications of this position.

If values are merely the customs of various cultures, this would mean that values are whatever the majority in a society believes is right. But if this were so, how could values change, as they obviously do? A change in cultural values begins with a minority arguing that some values are better than others, which would be unpersuasive if we really believed that all values are relative.

Changes in cultural values are evidence that experience and ideas have led many people to change their minds about what is right and good, or better. Cultures are not simply different games played by different rules, but instead reflect diverse patterns of reasoning that people modify as they experience alternative ways of living.

This argument against cultural relativism does not imply that it is reasonable to believe there is a single version of ethics, which every culture should accept. Nor does it prove the existence of universal or absolute values. As a discipline of thought, "Ethics has universal intent."[19] But as long as moral philosophers argue for different ethical theories, we should expect that cultures will continue to have diverse values.

Nonetheless, the nature of ethical reasoning presumes that some actions and ways of being are better than others. Moreover, the presumptions of international human rights law affirm that some actions, such as torture, are absolutely wrong, and other human rights, such as the presumption of innocence, are absolutely right—and that these rights should be universally enforced. The reasoning behind these claims is Western in origin, but has been affirmed within many cultures, which is evidence that our moral community is becoming global.[20]

Ethical Traditions

We begin our overview of the main traditions of thought in moral philosophy by noting an early fork in the path between teleological and deontological ethics.[21] The following discussion is limited to the Western tradition of moral philosophy, but part II considers teleological and deontological reasoning in indigenous traditions and in East and South Asian thought.

The word *teleological* comes from the Greek words *telos,* meaning purpose or goal, and *logos,* referring to science or study. Moral philosophers identify the ethical thinking of Aristotle (384–322 BCE) as teleological, because he argued that we discover our human nature and what it means to be good persons by discerning in nature that our purpose is to seek happiness and the civic virtues it requires. Thomas Aquinas (1225–1274 CE) adapted this view to a Christian perspective, and today this way of reasoning about ethics is known as the *natural law* tradition.

Five hundred years later—after Isaac Newton (1642–1727) proposed mathematical laws to explain nature (and thereby displaced its "purpose" with physics)—philosophers such as Jeremy Bentham (1748–1832) and John Stuart Mill (1806–1873) argued that ethics is simply doing what yields the greatest benefits. This form of reasoning (concerning utility, so it was identified as *utilitarian*) is also teleological, but in a different sense.

Philosophers in the natural law tradition hold that doing what is intrinsically right leads to happiness, whereas utilitarian philosophers (in what is now often called the *consequential* tradition of ethics) argue that actions resulting in greater happiness are "right" because they achieve the best possible results. These forms of teleological reasoning identify two of the main philosophical paths in moral reasoning.

A third way of reasoning is characterized as *deontological,* an adjective derived from the Greek word *deon,* meaning duty.[22] Immanuel Kant (1724–1804) argued persuasively for this tradition of moral philosophy. He asserted that human beings have the rational capacity to discern and do their duty, and he rejected consequential arguments that we should rely on the likely results of taking an action to determine what is right. Kant believed that we could act rationally with a good will, but accepted the view of Newtonian mechanics that overturned the science of Aristotle. Therefore, Kant believed it was irrational to look for any purpose in the laws of nature.

Ethics → Deontological → Right Action (Kant)
Ethics → Teleological → Being Good (Aristotle, Aquinas)
Teleological → Consequences (Bentham, Mill)

These three main traditions of moral reasoning are the context for doing environmental ethics.[23] Chapters 4 and 7 follow the deontological path to consider ethical arguments for duty and human rights. Chapters 5 and 6 pursue the teleological trek of being a good person, looking at issues of individual character and virtues and then at a concern for relationships and an ethics of care. Chapter 8 explores the teleological terrain along the well-traveled path of consequential ethics.

Doing Ethics Together

Our goal in doing ethics is to learn from diverse traditions of ethical reasoning how to bring our understanding closer to the truth that we cannot fully comprehend, as "*all* our reasoning extrapolates from limited experience."[24] To address environmental issues, we construct moral presumptions that we should act on, unless the likely consequences of doing so seem sufficiently adverse to justify revising a presumption or setting it aside.

Rule of Law

This approach to ethics involves reasoning by analogy to the rule of law. The rule of law is how we agree, as a society, to both disagree and aspire for greater agreement. The rule of law defines our society as a *moral community* by affirming ethical presumptions that should apply in creating and enforcing laws. Stated as two moral principles, the rule of law affirms that *no one is above the law* and *everyone is equal before the law.*

Ethical rules derived from these two principles are now asserted as human rights by international law, which affirms human rights as the necessary social conditions for human dignity. This means every person is included in the moral community defined by international human rights law. The conduct of governments and individuals often falls short of this high moral standard, but this fact does not make striving to enforce the rule of law any less important.

The rule of law provides an ethical framework for making public policy. It asserts ethical standards as legal presumptions, but also affirms that changing circumstances and new insights may lead to modifying some of these presumptions. The word *presumption* may only be familiar to most readers in legal phrases such as "the presumption of innocence" in criminal law, but this same meaning applies to doing ethics. What we take to be right or good is a presumption.

Reasoning by analogy, in doing ethics we rely on the same kinds of moral arguments that sustain the rule of law. We affirm that our moral community is defined by our moral presumptions and that those who challenge these presumptions bear the burden of explaining why some other action would be better. We assert that, "Ethics underpins law, criticizes it," and "becomes a guide to what law ought to be."[25] We resist rationalizations and strive to give reasons for doing our duty, acting with exemplary character, respecting and strengthening our relationships, and protecting rights.

Constructing Ethical Presumptions

Each chapter in part II explores how a pattern of ethical reasoning derived from the traditions of philosophy may help us define our moral community. Chapters 4–7 concern actions and ways of being that philosophers affirm have intrinsic worth and argue for revised presumptions that express these insights. Chapter 8 considers arguments that moral action involves doing whatever we think will result in the best consequences. In doing ethics, we rely on consequential reasoning to test presumptions affirming right actions and being good persons.

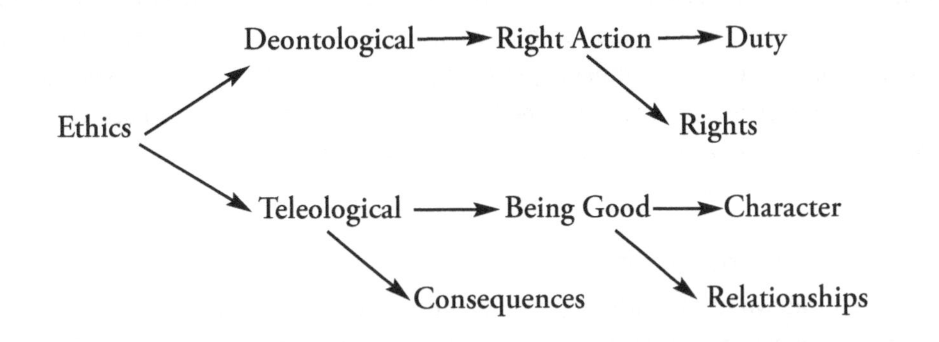

Chapter 4 assesses our *duty* to act on the basis of reason. Traditional deontological reasoning distinguishes between direct duties to persons and indirect duties that are implied by our moral duties to others. This means any duty we may have to the environment is by definition an indirect duty reflecting our actual duty to other persons. In environmental ethics, however, reasons have been given for affirming direct duties to nature. Now that science has confirmed the self-organizing character of every organism and ecosystem, might this analogy to human autonomy justify ascribing moral consideration to both?

Chapter 5 considers how individual *character* is relevant for ethics. Most moral philosophers who consider environmental issues rely on duty and consequential arguments to draw conclusions about human responsibility for nature. Yet there is a tradition of thought affirming that personal happiness, as well as a good and just society, can only be realized by good persons. Should environmental ethics encourage virtues such as integrity, gratitude, and frugality?

Chapter 6 argues that *caring relationships* should be at least as much the focus of moral philosophy as individual virtues generally have been. This concern is especially relevant for doing environmental ethics, because our cultural traditions have rationalized the abuse of women and nature. Might we now learn from nature and women how to live more ecologically?

Chapter 7 addresses deontological arguments about our duty to respect *rights*. Legal rights are supported by the secular argument that individuals have natural rights as autonomous and rational beings and by the religious affirmation that rights come from God. International human rights law affirms the right to social and economic development for every people and the right to a healthy environment for each person. Recent laws offer greater protection for animals, but generally do not grant them rights. How are we to resolve the moral and legal conflicts between protecting human rights and preserving endangered species and the earth's ecosystems?

In doing environmental ethics we explore these four patterns of reasoning to construct ethical presumptions about what we should do and the kind of persons we should be. These presumptions assert what we understand to be intrinsically right and good. We then use a fifth pattern of reasoning to test these ethical hypotheses by predicting the likely consequences of acting on them, to see if the possible or probable outcomes confirm or challenge our reasoning.

Most of us already think much like this, although we probably describe ethical presumptions as feelings or intuitions. We have a sense of what we believe to be right that is based on our experience, which we explain to others by referring to our feelings and the reasons that support these feelings. Also, we usually consider the likely consequences of acting on our sense of what is right, before we make a decision and carry it out. Doing ethics is a way of trying to clarify this reasoning about the moral choices we face.

Testing Ethical Presumptions

We test an ethical hypothesis (presumption) by predicting the likely consequences of acting on it. If we find evidence that seems to "falsify" our hypothesis,[26] we should take this into account. Evidence that seems to verify our presumption should be taken as supporting it.

As with the rule of law, some ethical presumptions may be stronger than others. For example, consider the presumption of innocence. To overturn this moral and legal presumption and find a person guilty of a crime, the law requires the state to present evidence that is beyond all reasonable doubt. In a civil lawsuit, however, the burden of proof on the party bringing the action requires showing only that the claim is supported by a preponderance of the evidence.

Reasoning by analogy, in doing ethics we may distinguish moral presumptions that require *compelling* adverse evidence to be set aside from those that may be set aside when the showing of adverse likely consequences is merely *convincing*. For example, an elected official should tell the truth about the threat of global warming, unless there is compelling evidence that the consequences of doing so are likely to be dire. Convincing evidence, however, that the consequences of telling the truth will likely be detrimental is all that is needed for an adult to justify setting aside the moral presumption to be completely truthful when a child asks, for example, if global warming will kill all the polar bears.

Because human rights are the social conditions necessary for human dignity, I argue that setting aside the moral presumptions affirmed by international human rights law requires compelling consequential arguments. Also, because the ecosystems of nature are necessary for sustaining all life on Earth, I argue that compelling evidence should be required to set aside our duty to protect the integrity of the earth's ecosystems.

Chapter 8 examines issues involved in predicting the likely consequences of acting on a moral presumption. Utilitarian reasoning and consequential arguments attack the use of deontological and teleological arguments by entrenched social elites to rationalize their power. Affirming that we should do whatever brings about the greatest good for the greatest number of persons has been an effective way of promoting political and economic freedom. Today consequential reasoning dominates environmental ethics.

Both natural science and social science utilize consequential methods of reasoning, and scientists and economists claim that their knowledge of the natural world is reliable. As these two disciplines of thought evolved from philosophy and now have an enormous impact on environmental decisions, the next two chapters consider the lessons we should learn from each.

Chapter 2 explains recent scientific arguments for the limits of our knowledge, the theory of evolution, and the discipline of ecology. It also considers the implications of current scientific research for ascribing moral consideration to nature. Chapter 3 argues that current economic theory and practice must be changed if economics is to fulfill its purpose of allocating resources for the common good.

QUESTIONS *(Always Explain Your Reasoning)*

1. Write a sentence using the words *right* and *good* that states an ethical principle. Would you characterize your statement as deontological, teleological, or consequential?
2. Provide three reasons why littering is unethical. Are any of these reasons religious? Deontological? Teleological? Consequential?
3. Use an analogy to defend an ethical presumption about the environment and assess the strength and relevance of the analogy.
4. Construct a presumption resolving a conflict of duties concerning the environment and predict the likely consequences of acting on this presumption.
5. Make a consequential argument for protecting national parks that avoids rationalizing.

Notes

1. The word *morality* comes from the Latin *mores*, which refers to custom. The *Stanford Encyclopedia of Philosophy* provides two meanings for morality. First, the word can be used to "refer to a code of conduct put forward by a society or some other group, such as a religion, or accepted by an individual for her own behavior." Second, morality may be used "normatively to refer to a code of conduct that, given specified conditions, would be put forward by all rational persons." http://plato.stanford.edu/entries/morality-definition.
2. "Ethics, or moral philosophy, asks basic questions about the good life, about what is better and worse, about whether there is any objective right and wrong, and how we know it if there is." Barbara MacKinnon, *Ethics: Theory and Contemporary Issues,* 3.

3 A thing has *intrinsic value* if it is valuable because of what it is in itself. Intrinsic value contrasts with *extrinsic* (or derivative) value, such as the *instrumental value* that things have because of their usefulness or because people are benefited through appreciating them. "[I]t is important to avoid the widespread confusions that misrepresent aesthetic value or even all non-instrumental values as intrinsic value." Robin Attfield, *Environmental Ethics: An Overview for the Twenty-First*, 12.

4 At http://www.merriam-webster.com/dictionary/right.

5 All these nouns may have slightly different meanings, depending on the context in which they are used, but I use them all to affirm the commonsense meaning for an ethical principle or moral standard.

6 At http://www.merriam-webster.com/dictionary/good.

7 Andrew Light and Holmes Rolston III, "Introduction: Ethics and Environmental Ethics," in Andrew Light and Holmes Rolston III, eds., *Environmental Ethics: An Anthology*, 3.

8 Sandra Blakeslee and Matthew Blakeslee, *The Body Has a Mind of Its Own: How Body Maps in Your Brain Help You Do (Almost) Everything Better*, 191. Research has "emphatically confirmed the network model of the brain as well as a long history of thought and metaphor. Reason and passion, thought and emotion, were indeed linked in a loop rather than stacked in a hierarchy. Neither stood as the other's slave. They engaged in a conversation that, to be healthy, had to be rich and balanced." David Dobbs, "Turning Off Depression," in Floyd E. Bloom, ed., *Best of the Brain from Scientific American*, 175.

9 The scientific method "changes and transforms its object." Werner Heisenberg, quoted in Jeffrey M. Schwartz, *The Mind and the Brain: Neuroplasticity and the Power of Mental Force*, 255.

10 Mary Midgley, *Animals and Why They Matter*, 43.

11 Benedict Carey, "Study Finds Brain Injury Changes Moral Judgment," *New York Times*, March 21, 2007, http://www.nytimes.com/2007/03/21/health/21cnd-brain.html. For the development of empathy and rational thinking, see Michael Schulman and Eva Mekler, *Bringing Up a Moral Child: A New Approach for Teaching Your Child to Be Kind, Just, and Responsible*, 8.

12 Evan Thompson, *Mind in Life: Biology, Phenomenology, and the Sciences of Mind*, 386.

13 Frans de Waal, quoted in Thompson, *Mind in Life*, 401.

14 Peter Singer, *Animal Liberation: A New Ethics for Our Treatment of Animals*, x.

15 At http://www.merriam-webster.com/dictionary/rationalize.

16 "Inference," *The Free Dictionary*, http://www.thefreedictionary.com/inference.

17 Aldo Leopold's land ethics and J. Baird Callicott's interpretation and articulation of this approach have been characterized as *holistic*. In the literature of contemporary moral philosophy, *ecocentric* ethics emphasizes ecosystems and ecology, whereas *biocentric* ethics is focused on individual animals.

18 Some moral philosophers have tried to reconcile these conceptions. "Although these ethics are generally considered to be polar opposites, in fact, I believe, both often make use of the same moral theory, namely, preference or 'interest' utilitarianism." Roger Paden, "Two Kinds of Preservationist Ethics," in Louis P. Pojman and Paul Pojman, eds., *Environmental Ethics: Readings in Theory and Application*, 209. See also James P. Sterba, "Environmental Justice: Reconciling Anthropocentric and Nonanthropocentric Ethics," in Pojman and Pojman, *Environmental Ethics*, 252.

COPYRIGHTED MATERIAL — DO NOT DUPLICATE, DISTRIBUTE, OR POST

19 Andrew Light and Holmes Rolston III, "Introduction: Ethics and Environmental Ethics," in Light and Rolston, *Environmental Ethics,* 5.

20 Chapters in part III offer evidence for this claim, as does Robert Traer in *Faith in Human Rights: Support in Religious Traditions for a Global Struggle.*

21 Teleological ethics refers to a theory of morality deriving duty or moral obligation from what is good or desirable as an end itself, opposed to deontological ethics, which holds that the standards for an action's being morally right are independent of the good or evil it generates.

22 "In contrast to consequentialist theories, deontological theories judge the morality of choices by criteria different than the states of affairs those choices bring about. Roughly speaking, deontologists of all stripes hold that some choices cannot be justified by their effects—that no matter how morally good their consequences, some choices are morally forbidden." "Deontological Ethics," *Stan-ford Encyclopedia of Philosophy,* http://plato.stanford.edu/entries/ethics-deontological.

23 Moral philosophers often identify social contract theory as a fourth main ethical approach. See James Rachels, *The Elements of Moral Philosophy,* 157–159. In his version of this theory John Rawls admits that "no account can be given of right conduct in regard to animals, and the rest of nature." *A Theory of Justice,* 512, quoted in Mary Midgley, "Duties Concerning Islands," *Encounter* 60 (1983): 36–43, reprinted in David Schmidtz and Elizabeth Willott, eds., *Environmental Ethics: What Really Matters, What Really Works,* 73.

24 Midgley, *Animals and Why They Matter,* 142.

25 Light and Rolston, "Introduction," 3.

26 Karl Popper uses this language in his writings about scientific reasoning. See Derek Stanesby, *Science, Reason and Religion.*

References

Attfield, Robin. *Environmental Ethics: An Overview for the Twenty-First Century* (Cambridge, UK: Polity Press, 2003).

Blakeslee, Sandra, and Matthew Blakeslee. *The Body Has a Mind of Its Own: How Body Maps in Your Brain Help You Do (Almost) Everything Better* (New York: Random House, 2007).

Bloom, Floyd E., ed. *Best of the Brain from Scientific American* (New York: Dana Press, 2007).

Light, Andrew, and Holmes Rolston III, eds. *Environmental Ethics: An Anthology* (Malden, MA: Blackwell Publishing, 2003).

MacKinnon, Barbara. *Ethics: Theory and Contemporary Issues,* 5th ed. (Belmont, CA: Thomson Wadsworth, 2007).

Midgley, Mary. *Animals and Why They Matter* (Athens: University of Georgia Press, 1983).

Pojman, Louis P., and Paul Pojman, eds. *Environmental Ethics: Readings in Theory and Application,* 5th ed. (Belmont, CA: Thomson Wadsworth, 2008).

Rachels, James. *The Elements of Moral Philosophy,* 4th ed. (New York: McGraw-Hill, 2003).

Rawls, John. *A Theory of Justice* (Cambridge, MA: Belknap Press of Harvard University Press, 1971).

Schmidtz, David, and Elizabeth Willott, eds. *Environmental Ethics: What Really Matters, What Really Works* (Oxford: Oxford University Press, 2002).

Schulman, Michael, and Eva Mekler. *Bringing Up a Moral Child: A New Approach for Teaching Your Child to Be Kind, Just, and Responsible* (Reading, MA: Addison-Wesley Publishing Company, 1985).

Schwartz, Jeffrey M. *The Mind and the Brain: Neuroplasticity and the Power of Mental Force* (New York: Regan Books, 2002).

Singer, Peter. *Animal Liberation: A New Ethics for Our Treatment of Animals* (New York: A New York Review Book, 1975).

Stanesby, Derek. *Science, Reason and Religion* (London: Croom Helm, 1985).

Thompson, Evan. *Mind in Life: Biology, Phenomenology, and the Sciences of Mind* (Cambridge, MA: Belknap Press of Harvard University Press, 2007).

Traer, Robert. *Faith in Human Rights: Support in Religious Traditions for a Global Struggle* (Washington, DC: Georgetown University Press, 1991).

An Act of Kindness

Thinking creates emotion, emotion creates behavior.

—Dianna Cunningham

Introduction

When I ask a group "What is kindness?" typically they describe acts of kindness or actions taken out of empathy and compassion such as smiling at someone as you walk by, words of encouragement, sending a thank-you message, volunteering at a hospital or soup kitchen, or being patient with someone.

From a psychological perspective, kindness is a reciprocal intrapersonal and interpersonal behavior and experience. Simply put, when we think kindly about ourselves, we tend to feel more positively about ourselves, and consequently our self-kindness increases (Field, 2017). When we think kindly toward another or others we are inclined to treat them with kindness; in so doing we generally think and feel more positively about ourselves (Simon-Thomas, 2008). This reciprocal intrapersonal and interpersonal experience of kindness is at the heart of prosocial behavior. Prosocialness is characterized by acts of helping, sharing, and comforting (Dunfield, 2014), in other words acts of kindness. To illustrate this, think about the acts of kindness mentioned in the opening paragraph. A smile and words of encouragement are helping and comforting. Thank-you messages share one's gratitude for the support and other gifts received from another. Volunteering is a way to lend help and comfort by sharing one's time and energy.

In Chapter 7 you were introduced to the six essential characteristics of an effective prosocial actor or sustainability agent. Recall that these characteristics were drawn directly from Seifert and colleagues, (2008) six outcomes of liberal arts education and that research in sustainability education revealed that these characteristics are in essence those demonstrated by effective sustainability agents (Chandler, 2014). Additionally, the six essential characteristics of the effective sustainability agent are the characteristics of individuals most likely to engage in acts of kindness. Therefore, it is clear that developing and understanding kindness and how to facilitate acts of kindness would be useful for encouraging sustainable behavior.

Theories and Concepts in Context of Sustainability

Study Figure 8.1 before reading how psychologists describe possible routes to and forms of kindness. Next review what was discussed in Chapter 3 "Who We are and Who We can Be" about Erikson's psychosocial stages of development and Kohlberg's types of moral reasoning. Now consider the relationship that these might have with kindness and by extension sustainability.

As you are reading the following descriptions of routes to and forms of kindness consider three things. First, morality and ethics neither ensure nor are necessarily related to acts of kindness. Second, the level of individual engagement (or agentic behavior) increases across the spectrum of routes to and forms of kindness from morals to altruism. Third, and keeping in mind the previous points, consider that research indicates a positive relationship between gratitude and kindness (Otake, Shimai, Tanaka-Matsumi, Otsui, & Fredrickson, 2006), as well as between gratitude and prosocial behavior (Bartlett & DeSteno, 2006; Grant & Gino, 2010).

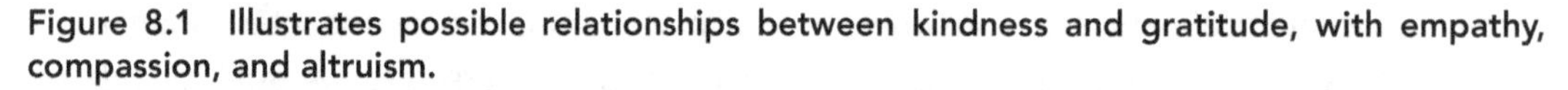

Figure 8.1 Illustrates possible relationships between kindness and gratitude, with empathy, compassion, and altruism.

Routes to and Forms of Kindness

Morals and Morality

A basic definition of morality is that it is the differentiation between beliefs or principals of right and wrong (i.e., morals). Tomasello and Vaish (2013) assert that "moral interactions are a subset of cooperative interactions" and that "the main function of morality is to regulate an individual's social interactions with others in the general direction of cooperation, given that all individuals are at least somewhat selfish" (p. 232). Morals and morality in some cases can facilitate kindness, for example an experience of sympathy, but this relationship is not as certain as you might think.

Ethics

While morals and ethics are often used interchangeably, these are considerably different constructs. Morals are personally held beliefs about right and wrong. Ethics on the other hand are a society's attempt to codify or prescribe moral behavior. The function of ethics is to establish a set of standards with which to guide or govern moral behavior.

Sympathy

Frans deWaal (2008), quoting Eisenberg (2000) defined sympathy as "an affective response that consists of feelings of sorrow or concern for a distressed or needy other (rather than sharing the emotion of the other—empathy). Sympathy is believed to involve an other-oriented, altruistic motivation" (p. 677). While sympathy does not involve sharing the other's emotional state it can give rise to empathic experience (Burton, 2015).

Empathy

Empathy is the experience of recognizing and sharing another's emotions (Burton, 2014). Jankowiak-Siuda, Rymarczyk, and Grabowska (2011) report that empathy has an automatic or "bottom up" component, as well as a deliberative or "top down" component. "Bottom up empathy is experienced via the mirroring representation systems that play a key role in the direct sharing of the emotional states of others" (Jankowiak-Siuda, Rymarczyk, Grabowska, 2011, p. 19). "Top down empathy known also as cognitive perspective-taking or theory of mind, occurs where the feelings of others are fully imagined and understood" (Jankowiak-Siuda, Rymarczyk, Grabowska, 2011, p. 20). Note that while individual engagement in empathy is higher than that of sympathy, the experience of empathy is not associated with action on behalf of the other.

Compassion

Compassion is associated with an active desire to alleviate the suffering of another (Burton, 2014). "With empathy, I share your emotions; with compassion I not only share your emotions but also elevate them into a universal and transcending experience. Compassion, which builds upon empathy, is one of the main motivators of altruism" (Burton, 2015, p. 3.)

Altruism

A general definition of altruism is an action taken on behalf of another or others even if the action has a cost or places the actor at risk. Frans deWaal (2008) presented three types of altruism: *directed altruism,* which is helping or comforting behavior directed at an individual in need, pain, or distress; *intentional altruism,* where the helper deliberately seeks to benefit the person being helped (intentionally altruistic altruism) or to benefit themselves (intentionally selfish altruism); and *empathy-based altruism*, where help and care are born from empathy with another.

About the Feature Article

As you read Newman and Erber's chapter *Prosocial Behavior and Altruism* first think about the relationship between gratitude, kindness, and prosocial behavior. Now consider the effect that acts of kindness might have had on your sustainability inclination. Finally, how would you employ kindness toward increasing sustainability inclination among your peers?

References

Bartlett, M. Y., & DeSteno, D. (2006). Gratitude and prosocial behavior: Helping when it costs you. *Psychological Science, 17*(4), 319–325.

Burton, N. (2015). Empathy vs sympathy. *Psychology Today. https://www. Psychology Today. com/blog/hide-and-seek/201505/empathy-vs-sympathy.*

Chandler, R. (2014). *I am the paradigm shift: A grounded theory of learners' sustainability outcome comprehension experience.* Ann Arbor, MI: ProQuest.

De Waal, F. B. (2008). Putting the altruism back into altruism: the evolution of empathy. *Annu. Rev. Psychol., 59,* 279–300. doi: 10.1146/annurev.psych.59.103006.093625

Dunfield, K. A. (2014). A construct divided: Prosocial behavior as helping, sharing, and comforting subtypes. *Frontiers in Psychology, 5,* 958.

Field, P. (2017). Researched-based reasons to be kind. *Huff Post.* Retrieved from https://www.huffpost.com/entry/kindness-research_b_7054652

Grant, A. M., & Gino, F. (2010). A little thanks goes a long way: Explaining why gratitude expressions motivate prosocial behavior. *Journal of personality and social psychology, 98*(6), 946.

Jankowiak-Siuda, K., Rymarczyk, K., & Grabowska, A. (2011). How we empathize with others: A neurobiological perspective. *Medical Science Monitor: International Medical Journal of Experimental and Clinical Research, 17*(1), RA18.

Otake, K., Shimai, S., Tanaka-Matsumi, J., Otsui, K., & Fredrickson, B. L. (2006). Happy people become happier through kindness: A counting kindnesses intervention. *Journal of happiness studies, 7*(3), 361–375.

Seifert, T., Goodman, K., Lindsay, Jorgensen, J. D., Wolniak, G, Pascarella, E., & Blaich, C. (2008). The effects of liberal arts experiences on liberal arts outcomes. *Research in Higher Education, 49(2),* 107–125. doi:10.1007/s11162-007-9070-7

Simon-Thomas, E. (2008). The cooperative instinct. *Greater Good Magazine.* Retrieved from https://greatergood.berkeley.edu/article/item/the_cooperative_instinc

Tomasello, M., & Vaish, A. (2013). Origins of human cooperation and morality. *Annual review of psychology, 64,* 231–255.

COPYRIGHTED MATERIAL — DO NOT DUPLICATE, DISTRIBUTE, OR POST

READING 9

Prosocial Behavior and Altruism

Leonard Newman and Ralph Erber

The Morning of a Busy Day

Ana knew she had a busy day ahead of her that morning as she watched the Weather Channel and munched on her Corn Pops. Her recent promotion by the ad agency had given her new responsibilities for a long-standing client known to have deep pockets. That client's ad proposal absolutely had to be done by the end of the week. The deadline made her somewhat anxious, but at the same time it excited her. The boost in her salary would allow her to replace that old Chevy her father had handed down to her when she was a college sophomore. It had served its purpose, dragging the laundry to and from her parents' house, but recently some ominous clanking sounds suggested it was time to look for a new car.

What Ana didn't know was that throughout the day, she would be busy fielding numerous requests for help, and at the end of the day, she would be asking for help from someone else. It all began with a pitch for donations that aired just before the local forecast. The short, commercial-length video showed the devastation a massive tornado had caused to the small town of Joplin, Missouri. Video footage of entire neighborhoods with completely destroyed homes alternated with images of the disaster's human toll. One particularly powerful photo showed a father embracing his son amidst a pile of rubble that used to be their home. And the narrator of the story was none other than Jim Cantore, Ana's favorite Weather Channel broadcaster, who asked viewers to make a donation to help the victims. Just ten dollars could go a long way, he said. Ana wanted make a donation right away, but looking at her watch, she realized she was running late. So she scribbled down the toll-free number and resolved to call it from the office during her lunch break.

COPYRIGHTED MATERIAL — DO NOT DUPLICATE, DISTRIBUTE, OR POST

The material and human toll of the Joplin, Mo. tornado.

For most social animals, humans included, helping others and receiving help are part of daily life. At times, we help others without being asked, such as when we slow down to let a fellow driver change lanes. At other times, we help in response to a specific request, agreeing, for example, to take notes for a fellow student or responding to a charitable appeal with a donation. On rare occasions, circumstances may require heroic effort from us, at considerable risk to our well-being. Although on the surface these responses may appear quite different, all ultimately benefit others. Indeed, that is the essence of prosocial behavior. In this chapter, we will look at the nature of prosocial behavior, asking two questions that have intrigued social psychologists: Why do people help? and why do people fail to help?

The Nature of Prosocial Behavior

Prosocial behavior refers to a broad category of actions intended to benefit others in socially defined ways (Piliavin, Dovidio, Gaertner, & Clark, 1981). This seemingly simple definition clarifies the nature of prosocial behavior in several ways. First, prosocial behavior is necessarily *interpersonal*, involving an interaction between a benefactor and one or more beneficiaries. Second, for a behavior to be prosocial, it must be *intentional*. If we slow down intentionally to enable a fellow motorist to change lanes, we are acting in a prosocial manner. If we slow down to change the radio station, we may accomplish the same thing, but the outcome is not the result of intentional, prosocial behavior. Third, to qualify as prosocial behavior, the act must benefit *others* more than ourselves. Interpersonal exchanges from which both parties benefit equally aren't really prosocial.

Finally, what benefits others is *socially defined*. That is, by and large, the social context defines which acts are prosocial and which are not. Years ago, before the dangers of smoking were well known, giving a stranger a cigarette would in all likelihood have been seen as a prosocial act. Today, however, that same act may not be seen as prosocial, because of the obvious drawbacks of smoking. Similarly, we don't generally think of relentless criticism as a form of prosocial behavior. However, to a student who is trying to get a paper published, offering the strongest criticism possible may well be a prosocial act.

The term *prosocial behavior* is sometimes used interchangeably with *helping* and *altruism*. These three terms are quite different, however. *Prosocial behavior* is an umbrella term that includes cooperation, helping, and altruism. This chapter focuses on helping and altruism.

Helping

Helping may be defined as any action that provides some benefit to or improves the well-being of another person (Schroeder, Penner, Dovidio, & Piliavin, 1995). It can be classified in three different ways (Pearce & Amato, 1980). First, helping can be seen as either spontaneous and informal (for example, holding the door for a fellow student), or planned and formal (say, making

SOCIAL PSYCHOLOGY AND HEALTH: THE STRESS-BUFFERING EFFECTS OF SOCIAL SUPPORT

Close others form a social network that can provide psychological and material resources to an individual who is coping with stress (Cohen, 2004). Social support provides three specific types of resources (House & Kahn, 1985). *Instrumental support* is material aid such as financial assistance or help with daily tasks. *Informational support* is advice and guidance on how to cope with one's problems. *Emotional support* includes empathy, caring, reassurance, and trust, along with opportunities for emotional expression. The lack of such social support can impede a person's ability to cope with a stressful event, promoting negative coping mechanisms such as smoking, drinking, and drug use (Cohen, Kessler, & Gordon, 1995).

Does that mean our ability to cope with stress increases with the *amount* of social support we receive? Not necessarily. A review of the extensive literature on social support and stress (Cohen & Wills, 1985) concludes that the mere *perception* that support is available tends to buffer the effects of stress, even if support is available from only a single source. In other words, simply knowing that social support is there when we need it can help us to cope with a stressful event. Unsurprisingly, the type of support that is available also matters. If we're suffering from romantic problems, for example, an offer of money will do little to help. At the same time, if we can't pay our bills, emotional support in the form of a shoulder to cry on will not get us very far.

a sizable charitable donation). Second, helping can be categorized according to the relative seriousness of the situation (for example, giving someone directions versus giving first aid to an accident victim). Third, helping can be seen as having indirect benefits (for example, a donation to a charitable fund) or direct benefits (perhaps the donation of spare change to a homeless person).

A slightly different classification scheme emerged when McGuire (1994) asked college students to list the kinds of help they had given to and received from others. Students' responses suggested four different kinds of helping. *Casual helping* includes small favors, such as lending someone change for the copy machine. *Substantial personal helping* involves considerably more effort—for example, helping a friend to move. *Emotional helping* includes social support given to a friend with personal problems. (See the Social Psychology and Health box above for some specific benefits of social support.) Finally, *emergency helping* includes assistance to a stranger with a severe emergency, such as an accident victim.

Regardless of how we classify helping, it is prosocial to the extent that it is intended to benefit another. Getting something in return matters very little. For the benefactor, the benefits of helping can be relatively small—for example, gratitude from the beneficiary, a good feeling about oneself, or the avoidance of guilt for not helping. Or they can be more tangible, such as receiving a picture of the child who benefits from one's donation. As long as the help is offered with the intent of benefiting another, it constitutes a prosocial act, regardless of whether it also benefits the helper.

Altruism

Altruism is characterized by the lack of any expectation that helping will bring external rewards (Macauley & Berkowitz, 1970). Because of the emphasis on expected or anticipated rewards rather than actual benefits, this definition is unrestrictive. That is, helping that has unexpected or incidental benefits would still by definition be considered altruistic. Defining altruism in this way makes sense. For example, the meaning of returning a lost wallet to its rightful owner changes, depending on whether or not we expect a finder's fee.

What about the less tangible rewards of helping? If you find yourself feeling good after helping someone in an emergency, does that make your act less altruistic than it would be if you had no (unexpected) good feelings? Some scholars (e.g., Krebs, 1982) have argued that helping isn't truly altruistic unless it comes at a cost to the helper. The self-sacrifice criterion puts a strong emphasis on the consequences of helping to the benefactor. That is, helping is not truly altruistic unless the cost to the helper outweighs any possible benefits. From this perspective, instances of helping that are truly altruistic are extremely rare.

Altruism implies helping others without expecting benefits for the self.

Others (Batson, 1991) have argued that whether or not a prosocial act can be considered altruistic should be defined not by the *consequences* to the helper, but by the helper's *motivation* for the act. From this perspective, help provided to ease a victim's suffering would be considered altruistic. Help provided with the expectation of some type of reward, or to avoid feeling guilty, would be considered prosocial because of its benefits to the victim, but it would not be considered altruistic because it is rooted in ultimately selfish motives.

Why Do People Help?

Serena Calls

It was only noon, but Ana's day at work had been far busier than she had imagined. To make matters worse, much of what she had to deal with had very little to do with work. Soon after arriving, she called Steve, the systems manager, to ask for a different e-mail account. Ana had always received more than her share of spam, but when she opened her e-mail today, it was out of control. Her feminist sensibilities were outraged by the multiple e-mails offering "male enhancement" and the avalanche of solicitations from adult websites. Steve had promised to get back to her ASAP, but he was living up to his reputation as a snail.

Serena, her older sister, had called to find out if Ana could babysit so she could go to a doctor's appointment that evening. Ana was reluctant at first because it meant leaving work early. Then again, it was her sister asking; how could she decline? And then at 10 A.M., Vicki, Ana's best friend, called to say she wanted to have lunch with her that day. Ana had planned to get a salad from the grocery store across the street, but Vicky was persistent, mentioning "boy problems," so Ana gave in. She checked her watch and realized she might have time to call that 800 number to make a donation toward hurricane relief. Before she could retrieve the piece of paper from her cluttered purse, however, Vicki arrived and motioned toward the door.

Ana put down the paper, grabbed her purse and coat, and accompanied Vicki down what she thought must be the slowest elevator in Chicago. At least it gave her time to convince Vicki they should go to the deli nearby rather than the Mexican restaurant on the river. As the two were about to cross the street, they were approached by a homeless person selling copies of *Streetwise*, a weekly publication meant to provide benefactors of the homeless with something in return for their money. Without breaking stride, Ana extracted a dollar bill from her purse and handed it to him as she grabbed the latest copy of the newspaper.

Prosocial Behavior as Egoism

To ask why people help each other may strike some of us as strange. After all, helping is the right thing to do, as prescribed by the norm of social responsibility or the idea that people are responsible for one another's welfare (Berkowitz, 1972). Yet philosophers from Socrates to Hobbes have espoused a view of human nature in which individuals are motivated first and foremost by self-interest. This view suggests that people comply with the norm of social responsibility primarily when doing so serves their self-interest. Not surprisingly, evolutionary psychology provides ample evidence that a great deal of prosocial behavior is indeed motivated by egoism.

Evolutionary Psychology I: Kin Selection and Helping

In evolutionary psychology, helping is explained through the principle of **inclusive fitness** (Hamilton, 1964). According to this principle, humans have a vested interest in preserving their genetic material, not only in their own offspring, but in the offspring of genetically related relatives. Consequently, they are more likely to help relatives than strangers and more likely to help close relatives than distant ones.

To illustrate this point, imagine that you've just arrived home for a family celebration, only to find your house engulfed in flames. Many of your relatives made it out of the house safely, but four people are trapped: your younger brother, your brother's son, your cousin, and the son of an acquaintance. These four are not beyond rescue, but they are scattered around the house, and the fire is burning with such a vengeance that you will be lucky to save just one, even if you act without hesitating. Who will you attempt to save first?

Burnstein, Crandall, and Kitayama (1994) presented scenarios like this one to a large number of American and Japanese undergraduates. Like them, you would probably opt to save your younger brother first, your brother's son second, your cousin third, and the son of an acquaintance last. The reason is simple and entirely compatible with the principle of inclusive fitness: you share 50 percent of your genetic material with your brother, but only 25 percent with his son, 12.5 percent with your cousin, and none with the son of a mere acquaintance. Consequently, saving your brother provides the best chance of your genes surviving into future generations—especially if you yourself don't survive your heroic actions. Interestingly, the results were similar when participants made decisions about helping that did not involve life-or-death consequences. This finding suggests that the tendency to help closely related kin first may be a generalized response that evolved in reaction to evolutionary pressures. As with most human behaviors that are rooted in evolutionary history, it does not require purposeful thought, but is executed outside of conscious awareness.

According to the evolutionary perspective on helping, we are particularly likely to help those who share our genes.

Using a similar methodology, Burnstein et al. (1995) identified some additional variables that support the evolutionary explanation of helping, particularly the imperative to save women and children first. They found that in a life-or-death scenario, participants were generally more willing to help females than males—but only to a point. As predicted by the principle of inclusive fitness, women lost their advantage when they reached the age of diminished reproductive potential. In general, the willingness of participants to help closely related others decreased as a function of the victims' age and declined at a particularly steep rate past the age of diminished reproductive capacity. With more mundane kinds of help, the decrease in helping as a function of age reversed as the other approached old age.

The favorable prejudice toward the young was so pervasive that participants were generally more willing to help their three-day-old brother than their 10- or 18-year-old brother, even though the latter was closer to the reproductive age. This general tendency prevailed primarily in environments that posed little threat to an infant's life, however. In situations marked by high infant mortality, participants showed a decreased tendency to rescue an infant brother, and an increased tendency to help a brother close to reproductive age.

One could argue that findings like those from Burnstein et al. (1995) are limited in value because they represent responses to hypothetical scenarios, rather than actual situations. However, the results of two studies of real-world helping suggest that the principle of inclusive fitness does figure prominently in people's responses to emergencies. Sime (1983) reported that survivors of a fire at a vacation complex were more likely, once they became aware of the fire, to search for relatives than for friends. And Laube (1985) found that emergency workers who were called on to help during a natural disaster reported to duty only after they had made sure their families were safe. Finally, the proclivity to help kin is not unique to humans; it is commonplace in the animal world as well (see Batson, 1995). Because the tendency to preserve inclusive fitness is innate and requires little in the way of higher-order cognitive processing, it can be considered a hidden influence on helping behavior.

Evolutionary Psychology II: Indirect Reciprocity and the Adaptive Value of Following Social Norms

Returning to our opening story, the principle of inclusive fitness can explain why Ana was willing to help her sister, even at considerable cost to herself. Although the situation was not a life-or-death matter, contributing to the welfare of her sister's offspring would ultimately contribute to her own inclusive fitness. However, inclusive fitness does not explain why Ana helped the homeless man, because helping him would provide no genetic benefit to her.

Why did Ana help the homeless man, then? More generally, why do we help others who are not genetically related to us? Evolutionary psychology offers two perspectives. The first is based on the idea of reciprocity (Axelrod, 1984; Trivers, 1971). If we help others, they become willing and available to reciprocate later. So Ana may not have helped the homeless man primarily to get something tangible in return (that is, the newspaper). Rather, she may have done so because he might be able to assist her in the future in some way. Helping based on the principle of **indirect reciprocity** (Alexander, 1987) is particularly likely when the benefit to the recipient exceeds the cost to the helper and when the helper and recipient recognize each other and are likely to interact in the future.

Of course, neither inclusive fitness nor indirect reciprocity can account for the anonymous help from strangers that is commonplace among humans, and at times can be dramatic. Less than two weeks after Hurricane Katrina devastated New Orleans and much of the Gulf Coast in September 2005, charitable relief organizations received pledges totaling $500 million. Only a fraction of them came from big donors like the Rolling Stones and the National Football League; most came from small donors—high school students who washed cars and grade-school children who sold bracelets to benefit the victims. Nine-year-old Johnny Wilson, who swam from Alcatraz to San Francisco's Aquatic Park, single-handedly raised $30,000.

Why do people help strangers, even when there is little chance of reciprocity and possibly a risk to their own inclusive fitness (when, for example, their heroic actions jeopardize their own well-being)? Evolutionary psychology suggests that the adaptive value of following societal and cultural norms can explain such behaviors. In general, those who follow societal norms are better off than those who ignore or defy them (Simon, 1990). Because humans tend to live together and are highly interdependent, cooperation and mutual responsibility for the welfare of others is paramount for a social group to function optimally and compete for resources with other groups (Tomasello et al., 2012). Consequently, most societies reward those who comply with social norms and punish those who do not (Cosmides, 1989). Because such rewards and punishments often operate outside of conscious awareness, they may serve as a hidden influence on people's willingness to help.

Societal mechanisms that promote help for strangers are complemented by two processes that operate on the individual level. McGuire (2003) identified an important cognitive bias that comes into play when people assess the perceived cost of helping to the benefactor, as well as the value of help to the beneficiary. Specifically, people show a modesty bias in estimating the cost of the help they provide relative to the help they receive. In other words, helpers tend to downplay both the cost of their actions to themselves and the benefits to the recipient. Beneficiaries, on the other hand, tend to overestimate the value of the help they receive. Although the modesty bias may sound counterintuitive, taking an "it was nothing" view of the perceived cost and value of our help ultimately promotes future helping, because it leaves us feeling chronically short in our attempts to be socially responsible.

Although the evolutionary account of helping is not without its critics (for example, Wood & Eagly, 2002), it is intriguing for a couple of reasons. First, because humans have acquired their propensity to help through evolutionary history, the processes that lead to their decisions to help generally operate outside of conscious awareness. For example, the decision to save your younger brother before you save your brother's son does not require a conscious calculation of relative fitness gains. Instead, the action occurs more or less automatically because evolution has rendered it the optimally adaptive response. The evolutionary account suggests that ultimately, every prosocial act arises from egoism. Help that is provided to genetically related others raises the odds that one's genes will survive into future generations. Help that is provided to strangers may result in reciprocal aid in the future, but even without reciprocal gains, helpers are rewarded through the many positive consequences of complying with social norms.

For the benefactor, these benefits of helping have two features in common. First, the gains often materialize over the long term. Inclusive fitness gains, for example, generally do not manifest themselves for generations. Other benefits of helping—such as reciprocal aid and rewards for complying with social norms—are likewise postponed. Second, the benefits of helping are far from certain. Saving your younger brother from a burning house at the cost of your own life will provide inclusive fitness gains, only to the extent that he survives future threats to his reproductive ability. Similarly, though doing someone a favor increases the *likelihood* that the person will return it in the future, there is no guarantee. And though society looks more kindly on those who comply with social norms, it also teaches us—at least occasionally—that no good deed goes unpunished. As we will see, however, helping has a number of benefits that are fairly immediate and certain.

Why Do People Help?: A Summary

Prosocial behavior is generally defined as behavior that is intended to benefit another. Helping, however, has been classified in different ways. One classification differentiates help in terms of its spontaneity, the seriousness of the situation, and the benefits, whether direct or indirect. Another scheme differentiates among casual helping, substantial personal helping, emotional helping, and emergency helping. Altruism is a form of prosocial behavior that is offered without expectation of a reward.

The evolutionary perspective on prosocial behavior suggests that all helping is selfishly motivated. According to the principle of inclusive fitness, humans have a vested interest in preserving their genetic material. Consequently, they are more likely to help others to whom they are closely related, particularly in life-or-death situations. Prosocial behavior that is intended to benefit strangers is explained on the basis of indirect reciprocity. When there is little or no chance that the beneficiary of help will reciprocate, people still help in order to comply with prevailing social norms because their compliance has adaptive value.

Think Like a Social Psychologist

Making Connections

Critics of the evolutionary approach to helping often cite alternative explanations. In that regard, how can the distinction between communal and exchange relationships, discussed in Chapter 10, be used to account for the human tendency to save family members rather than strangers from a fire? What other plausible explanations, not based on the concept of inclusive fitness, can you think of?

Prosocial Behavior as Mood Management

Helping has consequences for the way we feel. Although the modesty bias shown by McGuire (2003) suggests that we downplay the cost, helping nonetheless makes us feel good, and refusing to help often makes us feel bad. At the same time, the way we are feeling has consequences for our willingness to help others.

Protecting Good Moods

Imagine that your psychology instructor has just returned your first test. Much to your surprise, you did far better than you had expected. You leave the class with a sense of accomplishment and a feeling of elation. As you head for the exit, you see a fellow student slip on the stairs. He appears to be unharmed, but the fall has dislodged his backpack and spilled its contents all over the staircase. How likely are you to stop and help him gather his belongings? More specifically, will the good feelings that you experienced from doing so well on your test increase the odds that you will help? Research on the effect of good moods on helping suggests that the answer is an unqualified "yes" (Isen & Levin, 1972).

Good moods promote helping because they make us focus on the benefits of helping and the good in other people. They also promote helping because it preserves good moods.

What is it about a good mood that makes people more likely to help? A meta-analytic review that compared a large number of studies (Carlson, Charlin, & Miller, 1988) indicates that good moods promote helping through three mechanisms. First, people who are in a good mood tend to see the world through the proverbial rose-colored glasses (Clark & Isen, 1982), which allow them to see the benefits of helping more than the costs (Clark & Waddell, 1983) and the good in other people more than the bad (Isen, Shalker, Clark, & Karp. 1978). Second, helping is a good way to maintain or even enhance a good mood because of its positive consequences for the benefactor (Carlson, Charlin, & Miller, 1988; Isen & Levin, 1972). At a minimum, when we help someone in need, we can feel good for having done the right thing. We may also receive gratitude from the beneficiary. Both those outcomes can prolong a good mood. Not surprisingly, it helps when the appeal for help is positive (Cunningham, Steinberg, & Grev, 1980), and it hurts when the act of helping involves an unpleasant task (Isen & Simmonds, 1978).

Finally, even when helping is unpleasant, refusing to help could have disastrous consequences for a good mood. We may be haunted by thoughts of what we should have done, and we may feel bad for not helping, especially when the cost of doing so was small. Thus, a good mood may vanish with the cognitive and affective consequences of not helping.

Relieving Bad Moods

If good moods promote helping, do bad moods discourage it? Let's return to the example of the unfortunate student who has lost the contents of his backpack after slipping on the stairs. This time, however, imagine that you are in a bad mood because you performed much worse on the test than you had expected. Will you stop to help the student gather his belongings? As it turns out, research on the effects of a bad mood on helping suggests that the answer is again an unqualified "yes" (e.g., Carlson & Miller, 1987; Cialdini, Darby, & Vincent, 1973). How can that be?

Because helping can be a positive, mood-enhancing experience, people who are in a bad mood often engage in prosocial activities to make themselves feel better. According to the **negative state relief model** (Cialdini, Kenrick, & Baumann, 1982; Schaller & Cialdini, 1988), that is especially true for people who are experiencing sadness or guilt (Baumeister, Stillwell, & Heatherton, 1994; Cialdini, Darby, & Vincent, 1973).

In a clever test of the hypothesis that sadness and guilt would promote helping, Cialdini, Darby, and Vincent (1973) made some participants feel guilty by leading them to believe they had accidentally ruined a graduate student's research data. Other participants were made to feel sad by seeing the experimenter ruin the student's data. All participants then completed a task that required them to track a maze. Half the participants in the guilt and sadness conditions received praise for their performance; the other half received no praise. Then all participants were asked if they were willing to help another student, who was not part of the experiment, with a class project. **Figure 8.2** shows the effect of these experimental conditions on the dependent variable (willingness to help another student).

The results indicate that when participants who were feeling guilty or sad and received no praise for their performance on the maze-tracking task, they were quite willing to help the imaginary "other student." However, when participants' moods were alleviated by the praise they received for their performance, their willingness to help the other student dropped dramatically. In other words, participants looked at helping as a means to rid themselves of their guilt or sadness. The increased willingness to help observed among participants who are in a bad mood hinges on the extent to which other means of relief are available to them. Merely anticipating

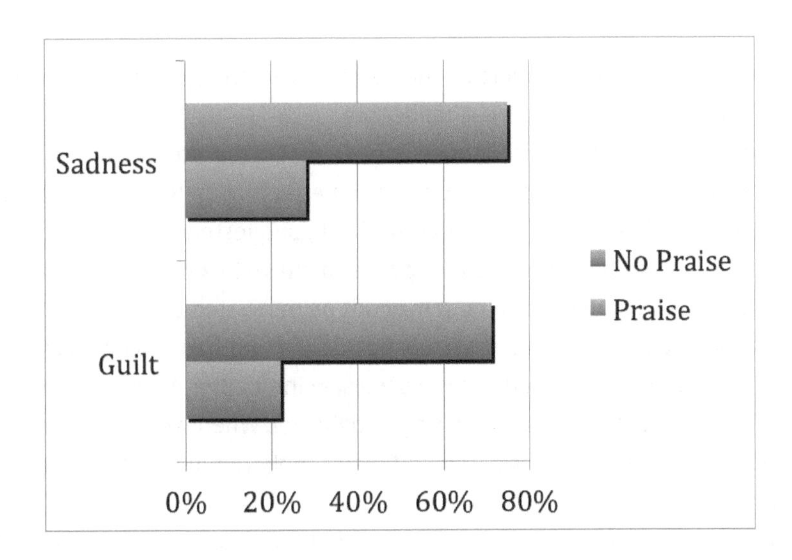

Figure 8.2 Willingness to help as a result of mood and guilt.

Source: Cialdini, R.B., Darby, B.L., & Vincent, J.E. (1973). Transgression and altruism: A case for hedonism. *Journal of Experimental Social Psychology*, 9, 502–516.

that one's mood will improve is often enough to reduce the willingness to help to levels more characteristic of those who are not in a bad mood. For example, Schaller and Cialdini (1988) found that sad participants who expected to watch a funny video helped less than sad participants who expected to watch a video described as not funny.

Our heightened willingness to help as a result of being in a bad mood also depends on the extent to which we believe that helping will in fact improve our mood. At times, we may feel so bad that we can think of absolutely nothing we could do to make ourselves feel better. Evidence that such extreme moods do not promote helping comes from a clever experiment in which researchers convinced some participants that their moods could not be changed (Manucia, Baumann, & Cialdini, 1984). In this study, all participants swallowed a pill that they believed was a fast-acting memory drug. It was, of course, a placebo that allowed the experimenters to "inform" participants of its effects. Half the participants were led to believe that the drug would freeze any mood they were experiencing and prolong it for 30 minutes. The rest of the participants were told that the drug would have no effect on their moods. Some participants then recalled and wrote about a sad event in their lives, while others wrote about an event that was not sad. Once they had completed their writing, all participants were given an opportunity to help another student with a project.

The results of this experiment supported the negative state relief model in two ways. First, participants who felt sad and believed that the pill had no side effects were more willing to help than participants who were in a neutral mood. Presumably, they expected helping to improve their mood. Second, sad participants who believed that the pill had frozen their mood—and that helping therefore would not improve their sadness—were less willing to help than sad participants, who believed their mood was malleable.

Although the negative state relief model is well supported empirically, it is not without critics. Citing a paucity of research demonstrating the effects of helping on mood, Carlson and colleagues (Carlson & Miller, 1987; Carlson et al., 1988) suggested that sad people's increased willingness to help may not be motivated by a desire to alleviate a negative mood. Furthermore, happy people's increased willingness to help may not be motivated by a desire to preserve their good mood. Instead, the researchers suggested, both good and bad moods may have an effect on helping, because both promote self-focus. As we saw in Chapter 4, directing attention to the self increases the salience of internal standards of behavior. When we encounter someone who is in need of help, being in a good or bad mood may simply remind us that offering to help is the right thing to do.

Researchers may differ on whether moods affect helping because people want to maintain or improve them, or because they make helping-related standards salient. However, there is little controversy that moods do promote helping. Still, understanding the link between mood and helping is important, because the two competing explanations have vastly different implications. If happy people help in order to maintain their mood and guilty people help in order to improve it, both groups are motivated ultimately by self-interest. If they help because of a heightened self-focus, then their motivation is not an issue.

Managing Emotions Related to an Emergency

The negative state relief model is concerned primarily with the effects of moods that exist independently of an emergency requiring help. However, seeing another who is in need of help can by itself cause a strong emotional reaction among those in a position to help. Ana's distress in response to Jim Cantore's appeal on behalf of victims of the Joplin tornado is a case in point. According to the **arousal/cost-reward model** of helping (Dovidio, Piliavin, Gaertner, Schroeder, & Clark, 1991; Piliavin, Dovidio, Gaertner, & Clark, 1981), her decision to take action may have been motivated partly by a desire to relieve her distress at the plight of the mother and child. More generally, the arousal/cost-reward model proposes that the decision to help is determined by the level of negative emotional arousal experienced by a witness to an emergency, along with a consideration of the cost of helping to the witness and the cost of not helping to the victim.

How much arousal a witness experiences depends to some extent on the severity of the emergency (Dovidio, 1984), but is also influenced by the victim's characteristics and the nature of the relationship between the victim and the witness. For example, the plight of an attractive victim and of victims we feel connected to psychologically elicit especially high levels of arousal, so those victims are most likely to receive our help (Piliavin et al., 1981). At the same time, witnesses are less likely to help when they attribute their arousal to something other than the emergency. Gaertner and Dovidio (1977) led some participants in a study to believe that any arousal they felt might be due to ingesting a pill with arousing side effects. When those

According to the arousal/cost-reward model of helping, the motivation to help stems from a desire to relieve the distress experienced at the plight of the children.

participants later encountered what appeared to be an accident involving another student, slightly more than half of them offered to help. Among participants who had not been informed about the arousing side effects of the pill, 85 percent helped. Thus, though the level of arousal is clearly important to helping behavior, the perception that the arousal stems from the emergency is equally important.

How do costs and rewards interact with arousal to predict helping? Not surprisingly, as the cost to the helper increases, helping decreases (Dovidio, 1984). That is particularly true when the act of helping is more unpleasant than the arousal produced by the emergency (Piliavin & Piliavin, 1972). At the same time, helping increases as the personal cost of not helping increases, because the victim might die as a result of our inaction (Dovidio et al., 1991). On the surface, this finding may suggest that helping is the result of a conscious, deliberate cost-benefit analysis by the helper. However, the strong arousal that is commonly felt by witnesses to an emergency often renders the decision to help automatic and spontaneous, thus serving as a hidden influence on helping. That would explain acts of heroic helping, including those displayed by participants in a study by Clark and Word (1974), who rushed to the help of a victim who was apparently being electrocuted. If participants had consciously thought about the consequences of touching the victim (almost certain death), few would have helped.

Of course, one could argue that the participants who risked their lives to save a fellow student from electrocution were motivated by something other than the selfish desire to relieve their distress. In fact, as we will see next, in many instances, people do help primarily out of a concern for the welfare of others.

Prosocial Behavior as Mood Management: A Summary

Models of helping that are based on the emotional antecedents and consequences of helping also suggest that helping is selfishly motivated. Both good moods and bad moods appear to increase helping. According to the mood management hypothesis, people who are happy help in order to maintain their happiness. People who are in a bad mood, such as sadness or guilt, help in order to make themselves feel better. An alternative hypothesis is that the relationship between mood and helping results from a heightened focus on the self brought on by a happy or sad mood. Presumably, a heightened focus on the self renders salient internal standards for behavior. The arousal/cost-reward model of helping explains helping in severe emergencies in terms of the emotional distress a witness experiences, the perceived cost of helping to the self, and the perceived cost of not helping to the victim.

Think Like a Social Psychologist

Thinking Critically

According to the mood management hypothesis, people who are feeling sad help others in order to make themselves feel better. To the extent that they consider the possible consequences of not helping, what related concern may motivate helping among people in a sad mood?

Designing Research

What kind of experiment would allow you to decide whether increased helping as a result of a happy or sad mood results from mood management or self-focus? What conditions would you need to include? What pattern of results would support the different explanations?

Prosocial Behavior as Altruism

Trying to Make the Call

By the time Ana arrived at her sister's apartment on Chicago's West Side, the irritation she felt when her sister asked her to babysit had waned. Instead, she felt exasperated by the horrendous rush-hour traffic and the difficulty of finding a parking space that wouldn't require her to walk several blocks. To make matters worse, the ominous clanking sounds from her car seemed to have gotten louder as she crawled from one light to the next. As much as she tried to convince herself that it was a product of her imagination, there was no denying that it sounded a lot worse than it had in the morning.

Fortunately, Serena was in a good mood and visibly grateful that Ana had come to her aid. Ana appreciated the chance to spend some time with her nephew, who was equally happy to see her, even though he was suffering from a cold and soon fell asleep on her shoulder. After putting the baby in his crib, Ana wandered into the kitchen to get something to eat. She and

Vicki had talked a lot over lunch, and had not had time to finish their sandwiches. But the kitchen cupboards didn't offer anything that appealed to her; Serena appeared to subsist entirely on diet soda and Tostitos. With nothing else to do, Ana straightened out the kitchen and washed a few dishes left in the sink before settling down on the couch with the day's newspaper.

As had been the case for days, the front page was once again devoted to the Joplin tornado. It featured the story of M. "Dean" Wells, the floor manager of the local Home Depot. As 200 mph tornado winds bore down, he ordered customers and employees to the back of the store. Hearing frantic knocking at the doors, he rushed to the front of the store to let another dozen people in. They all survived, but Dean Wells was killed when a wall collapsed on him. The story brought the Weather Channel's appeal back to Ana's mind. Remembering that she had meant to call that 800 number, she pulled her cell phone and the slip of paper from her purse. Before she could finish dialing the number, however, a noise from the nursery signaled that the baby's nap was over. He was awake, and he wasn't happy.

Was Ana's inclination to aid the victims of the Joplin tornado selfishly motivated? Probably not; none of the victims was genetically related to her. And because she felt neither particularly happy nor sad, helping them likely would not have changed her mood. Most important, the victims' plight didn't cause her emotional distress so much as it moved her. That is, Ana felt *empathy* for the victims.

According to Batson (1991, 2002), **empathy**—or helping that is designed purely to benefit another who is in need—lies at the heart of altruism. Empathy promotes helping for two reasons. First, it involves taking another's perspective (Davis, 1994; Krebs & Russell, 1981). Cognitively, we put ourselves in the shoes of the victim. Second, in doing so, we vicariously experience the victim's distress (Davis, 1994; Eisenberg & Miller, 1987). This combination of perspective taking and vicarious experience of distress produces empathic concern, a state in which we feel compassion for the victim (Batson & Shaw, 1991).

According to this definition, prosocial behavior is altruistic whenever empathic concern is present. This kind of compassion is very different from the aversive empathic arousal in the arousal/cost-reward model, however. Empathic arousal is about the self; empathic concern is for the victim. Whereas helping that is motivated by a desire to relieve one's own distress ultimately benefits the helper (Hoffman, 1981), helping that is motivated by empathic concern always benefits the victim.

To test the idea that helping can result from altruistic empathy, Batson and his colleagues (Batson, 2002; Batson & Powell, 2003) developed an experimental procedure that allowed them to differentiate altruism from egoistic motivations. In one study (Batson, Duncan, Ackerman, Buckley, & Birch, 1981), they asked participants to watch a video in which "Elaine," a fellow participant, reacted badly to a series of uncomfortable electric shocks. Participants could then volunteer to take the remaining shocks in her place, under one of several different conditions. To induce empathic concern, the researchers told a subset of participants that Elaine was similar to them in her interests and values. Batson et al. also told some participants that if they didn't help, they would continue to watch Elaine take the remaining shocks. They told others that they would not have to watch further shocks.

Varying the ease with which participants could escape from the aversive situation in this way was of crucial importance to the experiment. It allowed the experimenters to disentangle the extent to which helping may have been due to aversive arousal reduction from the extent to which it may have been due to empathic concern. If participants helped primarily to reduce their own arousal, as the arousal/cost-reward model suggests, empathy would matter only when escape from the situation was difficult. To the extent that participants could easily reduce their arousal by escaping the situation, helping rates should be relatively low (see the top part of **Figure 8.3**). However, if participants helped in order to alleviate Elaine's suffering, as the empathy-altruism model suggests, then their empathy should lead to helping regardless of whether or not they could escape from the situation (see the bottom part of **Figure 8.3**).

AVERSIVE AROUSAL REDUCTION HYPOTHESIS		
	LOW EMPATHY	HIGH EMPATHY
Easy Escape	Low	Low
Difficult Escape	High	High
EMPATHY-ALTRUISM HYPOTHESIS		
	LOW EMPATHY	HIGH EMPATHY
Easy Escape	Low	High
Difficult Escape	High	High

Figure 8.3 Helping Rates Predicted by Two Different Hypotheses in the Empathy by Escape Design.

Adapted from Batson, D. (1995). "Prosocial motivation: Why do we help others?" In A. Tesser (Ed.), *Advanced Social Psychology*. New York: McGraw-Hill.

Results from several such experiments (for example, Batson, Duncan, Ackerman, Buckley, & Birch, 1981; Toi & Batson, 1982) consistently favor the empathy-altruism hypothesis. That is, when participants are made to feel empathy for Elaine, they volunteer to take the remaining shocks themselves, even if they could easily escape witnessing her continued suffering. Evidently, for empathically aroused participants, physical escape does not translate into psychological escape (Stocks, Lishner, & Decker, 2009). This finding runs counter to the aversive arousal reduction hypothesis, which does not explain why even participants who could easily avoid arousal still helped Elaine.

Using a similar experimental procedure, Batson and colleagues ruled out another hypothesis for the high rate of helping among those with an easy means of escape. According to this alternative explanation, the high rate of helping may have been due less to feelings of empathy than to egoistic concern about the consequences of *not* helping. The general idea is that failing to help often produces guilt and shame—emotions that may be further amplified by empathy for the victim. So the high rate of helping among participants who felt empathy for Elaine, yet could easily escape, may have been generated by a desire to avoid guilt and shame. If that were the case, participants should help less when they can rationalize not helping, on the basis that no one else is helping. However, when Batson and colleagues (Batson et al. 1988) tested that idea experimentally, they found that empathic participants who had such an excuse still helped as much as participants who didn't. Thus, there is good reason to believe that true altruism—helping others solely for their benefit—does indeed exist: We find it whenever empathy is present.

Proximal Altruism as Ultimate Egoism?

Although the evidence for the empathy-altruism hypothesis seems overwhelming, some (Kenrick, 1991; Krebs, 1991) have argued that even helping that is born of empathy may be selfishly motivated. Kenrick (1991) in particular suggestsed that the factors that cause empathy are rooted in shared heredity. In the laboratory, empathy is frequently induced by similarity or by specific instructions to take another's perspective (Batson, 1995). In real life, however, similarity is something that we share, especially with our kin. Moreover, we can assume that during the course of our evolutionary history, communication based on empathic concern occurred most frequently with those who were genetically similar to us. Consequently, our propensity toward empathy may have been rooted, at least initially, in selfish concerns with inclusive fitness.

Of course, it is difficult to see how the participants in Batson's studies could mistake Elaine for a genetic relative. Nevertheless, helping strangers out of empathic concern may be a generalized, ultimately egoistic response that was once highly adaptive and now serves as a hidden influence on our behavior (Cialdini, Brown, Lewis, Luce, & Neuberg, 1997). Alternatively, empathy may be an evolved mechanism that directs helping toward familiar others and those who previously cooperated with us (de Waal, 2008). The finding that empathy has a stronger effect on helping when the helper and victim belong to the same cultural group, rather than to different cultural groups (Stuermer, Snyder, Kropp, & Siem, 2006), further attests to empathy's adaptive value.

Attempting to interpret what appears to be altruistic helping as a selfish behavior may strike some readers as odd or even misplaced. It flies in the face of countless cases of heroic helping, in which individuals risked—or even lost—their own lives to save someone in need. Was the unknown hero who survived the crash of Air Florida flight number 90, only to lose his life saving fellow passengers from the icy waters of the Potomac River in January 1982, motivated by some kind of self-benefit (the *Washington Post*, 1982)? Did the firefighters and police officers who rushed into the burning towers of the World Trade Center on 9/11 act out of self-interest? Did the Dutch family that hid Anne Frank from the Nazis act out of selfishness?

All these cases seem to represent altruism in its purest form: Helping not only with no self-benefit, but at considerable risk to the self. Why, then, would social psychologists doubt that altruism exists? The problem is that social psychology has traditionally subscribed to the doctrine of **psychological hedonism** (Allport, 1954), which originated in the writings of philosopher Jeremy Bentham (1789, 1879). Bentham proposesd that humans act simply to gain pleasure or happiness (positive hedonism) or to avoid pain (negative hedonism). At times, a person can gain happiness by contributing to the welfare of others, but as Mill (1863) argued, the pursuit of one's own happiness is ultimately what motivates the help.

A great deal of research supports this cynical view of prosocial behavior (see Batson, 1987). Thus, Batson's assertion that altruism exists is subject to ongoing, and at times heated, debate (Batson et al., 1997; Cialdini et al., 1997). Much of the debate revolves around the question of whether the experience of empathy blurs the usual distinction between self and other. To the extent that the vicarious experience of what another is suffering results in the incorporation of the self in the other, helping that is induced by empathy could indeed benefit the self (Cialdini et al., 1997). Regardless of whether that is the case, there can be little doubt that taking another's perspective increases our willingness to help.

Empathy, Collectivism, and Group Identity

Helping out of self-interest or to benefit another are by no means the only motives for prosocial behavior. At times, we may be less concerned about our individual welfare or the welfare of a specific other because we are motivated by a collective interest in the groups to which we belong. Imagine that you have received a letter from your local public radio station, asking you to make a donation. The request creates a **social dilemma** for you. On the one hand, public radio benefits everyone, including you. On the other hand, the benefit to you is somewhat diminished if you must pay for it. The prosocial thing to do would be to "do your share" and donate a small amount of money. However, self-interest would compel you to keep your hard-earned dollars, in the hopes that others will donate enough to keep public radio on the air. That way, you can reap the benefits without incurring any costs.

How you respond to such social dilemmas depends on the extent to which you approach it with a **collective interest**—that is, concern for the welfare of the group to which you belong, rather than for your own self-interest. Dawes and his colleagues (Dawes, van de Kragt, & Orbell, 1990; Orbell, van de Kragt, & Dawes, 1988) conducted a series of experiments that demonstrated the conditions that arouse collective interest, as well as its effect on the choices people make in social dilemmas.

In one study, participants who had been recruited for a study on group decision making received $5, which they could either keep or give away with the prospect of receiving a $10 bonus in return. The experimenters varied the rules by which each participant did or did not receive the bonus. Some participants were led to believe that they would receive the $10 bonus if four or more participants *other than themselves* donated their $5. (This rule is called a *noncontingent rule*—that is, receiving the reward was not contingent on the participant donating his or her own money.) Other participants were led to believe that everyone in their group would receive the $10 bonus if five or more participants, *one of whom could be themselves*, were to donate their money. (This rule is called a *contingent rule*—that is, receiving the reward is contingent partly on whether participants donate their own money.) In addition to manipulating the conditions under which participants would receive the $10 reward, the experimenters instructed some, but not all, groups of participants to discuss their choices.

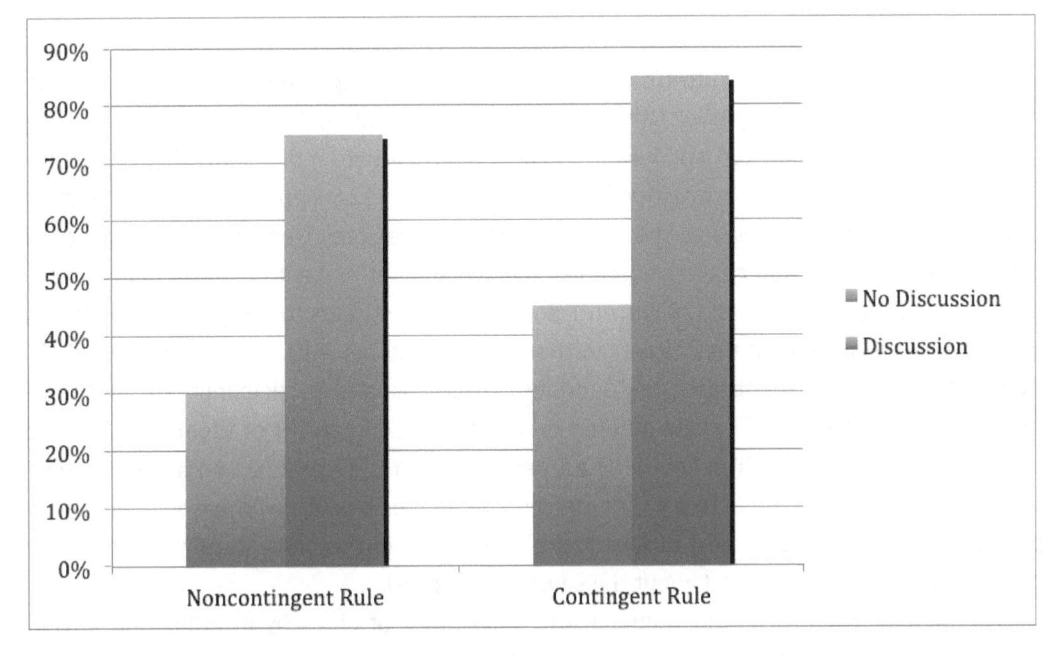

Figure 8.4 Effects of Rules and Discussion on Donation Rates.

Source: Dawes, van de Kragt, and Orbell (1990), Cooperation for the benefit of us—not me, or my conscience. In J. Mansbridge (Ed.), *Beyond self-interest* (pp. 97–110). Chicago, IL: The University of Chicago Press.

Figure 8.4 shows the results of this experiment. In the absence of any discussion, a higher percentage of participants who thought that receiving the reward was contingent on their own donations (45 percent) donated their $5 than participants who thought it was not contingent (30 percent). Interestingly, discussion increased participants' willingness to donate in both conditions (85 percent and 75 percent, respectively). Presumably, the discussions aroused a sense of collective interest that prompted even those who could have gained the most by holding on to their money to donate it to the group.

Additional experiments using a similar methodology indicate that prosocial behavior stemming from a collective interest is limited to the specific groups to which we belong. When asked to donate money to another group (for example, the one doing the experiment across the hall), participants were once again guided primarily by self-interest (Orbell, van de Kragt, & Dawes, 1988). This finding points to the importance of group identity in the development and influence of collective interest. The more we identify with a group, the more we are willing to act to benefit the group, even if doing so may result in a personal loss. At the same time, the more we identify with a group, the less willing we are to sacrifice for groups to which we don't belong.

We have already seen that empathy can supersede self-interest. How does empathy interact with collective interest? What happens when self-interest, collective interest, and empathy conflict? To answer this question, Batson et al. (1995) presented participants with a social dilemma that forced them to divide raffle tickets among themselves, their group, and another individual (Jenny or Mike), who happened to be the victim of a romantic breakup. Some participants received this news with the instruction to treat Jenny or Mike objectively, without getting caught up in how he or she felt (low empathy). Others were instructed to imagine how Jenny or Mike might feel as a result of the breakup, and how it had affected their lives individually (high empathy).

In the absence of such instructions, most participants (62.5 percent) allocated half their tickets to themselves and half to the group, suggesting that they were motivated by a combination of self-interest and collective interest. A much smaller percentage of participants acted purely in the collective interest (20 percent), donating all the tickets to the group, or in their own self-interest, by keeping all their tickets to themselves (12.5 percent). A mere 5 percent divided their tickets between themselves and Jennifer or Mike. Among participants who did receive instructions, the division of tickets differed dramatically: 37.5 percent of them wanted to split the tickets with Jenny or Mike. Another 32.5 percent based their decision on a combination of self-interest and collective interest. The percentage of participants who based their decision purely on the collective interest dropped to 15 percent, and the percentage who kept all the tickets to themselves remained about the same (15 percent).

The findings from this study reinforce the importance of empathy in predicting prosocial behavior. As we have seen, self-interest and collective interest are important motives for prosocial behavior. Under the right circumstances, collective interest trumps self-interest, but empathy trumps both. Interestingly, though the empathy-altruism link has been demonstrated primarily with individual victims, there is some evidence that it operates on the group level as well (Penner & Finkelstein, 1998). In one study of AIDS volunteers (Stuermer, Snyder, & Omoto, 2005), researchers found that empathy was a stronger predictor of helping when the victim belonged to an in-group. Among gay and lesbian AIDS volunteers for whom the victim was part of the in-group, empathy was the strongest predictor of helping. Among heterosexual volunteers for whom the victim was part of an out-group, helping was determined primarily by the victim's level of attractiveness.

Just how does empathy promote altruistic helping? It appears that people high in empathic concern or induced to feel empathy help, not so much because they perceive pressure from others or fear disapproval for not helping. They primarily help because they consider it an important choice that is consistent with their personal values and life goals (Pavey, Greitemeyer, & Sparks, 2012).

Are There Gender and Age Differences in Altruism?

The stereotype of the social role of females holds that women are more empathic than men. Research suggests that this stereotype may hold a kernel of truth. Numerous studies have shown women to respond with more empathy, using a variety of subjective and self-report measures, than men (Eisenberg & Lennon, 1983; Lennon & Eisenberg, 1987; Martin & Clark, 1982). Research further shows that this gender difference reflects differences in motivation rather than ability (Eisenberg & Lennon, 1983; Ickes, Gesn, & Graham, 2005).

To the extent that altruism depends on empathy, one would expect that women should also be the more helpful gender. However, by one measure, men seem to have the edge. Since 1904, the Carnegie Hero Fund Commission has awarded recognition to heroes who voluntarily risked their lives trying to save the life of another. As of 2003, 91 percent of those who received medals for their heroism were men (Becker & Eagly, 2004), even though Andrew Carnegie, the commission's founder, had left explicit instructions to not discriminate against women.

Before you conclude from these statistics that men are more altruistic than women, consider that Carnegie Hero Medals are typically awarded for acts of helping such as saving others from fires, drowning, animal attacks, electrocution, suffocation, and assaults by criminals (Wooster, 2000). Because such emergencies require immediate, physical intervention, they are more typical of men (Becker & Eagly, 2004). When one considers acts of heroism that require more sustained helping, women are the more helpful gender in many cases. Women were overrepresented among those who rescued Jews from the Nazi Holocaust, and women are more likely than men to donate a kidney or volunteer for the Peace Corps (Becker & Eagly, 2004).

How can we explain the gender differences in empathy-based altruistic helping? The finding that men are more likely to provide immediate help while women are more likely to provide sustained help fit well with a social role account (Eagly & Crowley, 1986) that emphasizes the different norms underlying the male and female gender roles.

Men are supposed to be risk takers and adventurous; women are supposed to be nurturant and caring. However, the observation that gender differences in empathy are evident in infancy (Martin & Clark, 1982) suggests that there may also be innate differences in the mechanisms underlying the experience of empathy among men and women.

In support of this speculation, fMRI studies of neural activity in the human brain suggest that empathy at the sight of another's pain can be divided into an early automatic emotional sharing component and a late cognitive evaluation process (Gu & Han, 2007). Although women and men show no differences in the automatic sharing component of empathy, women show more neural activity than men in the late cognitive evaluation process (Han, Fan, & Mao, 2008). However, it is not clear whether these differences necessarily translate into differences in helping. One study (Boeckler, Tusche, & Singer, 2016) suggests that while women describe themselves as more prosocial than men, they often behave less prosocially!

Age also matters when it comes to empathy-based altruism. Both seem to peak late in life. Sze et al. (2011) had groups of young adults (age 20–30), middle-aged adults (age 40–50) and older adults (age 60–80) watch videos of individuals in need. In addition, they were given an opportunity to make a monetary contribution to charities supporting these individuals. They found that the size of the contribution increased with age in a linear fashion: Young adults contributed the least, older adults the most. This finding resonates nicely with developmental models that indicate that generativity is a key component to successful aging (Erikson, 1982).

THINK LIKE A SOCIAL PSYCHOLOGIST: ADVENTURES IN RANDOM ASSIGNMENT

Bill Scholar, professor of psychology at Hats off to Science University, decides to conduct a study of the effects of priming of the positive emotional consequences of helping on rates of helping. He conducts the experiment with the help of the students in the two sections of his social psychology class. Bill delivers identical lectures in his day class, which meets on Tuesdays and Thursdays at 10 and his night class on Wednesday evening, except that he sprinkles his lecture to the day students with anecdotes about people who felt better after helping someone. (Bill flipped a coin to decide which section he would prime for helping.) At the end of both classes, he explains that he needs help with an experiment, and asks students to come to his lab on Friday afternoon. The percentage of students who show up from each section will be the dependent variable.

At the assigned time, almost 60 percent of the students from the day class visit Bill's lab, along with a little more than a third of the night students. Bill concludes that his experiment has failed, because the students in his day class were probably more helpful to begin with. What aspect of his method does not warrant his conclusion?

The answer is that Professor Scholar randomly assigned the two sections to the conditions of his experiment when he should have randomly assigned *individual* participants. The problem is that the two sections, or groups, may differ importantly in ways that could well affect the outcome of the experiment. In all likelihood, many of the evening students may have day jobs, which could prevent them from taking time off, especially on short notice. The lesson to be learned from this example is that in collecting experimental data, true random assignment should always take precedence over convenience.

Prosocial Behavior as Altruism: A Summary

According to Batson and colleagues, altruism—helping with no benefit to the self—is related to empathy. When a victim's plight triggers empathic concern, people will help, even if they can escape from the situation and/or they can justify not helping. Although the empathy-altruism model has garnered considerable empirical support, some researchers claim that what appears to be altruistic helping may ultimately be caused by selfish motives. For example, the variables that trigger empathy may arise from genetic relatedness. Others have argued that empathy blurs the distinction between the self and the other. Thus, any action that benefits the other ultimately benefits the self.

In a social dilemma, collective interest can lead to helping that benefits the group at the expense of self-interest. Under conditions that elicit empathy for a single member of a group, however, helping based on empathy replaces helping for the common good.

Gender differences in the experience of empathy compel men toward altruistic helping that is immediate and compel women toward altruistic behavior that is more sustained. Although these differences can be explained in terms of the norms underlying the male and female gender role, there is also evidence of an innate component. The finding that older adults show increased empathy-based altruism is explained by a developmental focus on generativity.

Think Like a Social Psychologist

Thinking Critically

According to one view, the variables that trigger empathy may also provide cues to genetic relatedness. Can you make an argument for why this relationship may, in fact, be maladaptive?

Making Connections

The doctrine of psychological hedonism holds that all human behavior, prosocial behavior included, is ultimately motivated by selfishness or egoism. To the extent that it is difficult to identify behavior that is not hedonistically motivated, what does that say about the doctrine's value as a basis for hypotheses about why people help?

Why Do People Fail to Help?

The Long Way Home

It was well past 7 P.M. when Ana drove home that day. Not unexpectedly, Serena had had to wait longer than expected at the doctor's office. When she finally returned, the two had chatted for a while and discussed their plans for Thanksgiving.

Traffic on the Eisenhower Expressway should have been light, since it was well past rush hour. However, a light but steady rain had settled over the city, just as the Weather Channel had predicted. The rain slowed traffic to a crawl. Ordinarily, Ana wouldn't have minded, because she considered traffic hassles a relatively minor price to pay for living in a great city. Tonight, though, she was tired and hungry, and quite anxious about the noise emanating from her car's engine.

SOCIAL PSYCHOLOGY AND THE LAW: CAN PROSOCIAL BEHAVIOR BE LEGISLATED?

Good Samaritan laws exist in many countries, including Japan, France, Germany, and Spain. Most of them require citizens to assist people in distress, unless doing so would cause harm to themselves. In Germany, failure to provide assistance in an emergency is a criminal offense. Citizens are obliged to provide first aid when necessary and are immune from prosecution if the assistance they provide in good faith turns out to be harmful.

In the United States, Good Samaritan laws protect those who help the injured or ill from blame. The intention is to reduce bystanders' hesitation or unwillingness to help, for fear of causing unintentional injury or wrongful death. Laws vary from state to state. Most, like the one in Illinois, exempt helpers from prosecution or liability in the event their actions cause unintended harm. Some, like Minnesota's law, declare a "duty to assist" in an emergency:

> A person at the scene of an emergency who knows that another person is exposed to or has suffered grave physical harm shall, to the extent that the person can do so without danger or peril to self or others, give reasonable assistance to the exposed person. Reasonable assistance may include obtaining or attempting to obtain aid from law enforcement or medical personnel. A person who violates this subdivision is guilty of a petty misdemeanor.

How effective are Good Samaritan laws in promoting help during an emergency? There is no clear answer to this question. The photographers at the scene of Princess Diana's car accident were investigated for violating France's Good Samaritan law, though they were later exonerated. Evidently, the law did not compel them to do the right thing. As we will see, failure to provide assistance often has little to do with the fear of prosecution (Latane & Darley, 1970). Consequently, Good Samaritan laws are probably less effective than legislators might think.

Figure 8.5 Helping in an Emergency: Five Necessary Decisions.

Source: Latane, B., & Darley, J.M. (1970). *The unresponsive bystander: Why doesn't he help?* New York: Apple-Century-Croft.

Just as she was about to exhort the old Chevy to get her home one last time, the engine sputtered and refused to turn over. As it took its last gasps, Ana pulled over to the shoulder. On impulse, she reached for her cell phone, only to realize that the battery was dead. Briefly, she entertained the idea of getting out of the car to wave down a fellow motorist, but the rain and the spray from passing cars discouraged her. Ana slumped down in the driver's seat, hoping someone would eventually stop to help her. Gazing out the driver's side window at the steady flow of cars, she figured it wouldn't be long.

Ana may have been unduly optimistic about her chances of getting help. Consider the circumstances that led to the death of Princess Diana on August 30, 1997. Trying to shake a group of rapacious papparazzi, her driver had crashed the car into a concrete pillar at high speed. The impact of the crash killed her fiancé, Dodi Fayed, and left Diana gravely injured. The papparazzi, who had followed closely, immediately pulled over and began snapping photos of the dying princess. Their apparent callousness caused an international uproar, prompting renewed calls for a Good Samaritan law that would make withholding help from the victim of an emergency a crime punishable by law (see the Social Psychology and the Law box on **page 229**).

Failure to help is not always the result of callousness. Consider an incident that took place more than 30 years before Princess Diana's death. During the early morning hours of March 13, 1964, Catherine (Kitty) Genovese was stabbed to death by an unknown assailant as she returned to her apartment in Queens, New York. A brief report of her murder appeared in the *Long Island Press* that same day. Two weeks later, a more grizzly account of the circumstances under which she died appeared on the front page of the *New York Times*. According to that account, Kitty died slowly. She was stabbed repeatedly over a period of about 30 minutes, while screaming for help and pleading for her life. Her cries were so loud that 38 of her neighbors rose from their beds to watch her die. Not a single one picked up the phone to call the police. Although the veracity of this part of the story has since been questioned (Manning, Levine, & Collins, 2007), it received widespread attention at the time. Some (for example, Rosenthal, 1964) suggested that the bystanders' inaction was brought on by callousness, or complete—and perhaps uniquely urban—disregard for the welfare of others. Rosenthal's (1964 account of the incident provoked a landmark research program (Latane & Darley, 1970) into the reasons why people often fail to help others in emergencies.

Latane and Darley (1970) reasoned that attributing the causes of inaction to bystanders' dispositions does not sufficiently explain **bystander apathy**. Instead, these researchers proposed that we must look at the situation from the bystander's perspective. Their cognitive model of helping suggests that before bystanders can offer assistance, they must make a series of sequential decisions (as shown in **Figure 8.5**). An incorrect decision at any point during this sequence will result in the failure to help (Latane & Darley, 1970).

Noticing the Event

Failure to help often is not the result of apathy, callousness, or disregard for the welfare of others. Instead, potential helpers frequently do not recognize an event as an emergency, particularly when they are in a hurry or otherwise distracted. In our opening story, although Ana hoped that one of the many passing motorists would pull over to offer assistance, the circumstances of her emergency suggested otherwise. It was dark and rainy. The traffic was making everyone late, feeling they were in a rush. Some drivers were undoubtedly talking on their cell phones, conducting business or telling their families they would be late for dinner. As a result, many drivers simply may not have noticed her car parked on the shoulder.

Most passersby will probably notice this man soliciting money, but whether they will offer assistance depends on whether they interpret his situation as an emergency.

Evidence for this speculation comes from an experiment in which participants were asked to walk to another building across campus and deliver a speech (Darley & Batson, 1973). Some participants expected to speak about the kinds of jobs they preferred; others expected to talk about the parable of the Good Samaritan. In addition, some participants were told they were running late and would have to hurry. Others were led to believe they were on schedule for their appointments. A third group believed they were running ahead of schedule.

On the way to their appointments, all participants came across a confederate of the experimenters, who was slumped in a doorway, acting as though he was in distress. The experimenters were interested in the percentage of participants who would stop to help the confederate under the different experimental conditions. As expected, whether or not participants stopped to help depended primarily on whether they were in a rush. Sixty-three percent of those who believed they were running ahead of schedule and had ample time to make their appointments offered to help. Forty-five percent of those who believed they were on schedule stopped to help. Among those who were in a rush because they were running behind, however, only 10 percent stopped to offer assistance.

MISTAKEN AS PRANK, BODY LEFT HANGING

Associated Press

FREDERICA, Del.—The presumed suicide of a woman found hanging from a tree went unreported for hours because passersby thought the body was a Halloween decoration, authorities said.

The 42-year-old woman used rope to hang herself across the street from some homes on a moderately busy road late Tuesday or early Wednesday, Delaware state police said.

The body, suspended about 15 feet above the ground, could be seen easily from passing vehicles.

State police spokesman Cpl. Jeff Oldham and neighbors said people noticed the body at breakfast time Wednesday but dismissed it as a holiday prank. Authorities were called to the scene about three hours later.

"They thought it was a Halloween decoration," Fay Glanden, wife of Mayor William Glanden, told the News Journal newspaper in Wilmington.

"It looked like something somebody would have rigged up," she said.

Whether participants expected to talk about jobs or the parable of the Good Samaritan made little difference to their rates of helping. When questioned at the end of the experiment, the majority of those who had rushed to their appointments indicated that they hadn't noticed the man slumped in the doorway. Ironically, the participants in this study were seminary students. Surely, if people who are training for a life of helping others—many of them with thoughts of helping on their minds—can fail to notice someone in distress, the power of distraction and time pressure must loom large.

Interpreting the Event as an Emergency

Noticing an event is necessary for helping to be offered, but by no means does it guarantee help. Once an event has been noticed, bystanders must still interpret it as an emergency. This is generally not an issue when the situation is clearly dangerous. In this case, people often rush to another's help as predicted by the arousal/cost-reward model, whether bystanders are present or not (Fisher et al., 2011). However, many situations carry some ambiguity as to whether they are real emergencies. The man slumped over in a doorway, coughing and groaning, may be in real need of assistance. Then again, he may only be sleeping off a drinking binge.

Ana's situation, too, was marked by ambiguity. From the perspective of passersby, the car on the shoulder may have held a motorist in distress. Then again, it may have been abandoned by its owner hours before. Frequently, the context in which an event is noticed contributes to the difficulties of recognizing it as an emergency, as the newspaper story in **Box 8.1** illustrates.

Two powerful contextual cues appear to have caused inaction among those who noticed the body dangling from the tree. First, on most days of the year, such a sight would be unexpected, and thus would alarm most passersby. Because the same sight is commonplace the week before Halloween, however, it takes on an entirely different meaning. Instead of being considered a potential emergency, it is seen as a decoration or a prank. Second, from the perspective of passersby, the apparent inaction of others who may have encountered the situation further complicated the matter. Those who may have been unsure about the dangling body may have concluded that it was a prank because if it had been an emergency, someone else would already have taken action. This phenomenon is known as **pluralistic ignorance**: because there is no evidence that others are concerned, we assume that nothing is wrong.

To demonstrate how pluralistic ignorance can shape the way people interpret an apparent emergency, Latane and Darley (1968) recruited participants for a study that required them to complete several questionnaires about their attitudes on a variety of issues. Some participants worked on the questionnaires by themselves; others, in the presence of two strangers. A third group worked in the presence of two confederates. As participants answered the questionnaires, the experimenters began to pump white smoke through a heating vent in the wall.

You may have guessed that the experimenters had little interest in the participants' responses to the questionnaires. Instead, they wanted to see how participants in the three experimental conditions would respond to the smoke. Would they continue marking their questionnaires, or would they leave the room to alert the experimenters? In most cases, smoke emanating from a heating vent signals a potential fire, but *white* smoke can indicate a more benign problem, such as condensation in the ventilation system. Of course, in light of such ambiguity, the safe thing to do would be to report the problem.

Because the presence of others diffuses responsibility for helping, having an automobile accident on a busy street reduces the chances that a motorist will receive assistance.

Most participants who worked on the questionnaires by themselves did just that: 50 percent of them went to see the experimenter within two minutes of noticing the smoke, and 75 percent did so within six minutes. However, when participants worked with two others, only 12 percent of them responded within two minutes, and 38 percent within six minutes. Some participants kept working, even when there was so much smoke in the room that they could barely see the questionnaires. Working with two confederates who acted unconcerned (for example, by shrugging their shoulders when participants made eye contact with them) did not reduce response rates much further. Evidently, subtle cues from others are sufficient to induce pluralistic ignorance. Although participants may have been worried about the smoke, realizing that neither of the other participants seemed concerned caused the majority of them to dismiss its importance.

Taking Responsibility for Helping

Pluralistic ignorance prevents helping because it prevents individuals from recognizing an event as an emergency. But what happens in situations that are not ambiguous? Does the presence of others promote or inhibit helping?

Kitty Genovese's murder suggests the latter answer. Remember that, by one account, it was witnessed by 38 neighbors, not a single one of whom did anything to help. Latane and Darley (1970) reasoned that their failure to take action was directly related to the number of bystanders. From their perspective, it was clear that others had noticed her screams as well. That recognition led to a **diffusion of responsibility**: Everyone thought that taking action was someone else's responsibility. This conclusion is unsettling, because it suggests that there is no safety in numbers. The more bystanders, the more responsibility can be diffused. Kitty Genovese's murder might have been prevented had it been witnessed by just two or three bystanders. Similarly, Ana's chances of getting help would be greater if her car had broken down on a street where traffic was light rather than on the busy expressway.

That the presence of others diffuses responsibility has been shown in numerous studies. In one particularly powerful demonstration, Latane and Darley (1968) asked participants to discuss personal issues related to their lives at the university. Participants sat in individual cubicles where they could not see one another. Ostensibly to avoid embarrassment to them, the discussion was held via intercom. Some participants were led to believe that the discussion took place with just one other student; others thought the discussion involved two others, and some believed it involved five others. In reality, there was only one participant in each discussion. The rest were prerecorded voices, and the "discussion" was rigged so that the participant was always the last to speak.

Early in the discussion, one of the "other participants" hesitantly volunteered that he was prone to seizures, especially during times of stress. As the discussion unfolded, it became clear that he was having a violent seizure, during which he repeatedly stated that he would die if he did not get help. The researchers recorded the percentage of participants who either tried to find him or alerted the experimenter to the problem. They also kept track of how long participants waited to intervene.

Figure 8.6 shows the results for the first measure. As expected, the number of bystanders affected the rate of helping. When participants believed they were having a discussion with just one other person, that person was necessarily the one having the seizure. Consequently, in that condition, participants were the only ones who could help. There was no possibility that their responsibility to take action could be diffused. Not surprisingly, 85 percent of the participants responded within 60 seconds in this condition. The remainder did so within two and a half minutes.

When participants believed there was one other participant who conceivably could intervene, only 62 percent helped within 60 seconds. Although the percentage increased to just over 80 percent within two and a half minutes, it never reached the 100 percent mark. When participants

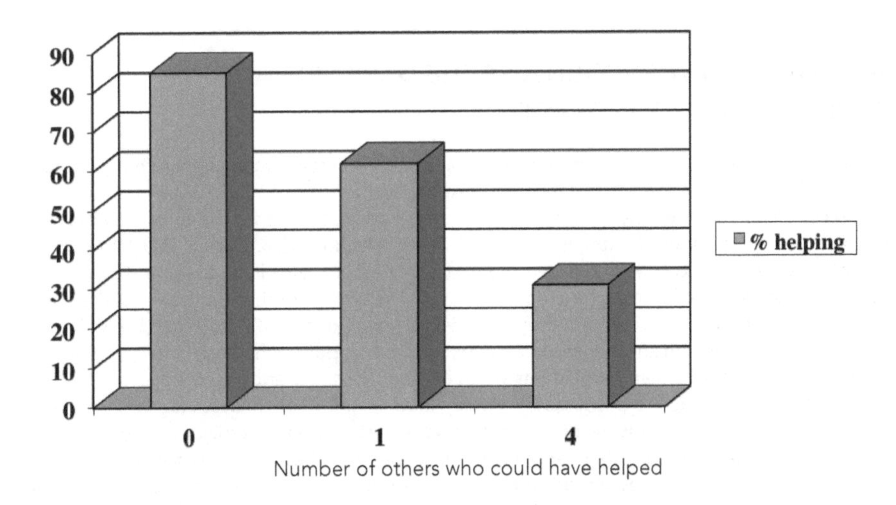

Figure 8.6 The Inhibiting Effects of Bystanders on Rates of Helping.

Based on: Darley & Latane (1968). Bystander intervention in emergencies: Diffusion of responsibility. *Journal of Personality and Social Psychology*, 8, 377–383.

thought there were three others who could help, the decrease in response was even more dramatic. In that condition, a mere 31 percent intervened within the first 60 seconds. Even after six minutes, when the experiment was terminated, well over a third still had not sought help.

The number of bystanders also had an effect on the time participants took before intervening (see **Figure 8.7**). When there was no one else who could help, participants took an average of 53 seconds to intervene. The presence of one additional participant increased response times to 93 seconds among those who intervened. The presence of four additional participants boosted it to 166 seconds.

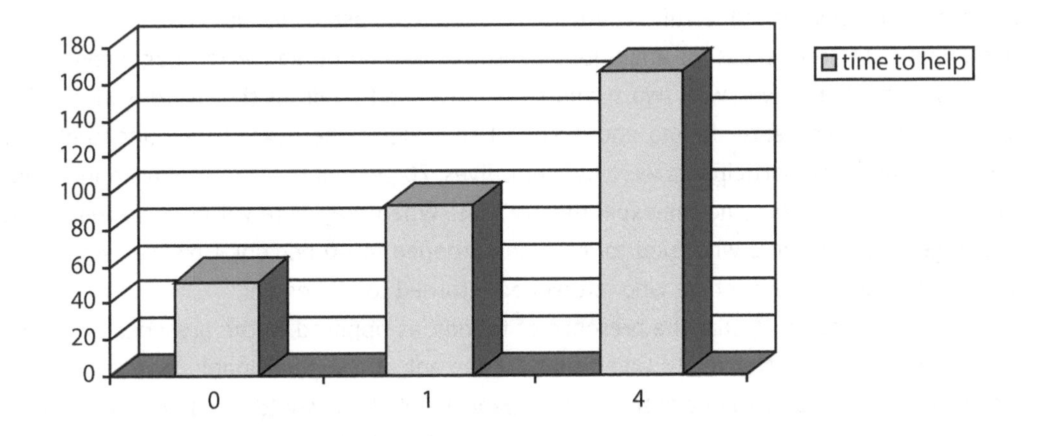

Figure 8.7 The Inhibiting Effect of Bystanders on Time Taken to Help.

Based on: Darley & Latane (1968). Bystander intervention in emergencies: Diffusion of responsibility. *Journal of Personality and Social Psychology*, 8, 377–383.

SOCIAL PSYCHOLOGY ENCOUNTERS THE DARK SIDE: THE IMPLICIT BYSTANDER EFFECT

The presence of bystanders greatly affects helping because it decreases the chance that people will recognize a situation as an emergency and thus feel responsible for offering aid. There is evidence that bystander effects will manifest themselves, even when others are not present. The *implicit bystander effect* was demonstrated in a series of studies (Garcia, Weaver, Moskowitz, & Darley, 2002) that primed the presence of others in various ways and noted the effect on helping rates in an unrelated situation.

In one study, participants first imagined they had won a free dinner for themselves or for themselves and ten friends. Later, during the experiment, they were asked how much time they would be willing to spend helping the experimenter with another study. As expected, participants who had imagined dinner with ten friends volunteered less time than participants who had imagined dinner by themselves.

A second study looked at the processes that may lead to the implicit bystander effect. Participants imagined that they and a friend were at a movie theater that was either crowded or empty. They then completed a lexical decision task that required them to decide whether words flashed on a computer screen for a brief time were indeed words on nonwords. All the critical words were related to unaccountability (*unaccountable, innocent, exempt*). As expected, participants who had imagined themselves in a crowded movie theater responded to the words faster than participants who had imagined themselves in an empty movie theater.

These findings suggest that bystander effects may not depend on the physical presence of others. Merely imagining their presence can reduce helping. Under such conditions, reduced help may result from a decreased sense of responsibility and accountability.

The identification of the implicit bystander effect complements earlier research in an important way. Though we may be the only bystander to an emergency, whether or not we feel compelled to offer help may depend on whether we have just exited an empty or crowded bus.

These inhibiting effects of bystanders, as demonstrated by Darley and Latane (1968), are dramatic, especially considering the fact that the gender of the "other participants" did not matter. It also made no difference when some participants were led to believe that another participant was a premed student, who would appear to be particularly well suited to help.

Would it make a difference if the other bystanders were friends rather than strangers? To find out, Latane and Rodin (1969) recruited participants for a study ostensibly meant to evaluate their game and puzzle preferences for a fictitious Consumer Testing Bureau. Participants completed their surveys by themselves, with two strangers, or with two friends. As they were working, they overheard the experimenter falling and hurting her ankle in the next room. Consistent with earlier findings, when participants were by themselves, 70 percent of them sought to intervene within two minutes of hearing the experimenter's fall. When they were with two strangers, the percentage of participants who tried to intervene dropped to 40 percent. However, when they were with friends, the percentage who intervened returned to 70 percent.

Does this finding mean that the presence of friends, as opposed to the presence of strangers, facilitates helping? Not really. Given that 70 percent of the participants who were alone helped, the odds that *at least* one of three participants would help would actually be higher than 70 percent. In other words, the presence of friends, too, inhibits helping.

Given the pervasiveness of this effect, the presence of bystanders may serve as a hidden influence that inhibits helping through processes operating outside of conscious awareness. The Social Psychology Encounters the Dark Side box above describes a series of studies of such implicit bystander effects.

Considering Appropriate Forms of Helping

Taking responsibility is clearly an important step toward helping, but a potential helper must still determine the appropriate response. In some cases, doing so may merely delay a response to the emergency. Consider, for example, the situation in which the participants of the Latane and Rodin (1969) study found themselves. After deciding that it was their responsibility to come to the aid of the injured experimenter, they could have done so in several ways. Most of them pulled down the room divider; a slightly smaller group simply yelled "Help!" A few participants left the room and entered the experimenter's room through a separate door.

Because this nurse is capable of providing assistance, the presence of bystanders is unlikely to reduce her willingness to help in an emergency.

In some emergencies, people may fail to help because they feel they are incapable of responding appropriately (Schwartz & Clausen, 1970). Put yourself in the shoes of participants in Darley and Latane's (1968) seizure study. It may be perfectly clear that the person needs assistance–and equally clear that you should help–but would you know what to do? If you were in the presence of others, would you be tempted to see whether someone else who might be better qualified to help would step up?

Unfortunately, the recognition that we are unable to help can have consequences beyond mere inaction. Instead of helping victims out of their predicament, too often we blame them for it. For example, we often derogate the destitute by (a) holding them responsible for their poverty (Henry, Reyna, & Weiner, 2004); and (b) assuming that any action we might take will make no difference (Lerner, 1980; Lerner & Miller, 1978). Such a response may seem odd, but it is firmly grounded in our belief in a just world (Lerner, 1980). We would like to believe that the world is a fair place in which people get what they deserve and deserve what they get. Learning that something bad happened to someone else has the potential to threaten our just-world belief. We deal with the threat by concluding that the person must have done something to deserve the bad luck.

As we might expect, people who feel incapable of helping have a difficult time choosing the appropriate course of action. Those who feel particularly capable are more likely to help. In one study (Cramer, McMaster, Bartell, & Dragna, 1988), education majors and registered nurses encountered an emergency involving a man who was trapped under a collapsed ladder. They were traveling either by themselves or in the presence of a confederate trained to behave as if nothing had happened. As in past research, the presence of the passive bystander affected the willingness to help among those students who did not feel particularly well-equipped to provide assistance (that is, the education majors). However, the passive bystander's presence did not affect the nurses, who went to help the trapped workman.

Implementing the Chosen Action

Once the appropriate form of assistance has been decided on, we might expect the chance that it will be implemented to be fairly high. That certainly is the case, although there are some notable exceptions. For example, the presence of visibly passive bystanders can reduce helping because their inaction can signal that an offer of help is inappropriate (Schwartz & Gottlieb, 1976). Fears that one's help may not be wanted can also reduce the chance of implementing a solution. Imagine you have witnessed a confrontation between a man and a woman. If you are like most people, you will probably assume that the two are romantically linked. That may lead you to conclude that an offer of assistance might not be welcome. Consistent with this conclusion, participants who witnessed a staged fight between a man and a woman were less likely to help when they thought the combatants were a married couple than when they thought the combatants were strangers (Shotland & Straw, 1976).

Even situations that are relatively unambiguous can sometimes be complicated because of confusion over who is responsible for the victim's plight. Imagine finding a person slumped over on a sidewalk. You rush to find out what is wrong; as you are doing so, other pedestrians join you. What do you think they will think about your relationship to the victim? What will you be thinking about what they are thinking? The results of two studies in which participants took either the helper's perspective or the onlooker's (Cacioppo, Petty, & Losch, 1986) suggest that you will expect the others to hold you responsible for the person's situation. This expectation isn't borne out of paranoia, but has an objective basis. Onlookers who observe a victim with another person generally assume that the other person had something to do with the victim's situation.

How Can Helping Be Improved?

Latane and Darley's decision-making model explains in detail why people often fail to help in an emergency. At each step, an incorrect decision leads to a failure to help. Frequently, the presence of mostly passive bystanders lies at the heart of faulty decision making. The behavior of others appears to serve as a source of information as we interpret the situation, decide whether or not to take responsibility, and choose and implement a course of action.

Others do not always have to be a negative influence on helping, however. They can model helpful behavior by being helpful themselves. Imagine the following scenario: The holiday season has arrived, and a Salvation Army volunteer has once again stationed himself at the entrance to the local grocery store. On your way in, you see a customer who is leaving drop some coins in the kettle. Would witnessing this act of kindness increase your willingness to make a donation on your way out?

Research suggests that it would, especially if the customer parts with her money cheerfully (Hornstein, 1970). That is why charities often frame their requests in terms of how many people have already responded. Along these lines, the typical bystander effect is reversed in situations that require many helpers rather than a single individual (Greitemeyer & Bruegge, 2015). This helps explain why people are often more than willing to "pull together" to help others victimized by a natural disaster, for example. There is also good reason to believe that exposure to helpful models increases helping in emergency situations. In a classic study (Bryan & Test, 1967), motorists were more likely to pull over and offer help to the driver of a disabled vehicle after they had witnessed another motorist doing the same thing.

More subtle contextual cues may also serve as hidden influences that promote helping. For example, the mere presence of a camera can attenuate the bystander effect (van Bommel et al., 2014). In one study, participants who had been primed with words related to helping were more likely to help someone pick up spilled pens than participants who had been primed with words unrelated to helping (Macrae & Johnston, 1998). Evidently, the priming task made helping thoughts more accessible, resulting in more help. Moreover, priming prosocial cues promotes helping, even in the presence of bystanders (Abbate, Ruggieri, & Boca, 2013). The Social Psychology Encounters the Bright Side box on **pages 240** describes a study that shows how a subtle priming technique influenced sustained helping (volunteering) in both hypothetical and real-world situations.

Finally, there is evidence from laboratory and field studies to suggest that helping promotes future helping behavior, especially when helpers reflect on their actions. In one study, participants who wrote about their thoughts, feelings, and actions related to a situation in which they helped another were subsequently more likely to help in an unrelated situation than participants who reflected on being the recipients of help. Presumably, reflecting on giving help encourages future helping because it increases the salience and strength of one's identity as a capable and caring human being (Grant & Dutton, 2012).

Why Do People Fail to Help?: A Summary

People often fail to help in emergencies, usually because of an incorrect decision somewhere in a sequence of steps that leads to action. First, people may fail to notice an event. Even if they do,

SOCIAL PSYCHOLOGY ENCOUNTERS THE BRIGHT SIDE: OF STUDENTS AND SUPERHEROES

If simply imagining the presence of others can decrease helping, could imagining someone who is particularly helpful increase helping? The answer appears to be yes, with one qualification. In a series of studies (Nelson & Norton, 2005), researchers asked some participants to list the characteristics of a superhero, and others to list the characteristics of an example of a superhero—Superman. Later, researchers asked both groups to indicate their willingness to volunteer as tutors to children in neighboring communities. Compared to participants in a control group, who had been asked to describe a typical dorm room, participants who had described the characteristics of a superhero volunteered more hours. However, those who had described Superman's characteristics volunteered for fewer hours than even those in the control group.

Why did the superhero prime increase helping, but the Superman prime decrease it? The answer lies in the comparisons participants may have drawn between themselves and the target of the priming. Participants who were primed with the category of superhero may have assessed the extent to which they were similar to a superhero. Because Superman is such an extreme example of that category, however, students who received the Superman prime may have focused on the extent to which they were *dissimilar* to Superman. Because their own powers paled next to Superman's, they may have underestimated their own, including their ability to help.

they may fail to interpret it as an emergency, to take responsibility, or to choose and implement the appropriate action. These failures are caused primarily by the presence of bystanders, whose behavior becomes an important source of information. Inaction on their part can lead to pluralistic ignorance, causing the situation to be misinterpreted. Bystanders' inaction can also result in the diffusion of responsibility—a situation in which individuals believe that others will take the responsibility for helping. Even when individuals do take responsibility, they often fail to choose the appropriate action, because they feel incapable of offering aid. Implementing a chosen action may be further complicated if bystanders believe that helping will bring social disapproval.

Think Like a Social Psychologist

Thinking Critically

When seminary students rushed across campus to give a speech on the parable of the Good Samaritan, many failed to help a man they passed, who was slumped in a hallway. This finding is generally interpreted as showing that it is all too easy not to notice an emergency, even for those who should have helping on their minds. Can you think of anything in the parable of the Good Samaritan that may not have been a good prime for helping?

Epilogue: All's Well that Ends Well

Ana knew that she only felt as if she had been sitting in her car for hours. She was tired and hungry, and there was little to occupy her mind other than wondering how on earth she was going to get home. A quick look at her wristwatch, however, indicated that she had waited less than half an hour when a car pulled over in front of her. A tall, heavy-set middle-aged man emerged from the car and knocked on her passenger-side window. "Need a tow?" he asked in a deep, booming voice. Grateful that he had stopped for her, Ana explained her situation, including the part about the inoperable cell phone. He handed her his phone and disappeared into his car.

Ana had no trouble reaching the emergency operator at the auto club, who told her that a tow truck would arrive momentarily, and asked her to wait by her car. When Ana went to return the phone to the Good Samaritan, she was prepared to thank him and send him on his way. To her surprise, he practically insisted that they wait together in his car, and even offered to drive her home. Unlike her own car, his had a working heater, so Ana was happy to accept his invitation. She was less sure about the offer of a ride home. As a single woman, she was keenly aware of the many cases in which young women were assaulted by strangers offering aid. She wasn't really afraid that harm might come to her, though; there was something avuncular about this man, which put her at ease. Instead, she worried that in accepting his offer, she might be imposing on someone who, like everyone else, was probably anxious to get home. He assured her, however, that taking her home was no trouble at all.

The tow truck arrived and put Ana's car on the hook, to be towed to the shop that had serviced it in the past. On the way to her apartment, the Good Samaritan did most of the talking. He explained that he had passed another disabled car a couple of miles back. He had thought of stopping then, but continued when he realized that someone else had already pulled over. He went on about how everyone seems to be in rush nowadays, and how people don't seem to look out for each other the way they used to. The only time he stopped talking was when the Beatles' song "Help!" played on the stereo system. Even then, he sang along to the tune: "Help, I need somebody—help, not just anybody ..."

Ana didn't mind listening to his monologue, because she felt too exhausted to carry on a conversation. When the car pulled up in front of her apartment building, she realized she had never asked the Good Samaritan for his name. "Name's Al," he said, as he handed her his business card. "Looks like you need some new wheels. Stop by the dealership and we'll see if I can fix you up. I sell new and used, and I'm there every day except Tuesdays."

Ana stuffed Al's card into her purse without looking at it. Later, as her frozen low-carb, low-fat, low-taste dinner entrée warmed in the microwave oven, she retrieved the card to see what kind of cars Al sold. With it came the little slip of paper on which she had scribbled the 800 number earlier that day. Ana dialed it and was greatly relieved when she heard a friendly voice ask, "Joplin Tornado Relief, would you like to make a donation?"

HIDDEN INFLUENCES ON HELPING: A SUMMARY

Inclusive fitness: An evolutionary principle that predicts we will help others to whom we are genetically related in order to preserve our genetic material

Reward-and-punishment mechanisms: Mechanisms that reward those who comply with cooperative norms and punish those who cheat. Compliance with such norms often occurs in the absence of conscious awareness

Arousal from witnessing an emergency: Arousal that directs our attention to the most central aspects of an emergency, making helping often automatic and spontaneous

Ultimate egoism: The idea that empathic concern is a generalized response that in evolutionary terms is highly adaptive and occurs without conscious awareness

Bystander effect: The inhibiting influence—often experienced outside of conscious awareness—that the presence of bystanders to an emergency exerts on those who could help

Contextual cues: The influence, for example, of surreptitious priming on a person's willingness to help

Key Terms and Definitions

Prosocial behavior: a category of actions intended to benefit others in socially defined ways

Helping: any action that provides some benefit to or improves the well-being of another person

Altruism: helping in the absence of any expectation that doing so will bring external rewards

Inclusive fitness: the human interest in preserving genetic material, not only in one's own offspring, but in the offspring of relatives

Indirect reciprocity: the expectation that helping others will make them available and willing to reciprocate later

Negative state relief model: a theoretical model that predicts that people who are in a bad mood will help others in order to make themselves feel better

Arousal/cost-reward model: a theoretical model that explains helping as being caused by the desire to relieve the emotional distress of witnessing an emergency

Empathy: a state in which we take another's perspective and vicariously experience the other's emotions

Psychological hedonism: a doctrine proposing that humans act primarily in order to seek pleasure and avoid pain

Social dilemma: a situation that pits the greater good of the group against the good of the individual

Collective interest: concern for the group to which we belong, rather than for the self

Bystander apathy: the tendency not to help when in the presence of others

Pluralistic ignorance: assuming that there is nothing wrong because there is no evidence that others are concerned

Diffusion of responsibility: the failure of individuals to take appropriate action in the presence of bystanders; in general, as the number of bystanders increases, the less likely we are to take responsibility for helping

References

Abbate, C. S., Ruggieri, S., & Boca, S. (2013). The effect of prosocial priming in the presence of bystanders. *Journal of Social Psychology, 153*, 619–622.

Alexander, R. D. (1987). The biology of moral systems. Chicago: Aldine Transaction.

Allport, G. W. (1954). *The nature of prejudice*. Reading, MA: Addison-Wesley.

Axelrod, R. (1984). *The evolution of cooperation*. New York: Basic Books.

Batson, C. D. (1987). Prosocial motivation: Is it ever truly altruistic? In L. Berkowitz (Ed.), Advances in Experimental Social Psychology (Vol. 20, pp. 65–122).

Batson, C. D. (1991). *The altruism question: Toward a social-psychological answer*. Hillsdale, NJ: Erlbaum.

Batson, C. D. (1995). Prosocial motivation: Why do we help others? In A. Tesser (Ed.), *Advanced social psychology* (pp. 333–381). New York: McGraw-Hill.

Batson, C. D. (2002). Addressing the altruism question experimentally. In S. G. Post & L. G. Underwood (Eds.), *Altruism and altruistic love: Science, philosophy, and religion in dialogue* (pp. 89–105). Oxford, UK: Oxford University Press.

Batson, C. D., Batson, J. G., Todd, R. M., Brummett, B. H., Shaw, L. L., & Aldeguer, C. M. R. (1995). Empathy and the collective good: Caring for one of the others in a social dilemma. *Journal of Personality and Social Psychology, 68*, 619–631.

Batson, C. D., Duncan, B., Ackerman, P., Buckley, T., & Birch, K. (1981). Is empathic emotion a source of altruistic motivation? *Journal of Personality and Social Psychology, 40*, 290–302.

Batson, C. D., Dyck, J. L., Brandt, J. R., Batson, J. G., Powell, A. L., McMaster, M. R., & Griffitt, C. (1988). Five studies testing two new egoistic alternatives to the empathy-altruism hypothesis. *Journal of Personality and Social Psychology, 55*, 52–77.

Batson, C. D., & Powell, A. A. (2003). Altruism and prosocial behavior. In T. Milton & M. J. Lerner (Eds.), *Handbook of psychology: Personality and social psychology* (Vol. 5, pp. 463–484). New York: Wiley.

Batson, C. D., Sager, K., Garst, E., Kang, M., Rubchinsky, K., & Dawson, K. (1997). Is empathy-induced helping due to self-other merging? *Journal of Personality and Social Psychology, 73*, 495–509.

Batson, C. D., & Shaw, L. L. (1991). Evidence for altruism: Toward a pluralism of prosocial motives. *Psychological Inquiry, 2*, 107–122.

Baumeister, R. F., Stillwell, A. M., & Heatherton, T. F. (1994). Guilt: an interpersonal approach. *Psychological Bulletin, 115*, 243–267.

Becker, S. W., & Eagly, A. H. (2004). The heroism of women and men. *American Psychologist, 59*, 163–178.

Bentham, J. (1879). *An introduction to the principles of morals and legislation* (First published in 1789). Oxford, UK: Clarendon Press.

Berkowitz, L. (1972). Social norms, feelings, and other factors affecting helping behavior and altruism. In L. Berkowitz (Ed.), *Advances in experimental social psychology* (Vol. 6, pp. 63–108). New York: Academic Press.

Boeckler, A., Tusche, A., & Singer, T. (2016). The structure of human prosociality: differentiating altruistically motivated, norm-motivated, strategically motivated, and self-reported prosocial behavior. *Social Psychological and Personality Science, 7*, 530–541.

Bryan, J. H., & Test, M. A. (1967). Models and helping: Naturalistic studies in aiding behavior. *Journal of Personality and Social Psychology, 6*, 400–407.

Burnstein, E., Crandall, C., & Kitayama, S. (1994). Some neo-Darwinian rules for altruism: Weighing cues for inclusive fitness as a function of the biological importance of the decision. *Journal of Personality and Social Psychology, 67*, 773–789.

Cacioppo, J. T., Petty, R. E., & Losch, M. E. (1986). Attributions of responsibility for helping and doing harm: Evidence for confusion of responsibility. *Journal of Personality and Social Psychology, 50*, 100–105.

Carlson, M., Charlin, V., & Miller, N. (1988). Positive mood and helping behavior. *Journal of Personality and Social Psychology, 55*, 211–229.

Carlson, M., & Miller, N. (1987). Explanation of the relationship between negative mood and helping. *Psychological Bulletin, 102*, 91–108.

Cialdini, R. B., Brown, S. L., Lewis, B. P., Luce, C., & Neuberg, S. L. (1997). Reinterpreting the empathy-altruism relationship: When one into one equals one. *Journal of Personality and Social Psychology, 73*, 481–494.

Cialdini, R. B., Darby, B. L., & Vincent, J. E. (1973). Transgression and altruism: A case for hedonism. *Journal of Experimental Social Psychology, 9*, 502–516.

Cialdini, R. B., Kenrick, D. T., & Baumann, D. J. (1982). Effects of mood on prosocial behavior in children and adults. In N. Eisenberg (Ed.), *The development of prosocial behavior* (pp. 339–359). New York: Academic Press.

Clark, M. S., & Isen, A. M. (1982). Toward understanding the relationship between feeling states and social behavior. In A. H. Hastorf & A. M. Isen (Eds.), *Cognitive social psychology* (pp. 73–108). New York: Elsevier.

Clark, M. S., & Waddell, B. A. (1983). Effects of moods on thoughts about helping, attraction, and information acquisition. *Social Psychology Quarterly, 46*, 31–35.

Clark, R. D. III, & Word, L. E. (1974). Where is the apathetic bystander? Situational characteristics of the emergency. *Journal of Personality and Social Psychology, 29*, 279–287.

Cohen, S. (2004). Social relationships and health. *American Psychologist, 59*, 676–684.

Cohen, S., Kessler, R. C., & Gordon, L. U. (1995). Strategies for measuring stress in psychiatric and physical disorders. In S. Cohen, R. C. Kessler, & L. U. Gordon (Eds.), *Measuring stress* (pp. 3–28). New York: Oxford University Press.

Cohen, S., & Wills, T. A. (1985). Stress, social support, and the buffering hypothesis. *Psychological Bulletin, 98*, 310–357.

Cosmides, L. (1989). The logic of social exchange: Has natural selection shaped how humans reason? Studies with the Wason selection task. *Cognition, 31*, 187–276.

Cramer, R. E., McMaster, M. R., Bartell, P. A., & Dragna, M. (1988). Subject competence and minimization of the bystander effect. *Journal of Applied Social Psychology, 18*, 1133–1148.

Cunningham, M. R., Steinberg, J., & Grev, R. (1980). Wanting to and having to help: Separate motivations for positive mood and guilt-induced helping. *Journal of Personality and Social Psychology, 38*, 181–192.

Darley, J. M., & Batson, C. D. (1973). From Jerusalem to Jericho: A study of situational and dispositional variables in helping behavior. *Journal of Personality and Social Psychology, 27*, 100–108.

Darley, J. M., & Latane, B. (1968). Bystander intervention in emergencies: Diffusion of responsibility. *Journal of Personality and Social Psychology, 8*, 377–383.

Davis, M. H. (1994). *Empathy: A social psychological approach.* Madison, WI: Brown Benchmark.

Dawes, R. M., van de Kragt, A. J. C., & Orbell, J. M. (1990). Cooperation for the benefit of us—not me, or my conscience. In J. J. Mansbridge (Ed.), *Beyond self-interest* (pp. 97–110). Chicago: University of Chicago Press. de Waal, F. B. M. (2008). Putting the altruism back into altruism: The evolution of empathy. *Annual Review of Psychology, 59*, 279–300.

De Waal, F. B. M. (2008). Putting the altruism back into altruism: The evolution of empathy. Annual Review of Psychology, 59, 279–300.

Dovidio, J. F. (1984). Helping behavior and altruism: An empirical and conceptual overview. In L. Berkowitz (Ed.), *Advances in experimental social psychology* (Vol. 17, pp. 361–427). New York: Academic Press.

Dovidio, J. F., Piliavin, J. A., Gaertner, S. L., Schroeder, D. A., & Clark, R. D. III (1991). The arousal: Cost-reward model and the process of intervention: A review of the evidence. In M. S. Clark (Ed.), *Review of personality and social psychology: Vol. 12. Prosocial behavior* (pp. 86–118). Newbury Park, CA: Sage.

Eagly, A. H., & Crowley, M. (1986). Gender and helping behavior: A meta-analytic review of the social psychological literature. *American Psychologist, 100*, 283–308.

Eisenberg, N., & Lennon, R. (1983). Sex differences in empathy and related capacities. *Psychological Bulletin, 94*, 100–131.

Eisenberg, N., & Miller, P. (1987). The relation of empathy to prosocial and related behaviors. *Psychological Bulletin, 101*, 91–119.

Erkison, E. H. (1982). *The life cycle completed: A review.* New York: Norton.

Fisher, P., et al. (2011). The bystander-effect: A meta-analytic review on bystander intervention in dangerous and non-dangerous situations. *Psychological Bulletin, 137*, 517–537.

Gaertner, S. L., & Dovidio, J. F. (1977). The subtlety of white racism, arousal, and helping behavior. *Journal of Personality and Social Psychology, 35*, 691–707.

Garcia, S. M., Weaver, K., Moskowitz, G. M., & Darley, J. M. (2002). Crowded minds: The implicit bystander effect. *Journal of Personality and Social Psychology, 83*, 843–853.

Grant, A., & Dutton, J. (2012). Beneficiary or benefactor: Are people more prosocial when they reflect on receiving or giving? *Psychological Science, 23*, 1033–1039.

Greitemeyer, T. & Muegge, D.O. (2014). When bystanders increase rather than decrease intentions to help. *Social Psychology, 46*, 116–119.

Gu, X., & Han, S. (2007). Attention and reality constraints on the neural processes of empathy for pain. *Neuroimage, 36*, 256–267.

Hamilton, W. D. (1964). The genetic evolution of social behavior. *Journal of Theoretical Biology, 7*, 1–52.

Han, S., Fan, Y., & Mao, L. (2008). Gender differences in empathy for pain: An electrophysiologial investigation. *Brain Research, 1196*, 85–93.

Henry, P. J., Reyna, C., & Weiner, B. (2004). Hate welfare but help the poor: How the attributional content of stereotypes explains the paradox of reactions to the destitute in America. *Journal of Applied Social Psychology, 34*, 34–58.

Hoffman, M. L. (1981). Is altruism part of human nature? *Journal of Personality and Social Psychology, 40*, 121–137.

Hornstein, H. A. (1970). The influence of social models on helping behavior. In J. Macauley & L. Berkowitz (Eds.), *Altruism and helping behavior* (pp. 29–42). New York: Academic Press.

House, J. S., & Kahn, R. L. (1985). Measures and concepts of social support. In S. Cohen & S. L. Syme (Eds.), *Social support and health* (pp. 83–108). New York: Academic Press.

Ickes, W., Gesn, P. R., & Graham, T. (2005). Gender differences in empathic accuracy: Differential ability or differential motivation? *Personal Relationships, 7*, 95–109.

Isen, A. M., & Levin, P. A. (1972). Effects of feeling good on helping: Cookies and kindness. *Journal of Personality and Social Psychology, 21*, 384–388.

Isen, A. M., & Simmonds, S. F. (1978). The effect of feeling good on a helping task that is incompatible with good mood. *Social Psychology, 41*, 346–349.

Isen, A. M., Shalker, T. E., Clark, M. S., & Karp, L. (1978). Affect, accessibility of material in memory, and behavior. *Journal of Personality and Social Psychology, 36*, 1–12.

Kenrick, D. T. (1991). Proximate altruism and ultimate selfishness. *Psychological Inquiry, 2*, 135–137.

Krebs, D. L. (1982). Psychological approaches to altruism: An evaluation. *Ethics, 92*, 447–458.

Krebs, D. L. (1991). Altruism and egoism: A false dichotomy? *Psychological Inquiry, 2*, 137–139.

Krebs, D. L., & Russell, C. (1981). Role taking and altruism: When you put yourself in another's shoes, will they take you to their owner's aid? In J. P. Rushton & R. M. Sorrentino (Eds.), *Altruism and helping behavior: Social, personality, and developmental perspectives* (pp. 137–165). Hillsdale, NJ: Erlbaum.

Latane, B., & Darley, J. M. (1968). Group inhibition of bystander intervention. *Journal of Personality and Social Psychology, 10*, 215–221.

Latane, B., & Darley, J. M. (1970). *The unresponsive bystander: Why doesn't he help?* Englewood Cliffs, NJ: Prentice-Hall.

Latane, B., & Rodin, J. (1969). A lady in distress: Inhibiting effects of friends and strangers on bystander intervention. *Journal of Experimental Social Psychology, 5*, 189–202.

Laube, J. (1985). Health care providers as disaster victims. In J. Laube & S. Murphy (Eds.), *Perspectives on disaster recovery* (pp. 210–228). Norwalk, CT: Appleton-Century-Crofts.

Lennon, R., & Eisenberg, N. (1987). Gender and age differences in empathy and sympathy. In N. Eisenberg & J. Strayer (Eds.), *Empathy and its development* (pp. 195–217). New York: Cambridge University Press.

Lerner, M. J. (1980). *The belief in a just world: A fundamental delusion.* New York: Plenum.

Lerner, M. J., & Miller, D. T. (1978). Just world research and the attribution process: Looking back and looking ahead. *Psychological Bulletin, 85*, 1030–1051.

Macauley, J. R., & Berkowitz, L. (Eds.). (1970). *Altruism and helping behavior.* New York: Academic Press.

Macrae, C. N., & Johnston, L. (1998). Help, I need somebody: Automatic action and inaction. *Social Cognition, 16*, 400–417.

Manning, R., Levine, M., & Collins, A. (2007). The Kitty Genovese murder and the social psychology of helping: The parable of the 38 witnesses. *American Psychologist, 62*, 555–562.

Manucia, G. K., Baumann, D. J., & Cialdini, R. B. (1984). Mood influences on helping: Direct effects or side effects? *Journal of Personality and Social Psychology, 46*, 357–364.

Martin, G. B., & Clark, R. D. III (1982). Distress crying in neonates: Species and peer specificity. *Developmental Psychology, 18*, 3–9.

McGuire, A. M. (1994). Helping behaviors in the natural environment: Dimensions and correlates of helping. *Personality and Social Psychology Bulletin, 20*, 45–56.

McGuire, A. M. (2003). "It was nothing"—Extending evolutionary models of altruism by two social cognitive biases in judgments of the costs and benefits of helping. *Social Cognition, 21*, 363–394.

Mill, J. S. (1863). *Utilitarianism.* London: Parker, Son, & Bourn.

Nelson, L. D., & Norton, M. I. (2005). From student to superhero: Situational primes shape future helping. *Journal of Experimental Social Psychology, 41*, 423–430.

Orbell, J. M., van de Kragt, A. J. C., & Dawes, R. M. (1988). Explaining discussion-induced cooperation. *Journal of Personality and Social Psychology, 54*, 811–819.

Pavey, L., Greitemeyer, T., & Sparks, P. (2012). "I help because I want to, not because you tell me to": Empathy increases autonomously motivated helping. *Personality and Social Psychology Bulletin, 38*, 681–689.

Pearce, P. L., & Amato, P. R. (1980). A taxonomy of helping: A multidimensional scaling analysis. *Social Psychology Quarterly, 43*, 363–371.

Penner, L. A., & Finkelstein, M. A. (1998). Dispositional and structural determinants of volunteerism. *Journal of Personality and Social Psychology, 74*, 525–537.

Piliavin, J. A., Dovidio, J. F., Gaertner, S. L., & Clark, R. D. (1981). *Emergency intervention.* New York: Academic Press.

Piliavin, J. A., & Piliavin, I. M. (1972). The effects of blood on reactions to a victim. *Journal of Personality and Social Psychology, 23*, 253–261.

Rosenthal, A. M. (1964). *Thirty-eight witnesses*. New York: McGraw-Hill.

Schaller, M., & Cialdini, R. B. (1988). The economics of empathic helping: Support for a mood management motive. *Journal of Experimental Social Psychology, 24*, 163–181.

Schroeder, D. A., Penner, L. A., Dovidio, J. F., & Piliavin, J. A. (1995). *The psychology of helping and altruism: Problems and puzzles*. New York: McGraw-Hill.

Schwartz, S. H., & Clausen, G. T. (1970). Responsibility, norms, and helping in an emergency. *Journal of Personality and Social Psychology, 16*, 299–310.

Schwartz, S. H., & Gottlieb, A. (1976). Bystander reactions to a violent theft: Crime in Jerusalem. *Journal of Personality and Social Psychology, 34*, 1188–1199.

Shotland, R. L., & Straw, M. (1976). Bystander response to an assault: When a man attacks a woman. *Journal of Personality and Social Psychology, 34*, 990–999.

Sime, J. D. (1983). Affiliative behavior during escape to building exits. *Journal of Environmental Psychology, 3*, 21–41.

Simon, H. A. (1990). A mechanism for social selection and successful altruism. *Science, 250*, 1665–1668.

Stocks, E. L., Lishner, D. A., & Decker, S. K. (2009). Altruism or psychological escape: Why does empathy promote prosocial behavior? *European Journal of Social Psychology, 39*, 649–655.

Stuermer, S., Snyder, M., & Omoto, A. M. (2005). Prosocial emotions and helping: The moderating role of group membership. *Journal of Personality and Social Psychology, 88*, 532–546.

Stuermer, S., Snyder, M., Kropp, A., & Siem, B. (2006). Empathy-motivated helping: The moderating role of group membership. *Personality and Social Psychology Bulletin, 32*, 943–956.

Sze, J. A., Gyurak, A., Goodkind, M. S., & Levenson, R. W. (2011). Greater emotional empathy and prosocial behavior in late life. *Emotion, 12*, 1129–1140.

Toi, M., & Batson, C. D. (1982). More evidence that empathy is a source of altruistic motivation. *Journal of Personality and Social Psychology, 43*, 281–292.

Tomasello, M., Melis, A. P., Tennie, C., Wyman, E., & Herrmann, E. (2012). Two key steps in the evolution of human cooperation. *Current Anthropology, 53*, 673–692.

Trivers, R. L. (1971). The evolution of reciprocal altruism. *Quarterly Review of Biology, 46*, 35–37.

Van Bommel, M., van Prooijen, J., Elffers, H., & van Lange, P.A.M. (2014). Intervene to be seen: The power of a camera in attenuating the bystander effect. *Social Psychological and Personality Science, 5*, 459–466.

Washington Post Editorial (1982, January 21). The unknown hero. *Washington Post*.

Wood, W., & Eagly, A. H. (2002). A cross-cultural analysis of the behavior of women and men: Implications for the origins of sex differences. *Psychological Bulletin, 129*, 119–138.

Wooster, M. M. (2000). Ordinary people, extraordinary rescues. American Enterprise, *11*, 18–21.

Figure Credit

Fig. 9.1: Copyright © KOMU News (CC by 2.0) at http://www.flickr.com/photos/komunews/5756447784/.

Fig. 9.2: Source: http://commons.wikimedia.org/wiki/File:USMC-110523-M-FG494-113.jpg.

Fig. 9.4: Copyright © 2013 Depositphotos/monkeybusiness.

Fig. 9.5: Copyright © 2013 Depositphotos/timbrk.

Fig. 9.6: Copyright © 2012 Depositphotos/zurijeta.

Fig. 9.7: Copyright © 2012 Depositphotos/monkeybusiness.

Fig. 9.9: Copyright © 2010 Depositphotos/Baloncici.

Fig. 9.10: Copyright © 2014 Depositphotos/iphemant.

Five Facets of Sustainability

When we deny the poor and the vulnerable their own human dignity and capacity for freedom and choice, it becomes self-denial. It becomes a denial of both our collective and individual dignity, at all levels of society.

—*Jacqueline Novogratz*

Introduction

Between 2008–2009 I worked with Water Atlas and Graduate School of Architecture faculty at University of South Florida (USF) to develop a new program entitled Ecological Urbanism. As part of this work I conducted an extensive literature review in search of a model that we could use to not only represent the essential aspects of a sustainable urban ecology but that could also be used as an assessment guide for sustainability projects. At the time the model that appeared in the literature most frequently was three pillars of sustainability (Viederman, 1994). Three pillars has been used for over 20 years in sustainability literature and in essence has been adopted as "the" model representing sustainability.

One troubling commonality that we found through our research with respects to sustainability projects in general was how few of those projects demonstrated long-term problem resolution. In the search to understand why many projects seemed to be ineffective at resolving sustainability problems, I met with Dr. Fenda Akiwumi, a geography professor at USF and natural resources democracy advocate. I told Dr. Akiwumi about the Ecological Urbanism program we were developing and that through this program we wanted to address the problem of limited sustainability project efficacy. Her response not only revealed the essential aspect of sustainability but illuminated why I was reluctant to adopt the three pillars of sustainability as a teaching and project assessment tool. She said, "You are asking why so few projects are truly effective at resolving these problems? Well the answer is quite simple; it is because no one is asking the people there what they think the solutions to these problems should be. The social context is ignored; therefore, it cannot be used to guide project development and implementation."

From my perspective, what was missing from three pillars was the perspective that every sustainability problem is at first a social problem, and therefore a psychological problem, and at the heart of every sustainability problem is the human experience. The *five facets of sustainability* (Figure 9.1) was constructed to address these realities by establishing the sum of human experience as dignity and placing human dignity at the center of sustainability problem resolution. Dignity is the composite experience of efficacy, esteem, agency, a sense of safety, freedom to be, and social capital. The first tenet of the psychology of sustainability, *any solution to a sustainability problem that does not first address factors negatively affecting human dignity will ultimately not be sustainable,* reflects this core value.

Overview of the Five Facets of Sustainability: Theory and Practice

The five facets of sustainability was developed as a guide for sustainability education, project planning, and assessment of sustainability project efficacy. The five facets of sustainability model illustrates the interconnectedness of all aspects of sustainability and their dependency on human dignity. Here, human dignity is the primary facet, and water, food, energy, and commerce are the secondary or resource facets. Please note that sociocultural and socioecological factors, and biodiversity are subsumed within each of the resource facets. These factors are critical to the health of all resource facets as well as to human dignity, as each is critical for social and ecological resilience. The psychology of sustainability helps us to understand our personal experience of dignity as well as others' experience of dignity in context of holistic sustainability. Developing this experience is exactly what you have been doing through each chapter of this textbook.

As you study Figure 9.1, think about what you have learned thus far and consider that any action taken to create a sustainable human ecology that does not also work to improve individual and societal experience of dignity ultimately will not be sustainable. Now contemplate relationship scenarios and consider, for example, how efforts to create a sustainable food system could also result in an improvement of individual and societal experience of dignity. Next, perform the same exercise using the other resource facets in combination with sociocultural and socioecological factors and biodiversity. Finally, share this exercise with others.

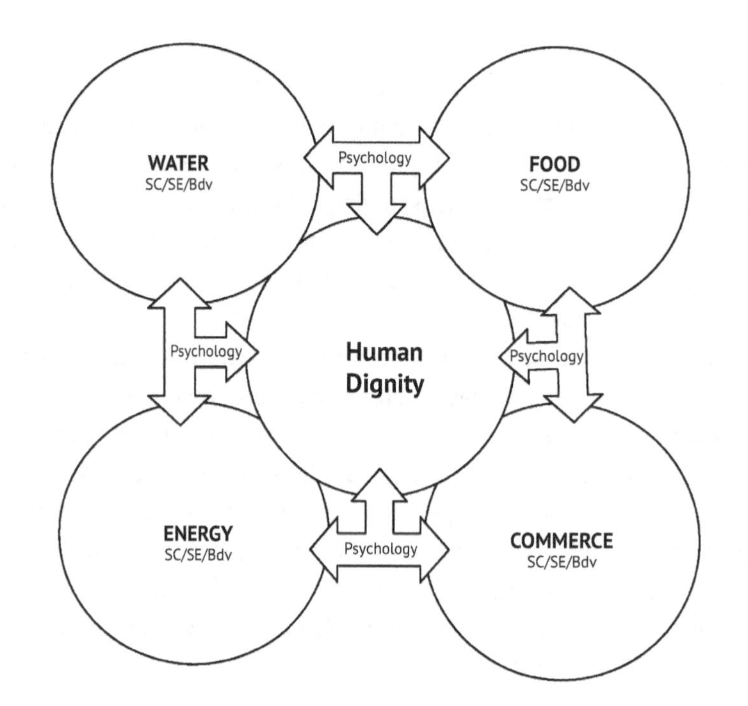

Figure 9.1 Five facets of sustainability model of holistic sustainability. Bidirectional arrows indicate the interconnectedness of all facets and psychology's role in understanding this interconnectedness. SC = sociocultural, SE = socioecological, Bdv = biodiversity.

About Feature Articles

You have four feature articles for this chapter. Please read these articles in the order in which they are introduced as this will help you recognize that all sustainability problems are human dignity problems.

Read Federico Mayor's *Seeking Alternatives in a Global Crisis* and keep in mind two quotes from this work: "The 21st Century will finally be the century of the people" (p. 121) and "The possible solution—that may render many of today's impossibilities as realities of tomorrow—must inevitably be based on equal dignity for all human beings and on social justice. Placing ethical and democratic values at the forefront of public and private activities so that social justice rather than the markets manages the economy at all levels will enable us in a few years to rectify our present misguided direction and get back on course" (p. 121). Think about how you would support Mayor's perspective using the psychology of sustainability.

Next, please read *Hydropower, Encroachment and the Re-patterning of Hydrosocial Territory: The Case of Hidrosogamoso in Colombia.* While this article is an account of a great tragedy, it is also an excellent example of what we are discussing in this chapter. As you are reading apply the five facets of sustainability to this situation as way to understand the inextricable connections of the resource facets to human dignity.

After reading Duarte-Abadía and colleagues' article please read *How to Finance our Sustainable Development Goals (SDGs): Socioecological Quantitative Easing (QE) as a Parallel Currency to Make the World a Better Place.* This is an intelligent discussion of different approaches to commerce for supporting sustainable development. Again, use the five facets of sustainability to consider why this approach might or might not be an effective as well as resilient approach.

Finally, please read *Children's Environmental Health Indicators as Tools to Measure Progress Toward Sustainability.* The authors reference the focus of past sustainability efforts on environmental and economic factors, and the neglect of human health (an aspect of dignity). As you read consider how the authors' perspective and recommendations align or not with the five facets of sustainability and especially the centrality of human dignity.

Reference

Viederman, S. (1994). Five capitals and three pillars of sustainability. *The Newsletter of PEGS, 4*(1), 5–12.

READING 10

Seeking Alternatives in a Global Crisis

Federico Mayor

"The 21st century will finally be the century of the people".

Abstract

Replacing the United Nations system and large international institutions with plutocratic groups (G-7, G-8, G-20) and universal principles with the laws of the market has led to multiple crises that require immediate reaction to prevent them from becoming irreversible.

Neoliberalism has placed military, energy, economic and media power in the hands of a very few (the "great domain"). The markets—for the most part undeservedly "rescued"—are now harassing political leaders, making democracies progressively more vulnerable and even appointing governments without elections (including in Greece, the cradle!).

For the first time in history we have the means for mobilizing people and involving citizens in local and global government, which enables us to affirm that we are living in fascinating times in which radical changes are now feasible.

The possible solutions—that may render many of today's impossibilities as realities of tomorrow—must inevitably be based on equal dignity for all human beings and on social justice. Placing ethical and democratic values at the forefront of public and private activities so that social justice rather

Federico Mayor, "Seeking Alternatives in a Global Crisis," *Cadmus*, vol. 2, no. 1, pp. 121-130.

COPYRIGHTED MATERIAL — DO NOT DUPLICATE, DISTRIBUTE, OR POST

than the markets manages the economy at all levels will enable us in a few years to rectify our present misguided direction and get back on course.

The "refounding" of the United Nations is one of the most important and urgent means of rectifying the present trends, to endow humanity with the required guidance, coordination and justice systems.

The reforms at the UN for global governance and actions to be urgently undertaken are presented. Access to food, water, health services, education and environment care is essential for the historical transition from a culture of imposition and violence to a culture of conciliation and peace. From force to word.

1.1 It is Impossible to Continue Sticking to Old Conventions as We have Done Until Now

As is to be expected, replacing the United Nations system and large international institutions with groups of plutocrats (G-7, G-8, G-20) and universal principles with the laws of the market has led to multiple crises that require immediate action to prevent them from becoming irreversible:

- Food crisis
- Climate crisis
- Social crisis
- Financial crisis

Neoliberalism has placed military, energy, economic and media power in the hands of a very few (the "great domain"). The markets, undeservedly "rescued" for the most part, are now harassing political leaders, making democracies progressively more vulnerable.

1.2 We are now at a Turning Point

Although the majority of political decision-making is still in the hands of men, for the first time in history the percentage of women in decision-making positions has increased; gender equality is advancing and civil society is becoming aware of its power, heralding a rapid transition from subjects to citizens which will prompt transformations that were previously unthinkable.

1.3 The Crucial Role of Communications

Communication has increased globally and despite the huge amount of biased and partisan information emanating from the media, there are still audiovisual and print media that provide reliable and independent news. Noteworthy among them is the emergence of *Al Jazeera* in the Arab world, which has prompted the dissemination of information and dialogue among other cultures and countries that until recently were virtually isolated.

But in that regard the most important change (to the extent that it will shortly prompt not only an epoch of change but also a change of epoch) is the "new beginning" proclaimed in the *Earth Charter*, which, thanks to cyberspace and new communications technology, will be facilitated by distant participation and will have an extraordinary impact in shaping the other possible world that humanity longs for and deserves.

2.1 The Current Great Challenges

- Attempts at world governance by the "G groups".[1]
- An economy based on greed, speculation and outsourcing of production. The result of neo-liberalism, in which the market has replaced values, has been catastrophic for mankind as a whole: social inequality has increased; multinationals have not only received economic power from nation-states but political responsibility as well, which is very troubling; and the lack of regulatory and sanctioning mechanisms to address supranational transgressions promotes sinister trafficking in weapons, drugs, people, patents and capital with total impunity... The existence of tax havens is likewise one of the greatest challenges for "normalization", which is required on a global scale.
- Immense military spending (4,000 million dollars daily) with the aggravating circumstance that the majority consists of outdated military hardware appropriate for past wars, which is useless in present-day conflicts.
- Exploitation instead of international cooperation, frequently implemented through huge consortia that blur the political responsibilities of governments and open wounds that are very difficult to heal in co-existence on an international scale.
- Untenable social inequality. Only 17% of mankind lives in the world's "wealthy neighborhood", the rest being distributed in progressive levels of hardship, with over 1 billion people living in conditions below poverty line. In that regard, food security[2] undoubtedly deserves special attention.
- Undue delays in courts, mechanisms, and legal institutions in charge of enforcing International law, resulting in numerous delinquents and offenders who act with total impunity.

The majority of these challenges began in 1989 or have increased ever since—the end of the "Cold War"—when expectations of global understanding, particularly through actions coordinated by a United Nations system duly endowed with the necessary personal, technical and financial resources, could have responded to the hope generated by the bloodless fall of the Soviet Union, the elimination of racial apartheid in South Africa and the successful conclusion of several peace processes (in El Salvador, Mozambique, Guatemala etc.).

"The possible solutions—that may render many of today's impossibilities as realities of tomorrow—must inevitably be based on equal dignity for all human beings and on social justice."

However, in just two decades, neoliberal "globalization" has prompted multiple (social, economic, food, environmental, democratic, ethical...) crises in which we are presently immersed; but for the first time in history we have the means for mobilizing people and involving citizens in local and global government, which enables us to affirm that we are living in fascinating times in which radical changes are now feasible.

3.1 Possible Solutions

... *"to face great challenges it is necessary to surpass the limits of what is possible".*
Dilma Rousseff, Brasilia, January 1, 2011

The possible solutions—that may render many of today's impossibilities as realities of tomorrow—must inevitably be based on equal dignity for all human beings and on social justice. Placing ethical and democratic values at the forefront of public and private activities, so that social justice, rather than the market, manages the economy at all levels, will enable us in a few years to rectify our present misguided direction and to get back on course.

- The "refounding" of the United Nations is one of the most important and urgent means of rectifying our present course, to endow humanity with the required guidance, coordination and justice systems. A transition from the current plutocracy to the "democracy" that the United Nations represents—certainly including within its scope the International Monetary Fund and the World Bank for Reconstruction and Development, as well as the World Trade Organization (deliberately placed in the early 1990s outside of the System's institutions), which along with a General Assembly with representation from member nations, international institutions and civil society—would provide the broad framework for governance and the international reference that the world needs. This multilateral framework must rapidly be adopted, if necessary through an immense mobilization of citizens, so that the

> power unduly ceded to the 20, 8, 7, 6... 2... 1 most wealthy countries of the world may cease. A diverse world urgently requires a plural system of governance, which must immediately be endowed with all the necessary resources.[3]

It is certainly true that the UN cannot be replaced by G groups that lack the institutional framework to enable them to implement any decisions taken.[4]

With all of the appropriate weighting of votes, but without veto rights, there would be three councils:

- Security Council
- Social and Economic Council
- Environmental Council

Together with BRIC (Brazil, Russia, India and China), other regional associations would be promoted: in addition to the United States (with Canada) and the European Union, in a few years, UNASUR in Latin America, the African Union, Central Asian and Southeast Asian organizations would become well established to facilitate world governance and the rapid formation of great alliances in the aforementioned areas, to avoid conflict to the maximum extent possible.

The capacity for foresight that must be present, especially in this type of systems, would likewise facilitate adoption of preventive measures and the means for reducing the impact of natural catastrophes.

In addition, the International Court of Justice and its associate legal institutions must be afforded greater efficiency to ensure strict enforcement of international law.

In that regard, over the years the United Nations has issued a series of essential document guides that, if implemented, would resolve many of the problems addressed.

In addition to the "classic" documents (United Nations Charter, Universal Declaration of Human Rights, Agenda 21, Commitments for Social Development, Declaration and Action Plan for a Culture of Peace), I would like to mention other more recent ones that could free us from the latest "pitfalls" of neoliberal globalization, such as the Declaration of the Latin American and Caribbean Unity Summit and the Cancun Declaration (on the international financial crisis; trade; energy; science and technology; social programs and the eradication of hunger and poverty; food and nutritional solidarity; education, health and public services, migration, gender; sustainable development, climate change; natural disasters; human rights; the global drug problem; terrorism ...).[5] In that regard the Cancun Declaration addresses practically all of the great challenges of our times... The problem is that the market still dictates the guidelines for politicians' conduct. But as I have already indicated, this undoubtedly won't last much longer.

Regarding Spain, an excellent report entitled "Global Change for Spain 2020/2050—Energy, Economy and Society"[6] was recently published.

"It is important to rapidly implement a genuine policy of alliances, summits and dialogues to increase transparency in relationships and behavior that at present, and unfortunately as is quite obvious, is motivated exclusively by profits."

3.2 Some of the Measures that Should be Adopted by the Abovementioned Councils of the New United Nations "System":

Security Council

- Nuclear Disarmament. Implement the decisions concerning progressive arms reduction (September 2009) recently agreed at an extraordinary session of the Security Council presided by President Barack Obama.
- New strategies. New weapons. The weapons industry "colossus" must adjust itself to the world's real security needs, ceasing to manufacture and impose on the "allies'" military equipment designed for past conflicts.
    - A "reasonable" level of disarmament is essential in the fight against poverty and in promoting universal access to education.[7]
- Coordination to reduce the impact of natural and man-made catastrophes. It is as incomprehensible as it is unacceptable that powerful countries that are armed to the teeth are totally helpless when faced with natural disasters, even recurring ones. There already exist appropriate closely-studied measures for different types (earthquakes, floods, fire volcanic eruptions etc.).[8]
- Capacity to arbitrate and resolve conflicts. When warranted, Blue Helmets and technology can be deployed proportionally in those conflicts that can't be prevented. They would likewise have the capacity to resolve disputes involving authoritarian regimes such as China, and in inadmissible situations of dominance, as is the case of Israel with respect to Palestine.
- Broad powers concerning legal systems that contravene human rights (the death penalty, for example).
- Peaceful co-existence. Security forces must ensure compliance with law, progressively reducing the hugely expensive military installations that to-date represent a large part of domestic spending in addition to the armed forces, with citizens being obliged to submit to the will of the states with power. The transition from a culture of violence and war to a culture of dialogue and peace would provide not only positive benefits in welfare and quality of life, but also boost citizens' self-esteem and reduce one of the largest and most inefficient areas of national economies. For this reason it is important to rapidly

implement a genuine policy of alliances, summits and dialogues to increase transparency in relationships and behavior that at present, and unfortunately as is quite obvious, is motivated exclusively by profits, while distractedly looking the other way.

- "It is important for us... to make sure that we are talking with each other in a way that heals, not that wounds", declared President Obama recently in an excellent speech in Tucson, Arizona. As he likewise did in El Cairo in June 2009 when offering an outstretched hand to Islam instead of declaring it an "axis of evil" as his predecessor George Bush did, the current President of the United States is attempting both at home and abroad to prompt a genuine "change of culture", which would have so much impact and significance on the legacy that we must leave to the coming generations.

Social and Economic Council, to achieve throughout the world:

"[The world needs] Foresight and capacity for immediate action to correct speculation and outsourcing of production, with profits that conceal precarious living and working conditions."

- Monetary, financial and trade regulation, especially through the corresponding, duly "re-modeled" institutions (IMF, WB and WTO).
- Immediate elimination of tax havens.
- Strict supervision of supranational trafficking, particularly of drugs that, like tobacco and alcohol, would be available at moderate prices, since it has been proved that high prices have no dissuasive effect and only promote mafias and narco-terrorism—currently experienced by conflict-prone countries such as Mexico—especially because the largest consumers (such as the United States) insist on reducing offer (exterior) rather than demand (interior).
- Foresight and capacity for immediate action to correct speculation and outsourcing of production,[9] with profits that conceal precarious living and working conditions.
    - "The financial markets have demonstrated their nearsightedness", wrote Nobel Prize winner Joseph Stiglitz[10]... "Only political change will put Europe and the United States back on the road to growth". Only with this global capacity can foresight prevent not only the markets' harassment of political governance but also the emergence of new "bubbles", such as the communications technology bubble in 1993 and the real estate bubble of 2008, while preventing tax fraud.[11]
- Raising funds by charging fees on electronic transactions,[12] essentially to be used in the fight against poverty[13] and major social objectives. Income generated by copyright of works in the public domain must also be used.[14]

- Implementation of a "basic income" in ways that are most appropriate for the most vulnerable sectors of the population.[15]
- Redesign global economic directives based on a new general consensus (such as the Barcelona Consensus)[16] and inspired in recent practice which deserves close analysis, such as the sustainable "blue economy" expressed in GNH (Gross National Happiness) implemented in Bhutan.[17]
- Economy based on sustainable global development to ensure the minimum conditions for a reasonable quality of life for all citizens. Specifically:
    - *Nutrition*:[18]
        - agriculture
        - aquaculture
        - biotechnology
    - *Water*:[19] collection, transfer, management, and adequate production through desalinization, particularly through the use of thermo-solar energy.
    - *Health*: access to the appropriate technical, clinical and therapeutic services. Demographic decrease has been compensated by greater longevity, which increases chronic treatment and neuro-degenerative illnesses. Promoting preventive measures, particularly with respect to potentially irreversible diseases such as loss of mental faculties resulting from genetic or post-natal alterations, undoubtedly constitutes the greatest victory both in medical as well as social and economic terms.
    - *Education*: Access for all citizens to an education that would enable them to make full use of their distinctive aptitudes (the capacity to think, imagine, invent, create) based on their own reflections and without being subjected to the dictates of others.

Environmental Council

This Council would coordinate and supervise compliance with guidelines for maintaining the world's conditions for habitability, based on important documents such as the Earth Charter.[20] In that regard Leonardo Boff has written about "safeguarding our Common Home".[21] Containing climate change and ensuring an ecological future are our personal daily responsibility and commitment. Briefly summarized, the following matters must be addressed:

- Sustainable energies:[22] Consumption of oil and other fossil fuels that produce carbonic anhydrase and other greenhouse gases is largely the cause of climate change and environmental degradation. The greed of oil producers is manifested in the fact that for many years they have attempted to hide the negative impact of using oil as practically our sole energy source.[23] In the present crisis, oil prices have played the greatest role in financial collapse, posing a serious threat to the slight economic recovery that was just commencing. It is essential to increase the renewable energy consumption levels to 40–45% within the next few years, especially in cities, using solar energy (photovoltaic and thermo-solar), wind energy, sea energy, nuclear fusion when possible and, in the meantime, nuclear fission, progressively introducing other sources such as thorium. Only then will it be possible to slow climate change before irreversible damage is done to the environment. Production of large quantities of thermo-solar energy in deserts could now be achieved with the use of graphene, obtained from an abundant mineral (graphite), which given the difficulty of storing energy would enable massive amounts to be transferred from production sites to distant places where it could be used.

Moreover, it is limiting consumption of oil and other fossil fuels that would ultimately enable us to enjoy this fundamental substrate for all organic chemistry syntheses for a longer period.

The geostrategies of "black gold" will rapidly change in a very short time. In fact, the petroleum industry's center of gravity is now shifting toward China, Russia and Brazil.[24]

- Quality of the seas: The majority of carbonic anhydride recapture takes place in the oceans in which phytoplankton, with chlorophyll (as is the case with green plants), captures the most oxidized form of carbon (CO_2) together with the most oxidized form of hydrogen (H_2O) and produces reduced compounds (fuels), thanks to solar energy. In consequence, deforestation must be regulated and the quality of the seas monitored; seas are presently affected by large oil tankers that, once again due to greed, discharge tank washing oil sludge into them instead of using the appropriate in-port installations, thus creating low-density oil residue on the ocean surface that asphyxiates phytoplankton cells, depleting their capacity as the "world's lungs". They occupy over 70% of the earth's surface.
- Soil quality: Particularly, regulation of the use of fertilizers and pesticides by the appropriate use of transgenics, conducting thorough research projects such as the transfer of nitrogenase systems typical in legumes to rice roots, rendering them capable of directly capturing atmospheric nitrogen, thus significantly reducing the consumption of nitrogen fertilizers.

"How can the transition be made at the speed required by the most powerful from nation-centric governance to world governance within the framework of a truly efficient United Nations system?"

4.1 At this Point We have Made Concrete Proposals to Meet the Current Great Challenges and to be Able to Commence Genuine "World Governance Based on Knowledge And Scientific Rigor".

But a question immediately arises: How can the transition be made at the speed required by the most powerful from nation-centric governance to world governance within the framework of a truly efficient United Nations system? Until now the answer was really difficult because the intervention of citizens in public matters was very limited. But finally, in the last few decades the possibility of participation via cyberspace has opened previously unimaginable opportunities not only to strengthen democracy, but also to promote policies, strategies and actions through massive virtual mobilizations that were heretofore impossible. The enormous powers of the media[25] attempt to maintain us as passive spectators, as distracted recipients, but I have no doubt—and this is our greatest present hope—that thanks to new communications technologies, citizen participation will greatly increase, intervening directly in decision-making. Citizen power and awareness of the need to speak for the voiceless, for those who are invisible,[26] will provoke profound changes throughout the world.

> *"Each citizen must be aware that he is capable of inventing his own future."*

Now more than ever, it is essential to recapture time, to eradicate the political inefficiency, detachment and indifference of so many citizens who have been badly misinformed by the partisan and biased communications media.

The outward changes required must commence with changes in each person's daily behavior. To achieve this great historic change, each citizen must be aware that he is capable of inventing his own future, fleeing the fatalism of what is perceived as inevitable or invincible.

Only then will it be possible to achieve the "new beginning" announced in the Earth Charter as the great objective of an inhabitable world for all, without exclusions. Yes, the 21st century can indeed be the century of the people because, as in Miquel Martí i Pol's poem, everyone will repeat: "...let me say that now is the time for love".

Author Contact Information
Email: fmayor@fund-culturadepaz.org

Notes

1 Carrillo Salcedo and Juan Antonio in "Las formaciones G en las relaciones internacionales contemporáneas. Entre el poder y la legitimidad: dos modelos para la gobernabilidad mundial", November 23, 2010, *Real Academia de Ciencias Políticas y Morales*

2 Federico Mayor, *Tiempo de acción* (Granada: University of Granada, 2008)

3 Mario Soares, "Los grandes desafíos de nuestro tiempo," *Other News,* 15th April 2008

4 Federico Mayor Blogs *"Naciones Unidas, sí. G-8, no; G-7 à G-8 à G-13 à Gà 20 ... à¡G-192!"; "Inermes frente a las catástrofes"; "¿El mundo tiene arreglo?"; "Alianza contra la pobreza"; "¡Peligro!: no hay tiempo para pensar; ¡La incontenible marea del ciber espacio ha comenzado!"; "Precio del petróleo y de los alimentos ... ¿volvemos a las andadas?"*

5 "Declaration of Cancun," *Cuadernos Americanos* 2, no. 132 (2010): 184–208

6 *Cambio global España 2020/2050. Energía, Economía y Sociedad* (Madrid: Centro Complutense de Estudios e Información Medioambiental, 2011)

7 *Una crisis encubierta: conflictos armados y educación* (Paris: UNESCO, 2011)

8 Federico Mayor, *Normas internacionales para la reducción del impacto de catástrofes naturales* Inaugural speech included in the published papers delivered during the International Conference on Natural Disasters held to commemorate the 75th anniversary of MAPFRE, Madrid, October 8–9, 2008

9 Heriberto Araujo and Juan Pablo Cardenal, "El mundo chino ya está aquí," *El País,* 11th February 2011

10 Joseph Stiglitz, "¿Qué nos depara el 2011?," *Other News,* 18th January 2011

11 Guillermo De la Dehesa, "¿Cómo recuperarse de la recesión?," *Revista de Occidente,* no. 348 (2010): 71–90

12 UBUNTU, "¡Es la hora de aplicar un impuesto sobre las transacciones internacionales de divisas!", *Comunicado* 30, September 17, 2010

13 "Manifiesto en favor de la vida, la paz y la igualdad," *Fundación Cultura de Paz,* 2006

14 Propuestas de *tasas de propiedad intelectual en obras de dominio público.* UNESCO proposal, Meeting in Castellón, 1998

15 *En tiempos de crisis, soluciones para la gente,* Fundación Cultura de Paz, December 10, 2008

16 *Nuevo Consenso: por un mundo habitable para todos,* Barcelona, Nova and Fundación Cultura de Paz, 2011

17 Gunter Pauli, *The Bhutan Blue Economy Initiative Global Signatories* (Winterthur: Club of Rome, 2010)

18 Federico Mayor, "Hambre, nutrición y crecimiento: panorámica mundial," *Real Academia Nacional de Medicina* 127, no. 1 (2010)

19 Federico Mayor, *La gestión del agua más allá de los países* (Zaragoza: EXPOAGUA, 2008)

20 *Earth Charter,* 2000

21 Leonardo Boff, *Teología para otro mundo posible* (Mexico City: PPC Ediciones, 2011), 220–230

22 Federico Mayor, *"Monografía sobre el mercado de emisiones de carbono"*, published in an issue of Revista de *Política Exterior* devoted to climate change and carbon trade (Winter, 2011)

23 "The Truth about Denial," *Newsweek,* 13th August 2007

24 Miguel Ángel García Vega, "El petróleo estrena geoestrategia," *El País*, 6th February 2011

25 Ignacio Ramonet, "El desastre mediático," *Other News,* 29th April 2008

26 Federico Mayor, "Los invisibles," *La Vanguardia,* 25th October 2007

READING 11

Hydropower, Encroachment and the Re-Patterning of Hydrosocial Territory

The Case of Hidrosogamoso in Colombia

Bibiana Duarte-Abadía, Rutgerd Boelends, and Tatiana Roa-Avendaño

Mega-hydraulic projects tend to produce severe social and environmental impacts, with burdens and benefits unevenly distributed among different social groups, regions, and scales. This triggers socioenvironmental conflicts, since "territory" has incommensurable functions and values for the diverse parties. This article examines the dominant human-nature interactions that underlie recent hydropower developments and the reconfiguration of the hydrosocial network in Colombia's Sogamoso basin. We use the Echelon of Rights Analysis (ERA) to examine conflicts over hydrosocial patterning, involving struggles over resources, norms, authority, and discourses. The Sogamoso mega-project highlights how modernist policies discursively frame clean energy, sustainable development, and public utility, while breaking up existing socioecological relationships and aligning water users, rights, and uses in new hydro-political network hierarchies. In Sogamoso, hydropower development discourse ends up declaring local subsistence activities illegal while denying existing rights frameworks. Therefore, crucial questions about water rights, legitimacy, and justice remain unasked and unanswered within political arenas.

Key words: hydropower, water governance, hydrosocial territories, natural resources conflict, Colombia

Bibiana Duarte-Abadía, Rutgerd Boelens, and Tatiana Roa-Avendaño, "Hydropower, Encroachment and the Re-patterning of Hydrosocial Territory: The Case of Hidrosogamoso in Colombia," *Human Organization*, vol. 74, no. 3, pp. 243-254.

COPYRIGHTED MATERIAL — DO NOT DUPLICATE, DISTRIBUTE, OR POST

Introduction

> *June 8, 2014. Environmental tragedy ... the Sogamoso River, Betulia, Santander has fallen completely dry. ISAGEN recognizes its error in operating the dam reservoir, but says that few fish died. Fishermen assure however that thousands of fish have died. ... The Sogamoso River's riparian areas turned into mud and stone beaches. ... Communities close the road and claim ISAGEN to take responsibility. Chronicle of a death foretold.*[1]

Contemporary intervention processes involving large-scale ecosystem transformation have major redistributive effects. In the case of mega-hydraulic projects and large-scale river diversion schemes, these impacts are usually to the advantage of powerful stakeholders outside the project area (such as mega-cities and industries) and mostly to the disadvantage of the vulnerable groups in the affected river basin territory (McCully 2001; Moore, Dore, and Gyawali 2010; Sneddon and Fox 2008; WCD 2000). Development of hydropower plants is an important driver of such transformations, and the case of Hidrosogamoso in the Department of Santander in northeast Colombia is illustrative. Construction of the hydropower plant in the Sogamoso River started in 2009 and was finished at the end of 2014. At the moment, the dam inundates an area of thousands of hectares, affecting a large number of communities and the territory-based livelihoods of many people (Roa-Avendaño and Duarte-Abadía 2012).

The project received strong support from international institutions, the national government, and the private sector, which used arguments of overall public interest, "clean" energy, the environment, and the national economy to legitimize it. Support for the project implies a prioritization of high-value urban electricity over the water needs of fishermen and peasant subsistence agriculture. However, project plans claim that the hydropower plant's so-called non-consumptive water use is not competing with the diverse consumptive and livelihood-based water uses of the territory's stakeholders (DNP 2007).

In Sogamoso, this claim is contested by local residents. They are confronted with the re-patterning of their existing hydrosocial networks and profound changes in the ecosystems on which their livelihoods depend. Experiences to date show how some collective land and water user groups have been forced to privatize and sell their properties while other properties were outright expropriated. In Colombia, constitutional and legal norms for building infrastructure projects in indigenous and community territories require agreements between companies, the Government, and the people affected. The Sogamoso basin experience, however, seems to indicate that the interplay of negotiations is significantly asymmetrical. Values placed on territories are different for the diverse parties and often incommensurable (see also Escobar 2011; Martinez-Allier 2002). Socioenvironmental conflicts have been growing since the early phases of hydroelectric construction, while deterritorialization profoundly challenges the local social fabric.

This article examines the profound alterations in the existing human-nature interactions triggered by Hidrosogamoso hydropower development and analyzes the impact and effects of such changes in the local, socionatural territory, conceptualized as a hydrosocial network intersecting biophysical, ecological, sociocultural, and political-economic domains.[2] The section below reviews the broader debate and conceptual background of hydropower and large dam interventions that trigger the profound socioecological transformation of hydrosocial territories. It also proposes a conceptual framework for analyzing water conflicts in terms of struggles over resources, norms, authority, and discourses. The third section describes the reconfiguration of the territory that is affected, and the fourth analyzes the socioenvironmental conflicts that emerge as a result of changing control over water in the river basin. It examines how the negotiation strategies used by the Electrical Interconnection Company (ISA, currently known as ISAGEN, a government-owned company with private shareholders under the control of the Ministry of Mines and Energy), weaken and fend off any political action by affected communities to defend their territory-based livelihoods. The fifth section presents the responses by affected groups and their support networks and analyzes how the capacity to decide about territorial reaccommodation and control over water is significantly geared toward serving the Company's interests. We conclude that mega-hydropower projects (such as the one in the Sogamoso basin), presented as a symbol of progress and modernity under the powerful discourse of globalizing development, profoundly undermine existing livelihood practices and hydrosocial territoriality in order to re-pattern humans, hydraulics, and nature in a dominant, externally driven, hydro-political network hierarchy. They produce and legitimize structural violence, in which political debate, local ecological-cultural values, and alternative human-nature worldviews regarding the river's life cycle, are delegitimized and made invisible.

Hydropower and the (Re)patterning of Hydrosocial Territories

Large Dam Development and the Revival of Hydropower

In the last decades, the development of hydropower and large hydraulic infrastructure has become an increasingly controversial issue, generating intense disputes between proponents and protesters and triggering broad societal struggle. Building large-scale water infrastructure has proven to have huge social and environmental impacts, whereby burdens and benefits are unevenly distributed among different social groups, regions, and scales (McCully 2001; Molle and Floch 2008; WCD 2000). Large dams grossly change hydrological regimes and tend to irreversibly alter local community livelihoods. Often, in many places around the world, hydropower projects result in dispossession, expropriation, or resettlement without compensation (see Cesnea 1999; Steiner 2010).

Large-scale interventions in hydrological regimes have received growing scholarly and public critique, as embodiments of mono-disciplinary, top-down, and supply-side water resources development. However, more recently, their worldwide planning has gained a new impetus through their representation as important ingredients of the new "green economy" (Sneddon and Fox 2008; Swyngedouw 2014). Hydropower generation is currently a key justification for large dam projects, supported by the discourses of clean development and climate change control. New mega-works, however, often ignore the lessons of past decades, while disregarding their own contribution to climate change (Jasanoff 2010; Moore, Dore, and Gyawali 2010). A continuing controversy relates to how new mega-hydraulic projects prioritize industrial and large urban interests over those of indigenous territories, peasant livelihoods, and local food security issues.

It seems that the iron triangles of state bureaucracies, politicians, and engineering schools—in interaction with private companies—are a decisive factor in preferring large-scale hydraulic works over more context-adapted, interactive, and less expensive alternatives. Large hydropower facilities, indeed, are normally embedded in powerful hydrosocial networks (Boelens and Post Uiterweer 2013; Molle, Mollinga, and Wester 2009; Swyngedouw 2014). Entwining political and economic power, they strategically deploy the globalizing discourse of water scarcity, efficiency, rational planning, and national progress to legitimize their plans, sidelining proposals with less socioenvironmental impact and more support for local socioeconomic development and cultural practice.

Society-Nature-Technology Interaction and the Reconfiguration of Hydrosocial Territories

Territorial places such as the Sogamoso basin, commonly presented as natural environments, are actively constructed and historically produced "sociophysical realities" or "waterscapes" (Swyngedouw 2007, 2014). They are the outcomes of socioenvironmental interaction processes. The boundaries between nature and society, besides exposing "actual reality," are the products of human imagination and social and scientific agreements (e.g., White 1995). Political ecology and Science and Technology Studies have argued how these socionatural (hydrosocial) networks, entwining the social, the biophysical, and the technological, are constituted (see, e.g., Latour 1993; Swyngedouw 2007). Water flows, water use systems, hydrological cycles, etc., and their linkages at micro, meso, and macro scales, are mediated by power relations and human intervention, thereby constituting new hydrogeographies (see, e.g., Bakker 2010; Boelens 2014; Budds 2009; Swyngedouw 2014; Whatmore 2002). "Hydrosocial territory" refers to:

> The contested imaginary and socioenvironmental materialization of a spatial, multi-scalar network in which humans, water flows, ecological relations, hydraulic infrastructure, financial means, legal-administrative arrangements, and cultural institutions and practices are interactively defined, aligned, and mobilized through epistemological belief systems, political hierarchies, and naturalizing regimes of representation. (Boelens et al. n.d.)

Given its contested cultural and political nature (see Hoogesteger, Boelens, and Baud n.d.; Saldîas et al. 2012; Seemann n.d.), the question of how the boundaries between nature and society are conceptualized, how the interlinkages among particular natural, social, and technological elements are established to pattern hydrosocial networks, by which actors and with what interests and consequences, is fundamental (McCarthy and Prudham 2004; Robbins 2004; Swyngedouw 2014). By de-patteming existing water territories and hydrosocial networks and re-patterning them in particular ways through new alliances among humans and non-humans, hydropower and large dam projects induce development and marginalization, and benefits and burdens, in differential ways for different groups of people (Zwarteveen and Boelens 2014).

Dominant hydroelectric powers often tend to obscure this "man-made," political construction of socionatures, for instance, through the naturalization of rivers, hydrological cycles, and even water distribution systems. Denying water's "humanized nature" (see Boelens et al. n.d.; Mosse 2008; White 1995) and locating the latter in the realm of (purified) nature (Latour 1993), of natural laws, and of naturally best solutions is a common strategy to depoliticize water questions that deeply influence politics and decision making (Zwarteveen and Boelens 2014; see also Swyngedouw 2014). In other words, water flows actively shape, connect, invigorate, destroy, and mediate society and nature, and they are also a deeply contested resource steered by politics (Kaika 2006; Swyngedouw 2007, 2014). Therefore, understanding how river basin configuration and hydropower development are based on socionatural politics provides opportunities to critically scrutinize the power-laden contents of dominant hydrosocial regimes and networks.

To examine the water conflict in the Sogamoso basin, we use the Echelons of Rights Analysis (ERA) (e.g. Boelens 2009; Zwarteveen and Boelens 2014). It distinguishes four interlinked echelons, associated with the levels at which contestation over water occurs. The first echelon, involving the domain of resources (e.g., water, land, labor) and technologies, looks at conflicting interests regarding water flows and patterns of use and access, commonly mediated by technologies (e.g., hydraulic infrastructure). It therefore relates to conflicts over how water access—in terms of quantity, quality, and timeliness—needs to be patterned among societal and ecological uses and user groups. The second echelon considers conflicts over the norms and rules defining water allocation, contamination, and water-related risks. It highlights the dynamics of water rights and claimmaking powers, illuminating how diverging norms, rules, laws, and policy regulations conflict in the water arena. The third echelon regards the question of who has the authority and legitimacy to define the rules and norms of water allocation, contamination, and risk. Here, we see a diversity of competing values and decision stakes and a multitude of interest groups with different views and frameworks of interpretation. The third echelon focuses on power, legitimacy, scales of water governance, and how water decision making among diverse groups is organized. Finally, the fourth echelon deals with the conflicting discourses and worldviews for justifying or articulating particular water realities and policies. This echelon links the foregoing ones and enables the critical analysis of conflicting water policies, theories, and models. It reveals how discourses are strategically used to contest particular allocations of water.

The Cultural Politics of Violence and Dispossession

The interlinked echelons demonstrate that both overt conflicts and encounters and, importantly, the underlying societal contradictions deeply structure, energize, and color the tensions that manifest above and beneath the surface. As Galtung (1990) explains, these contradictions are ingrained in the structure of class domination and political-economic inequality and are the foundation of structural violence (or as Zizek [2009] (re)conceptualized it: "systemic violence"). Structural/systemic violence connects in a triangular way to direct violence (based on attitudes) and cultural violence (particularly along lines of ethnicity, race, and gender). In Latin America and in countries such as Colombia in particular, capitalist accumulation and dispossession are profoundly ethnicized and racialized, and moreover, the conflict is deeply determined by para-military violence (e.g. Rosero 2007). Together, the forms of violence find permanent backing through discursive violence, or the creation and reproduction of a world of meaning that is taken for granted. In many different configurations, these forms of violence entwine and are naturalized: they become the "normal state of being" (Foucault 1982, 2007; Zizek 2009).

Pécaut (2000) and Oslender (2008), among others, elaborate on how these "geographies of terror" are constituted and normalized in the case of Colombia, with strong support and complicity across multiple layers of government, national elites, and transnational companies. Rodrîguez-Garavito and Orduz-Salinas (2012) and Vélez-Torres (2012), among others, show how these forms of class-based, ethinicized, and racialized violence and dispossession are importantly linked to hydropower development in Colombia. In exemplary cases politics of disciplining and cultural categorization (superior/inferior) are deployed. In other words, cultural politics deeply color the contestations that take place within each of the four Echelons of Rights (that is, in terms of distributing fundamental resources; setting the rules, rights, and obligations; sanctioning the culturally appropriate forms of authority and decision making; and naturalizing particular worldviews). Politics of cultural disciplining aim to generate values, beliefs, and behaviors that provide legitimacy to dominant water policies and unequal resource distribution practices. In practice, however, subaltern water user groups and communities employ strategies of deviance and resistance to counteract these politics. Before examining how water conflicts unfold within the four echelons, we present an outline of territorial change under the Hidrosogamoso hydropower development.

Hidrosogamoso: Deterritorialization and the Reconfiguration of a New Water Territory

Colombia, like most countries on the continent, is racing headlong to promote the extraction-export model in the quest for economic growth. Under neoliberalism the country has laid the legal and institutional foundations to protect and institutionalize large national and transnational companies' rights. It aims to attract foreign investors by providing them with natural resources, subsidies, and large amounts of energy (see Baud, de Castro, and Hogenboom 2011; Roa-Avendaño and Duarte-Abadîa 2013; Svampa 2011). Accordingly, numerous hydroelectric projects have emerged, since petroleum reserves are running dry, and fuel prices are escalating.

The Hidrosogamoso project is illustrative of these large-scale developments. It was planned in the 1970s but was more recently revived when financial and political conditions to construct and operate it developed. The dam, owned by ISAGEN, is part of an array of projects in the mid-basin of the Magdalena River, with both national and international economic stakeholders.[3] The project, with a projected hydropower generation capacity of 820 megawatts, aims to cover 10 percent of the national energy demand and export electrical energy to neighboring countries. The hydraulic mega-project activities of Hidrosogamoso are located in the Department of Santander, in the canyon where the Sogamoso River crosses the La Paz Mountains, down to the Magdalena River, forming an extensive alluvial zone that floods during the rainy season (see Map 9.1).

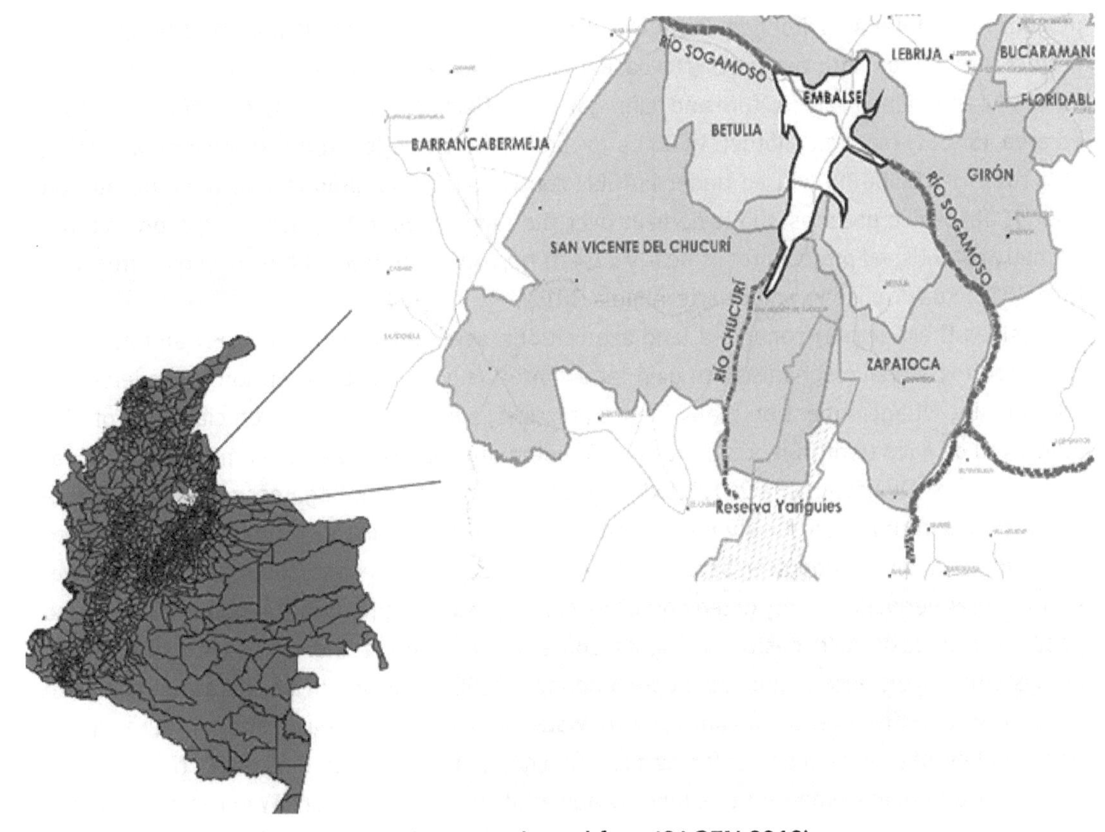

Map 9.1 **Project Influence Area (Source: Adapted from ISAGEN 2013)**

For centuries, fishing people, landless rural villagers, and settler farmers have taken advantage of the regular flooding in the lower basin of the Sogamoso. Historically, they established complex networks of food exchanges with indigenous communities. More recently, they have traded with local communities settled in the Yariguies mountains, the upper basin, and toward the wetlands and surrounding areas, following this "amphibian rhythm." That is, local population groups strategically use the river and swamps intermittently, depending on the time of year (Baleta 2005; Fals Borda 2002). Historically, the wealth of fish in the Sogamoso lower river and its wetlands enabled fishing-based livelihoods: since the end of the 19th century, people from diverse regions have resettled in the alluvial plains because the river ecosystems (gallery forests, broad beaches, islets, and wetlands) provided livelihood opportunities for those who came to escape from war and hunger (Archila 2006).

The Hidrosogamoso dam is 190 m high, with a storage capacity of 4,800 millions of cubic metters. Currently, by damming the waters of the Sogamoso River, the hydropower project is flooding an area of 7,000 ha upstream, affecting the eight municipalities where the Sogamoso empties into the Magdalena River: Girón, Betulia, Zapatoca, Los Santos, Villanueva, Barichara, San Vicente de Chucuri, and Lebrija. Although Girón loses the most land to the project with 32 percent of its total area flooded, Betulia will be the municipality most impacted because the project is dividing it into two parts (Novoa, Pardo, and Rico 2011). According to official data, 900 families dependent on agriculture and fishing will be affected. In addition to the reservoir-flooded area, ISAGEN requires another 3,500 ha for project construction and conservation activities, so a total of 10,500 ha will be under ISAGEN control. And, according to Executive Resolution 230 (2008) which declares public domain over the land required to construct the project, the formally established project area is nearly 21,420 ha, triple the flooded area (Novoa, Pardo, and Rico 2011; Roa-Avendaño and Duarte-Abadía 2012).

Besides these legally condoned land acquisitions, as detailed below, ISAGEN and its allies also used extralegal mechanisms to gain land control (e.g., financial co-option of leaders) and, additionally, villagers mention many illegal practices, such as corrupting officials, use of violence, and *de facto* territorial occupations by flooding and dispossession of common lands (Roa-Avendaño and Duarte-Abadía 2012). Existing territories along the Sogamoso River are deeply de-patterned through the newly introduced social and power relationships, and re-patterned according to a new hydropower-based configuration (see also Manzano 2009). The hydro-power socionatural network actively deterritorializes existing ways of life, creating boundaries around people's previously held customary rights and severely limiting their access to the aquatic ecosystems' subsistence resources (Roa-Avendaño 2010). Construction of Hidrosogamoso will give ISAGEN control over local communities' water: it changes the seasonality of flooding and non-flooding of their land and enforces a radical change in ownership because of the appropriation, use, and management of this land by powerful third-party sectors. Water is accumulated or dammed up, first of all, to generate energy. Then other fields of domination come, one after the other, such as industrial fishing, commercial tourism projects, and control over allocation of water for agriculture, drinking water supply, and other productive activities. In short, this is a form of "accumulation by dispossession" (Harvey 2003): capitalist hydropower development intensifies the number of people excluded from their territories, obliging them to abandon their biodiversity-based livelihoods. Dispossession of water needs to be understood beyond simply the accumulation of the liquid water: it entails a wholesale of transformation of nature-society water dynamics.

Now, five years after beginning construction on the hydropower project, the river's transformed hydrological regime has generated important changes in the quality and quantity of water flows. Water quality is affected by five factors: first, geochemicals are released from rocks during dynamiting to build tunnels and the dam wall. Second, the capacity to regulate and ecologically filter the water is lost by damming the water and increasing the rate of deforestation in the La Paz mountains. The latter also increases the occurrence of natural disasters during extreme flows.[4] Third, non-organic building materials and sewage from camps pollute the area. Fourth, geomorphological changes in the riparian ecosystem of the basin destabilize the slopes during project construction. And fifth, high migration into the zone increases the demand for water and the dumping of solid and liquid wastes. Just as important are the water quantity problems that result from deviating the river and damming its water. All these environmental transformations have a deep, negative impact on the livelihoods of the people who depend directly on the river for fishing, small-scale mining, and subsistence agriculture.

On the one hand, their food sovereignty is threatened by the high, uncontrolled death of fish. Currently, fish have become scarce in the region while the remaining fish may be too contaminated to eat. In the Llanito wetlands, community leaders affirm that fishing activity is reduced by 70 percent: over 20 tons will no longer be sold, affecting 1,200 fishers (Gamarra and Suárez 2011). On the other hand, fishers, women who sell fish, and small farmers have been displaced by the project, and their activities have been prohibited or restricted. This has eliminated the people's food security and autonomy, making their livelihoods increasingly dependent on the outside market. Fishers are kept out of fishing areas while shops have increased product sales and prices; further, destruction of the dry parts of rivers (beaches and dunes) prevents planting of subsistence crops. So, at the same time that the cost of living (rent, services, food) rose sharply in the zone around the hydroelectric construction, residents have lost access to their livelihoods. Similarly, people living downstream from the worksite have no water supply and have to drink water directly from the river and nearby gullies. Many residents who lost their livelihoods now offer cheap labor for the operating companies and contractors; the women seek alternative income sources or depend on their children or husbands who work for the company.

These socioecological impacts, generated in the first phase of construction, are kept quiet by offering alternative development proposals, to be pursued by the hydroelectric company after construction is completed. Most of these proposals involve transforming the Sogamoso River into a tourist asset. In the wetlands, commercial fishing is already largely replacing local families' subsistence-based fishing practice. Rather than addressing the impacts generated by the dam on water security, food sovereignty, and self-esteem, people are induced to participate in new, externally constituted social institutions, in which local water flows are governed by market dynamics. This implies a break in socioecological interactions grounded in a cultural legacy and local production of the knowledge necessary to maintain equilibrium in riparian ecosystems. Instead, people's social insecurity becomes more intense. In the words of a village leader, "It is clear to see that this changed our lives, but for the worse. They promised us work, but then they hired contractors. … For instance, we have our communal neighborhood aqueduct, but now they are building a municipal aqueduct, to charge us more and make us beg for water" (personal communication, July 2011).

Despite ISAGEN project statements, people lack the opportunities to prevent risk in relation to hydropower development impacts. In general, people are uninformed of their rights, and the Company takes advantage of this situation. The alternative "social inclusion projects," in everyday practice, appear to be a means to exclude the riverside population from the newly established patterns of appropriating natural assets within the new territory.

Conflicting Interests and Negotiations over Hydrosocial Patterning

We use the four levels of water conflict analysis (developed in the ERA) to examine the negotiation strategies defining the new water control and management patterns in the Sogamoso basin. To understand the dynamics of water conflicts, we focus on the struggle over the redistribution of natural assets and resources; over the contents of rules, rights, and regulations; over the legitimate authority to establish those rules and institutions; as well as the different discourses that orient human behavior and sustain (or challenge) water development policies, regulation, and particular authority. Struggles over the fourth echelon, of conflicting discourses, aim to coherently link and give particular shape to the foregoing three echelons, establishing a convincing regime of representation for water governance in Sogamoso's hydrosocial territory.

Conflicts over the Redistribution of Natural Assets and Water-Related Resources

In the Sogamoso basin, the fundamental change to the river's hydrological regime has generated enormous impact. Some communities will get flooded, others will lay dry. Changes occur in water volumes and flows as a result of hydropower water storage regimes and because of release flow practices affecting downstream communities. Hidrosogamoso has also profoundly changed the river's ecological base flow regime. Consequently, fishermen and farmers have seen a dramatic loss of water and water-related resources. For many of them, this has meant a destruction of their subsistence livelihoods. Meanwhile, capital accumulation remains externally oriented.

This re-patterning of the distribution of water resources and related assets is skewed towards the new power structures in the basin. Job offerings and a myriad of socioeconomic projects proposed by the company for local residents, such as improving roads, upgrading housing, and public services (e.g., sewerage and water supply) are neatly suited to ISAGEN's own needs. They help foster acceptance of the project and benefit the establishment of settlements that are conducive to the ISAGEN's own interests. Nevertheless, these proposals are advertised as the benefits of progress and development that the river population will receive. Formulating alternative projects to compensate for the negative effects of the hydroelectric projects is mediated by environmental NGOs directly working for the company.

The Hidrosogamoso project has powerful political support from the government at all levels, which makes communities feel that they are at a strong disadvantage during negotiations. The resources promised by the company, rather than constituting tangible alternatives for livelihood development, consist of strategies to reaccommodate their territory and co-opt stakeholders. For instance, several local residents already have accepted the compensation plans offered by ISAGEN, which include indemnities, job offers, and/or land purchases. This situation is provoking divisions and conflicts within the community over access to the promised resources.

Economic and social compensations for affected groups are framed in a production/reproduction logic that is totally different from the livelihood rationalities that used to prevail in the Sogamoso basin. The ways of valuing the fundamental assets and their place within socioeconomic and cultural production systems are deeply incompatible (see also Martinez-Alier 2004). In practice, this worsens ecological-distributive conflicts. The monetary compensations, for example, are not just minimal but especially reductionist in the eyes of the local communities; they can never compensate for the social, cultural, and environmental damage generated by alterations in the river's natural dynamics.[5]

The Contents of Rules and Norms

From the outset, the Hidrosogamoso project has contradicted both the customary rulemaking and governance systems in the basin and the formally established rights to participation, information, and a healthy environment (see also Vos, Boelens, and Bustamante 2006). Work was begun without respecting these rights, which are recognized in Colombia's Constitution. In fact, the environmental public hearing was held after construction had begun (Roa-Avendaño and Duarte-Abadía 2012). When Hidrosogamoso was declared to be of public interest, over 10,000 ha were expropriated from the farmers in the region. The Sogamoso events show how customary rights become invisible and come to fall outside official recognition frameworks when powerful commercial interests are at stake. ISAGEN obtained its environmental license without holding a public hearing, while large landowners and ranchers negotiated with the Company behind closed doors to get their rights claims materialized. At the same time, fishers in El Llanito (the lower Sogamoso River—Barrancabermeja), who seek to practice their customary rules and rights and maintain intergenerational ecological balance in the zone, are denied the right to regulate their wetland, unless this is approved within the project's physical planning.

Although leaders of the fishers' organization recognize the impacts that the dam will have on the river and wetlands, they do not feel they have the social force to curb the project, and therefore they have been negotiating with ISAGEN in order to survive. Fishers try to take advantage of the backing provided by Law 99, a Colombian Environmental Policy created in 1993, which obliges hydroelectric plants to finance watershed planning, fishing, and aquiculture plans. Following a pragmatic strategy, they strive to be recognized as stakeholders in the territory.

However, they have not renounced the possibility of posing resistance if their expectations for negotiation do not materialize. Formally, national legislation views wetlands as collective areas for common use, where civil works cannot be built if they affect territorial livelihoods. However, in Colombia's everyday, power-laden practice, agglomeration of large properties for cattle raising, agroindustrial projects, and petroleum activities have interfered with the development of collective territoriality and the ecological regulation of Sogamoso wetlands. In this context, local fishers' negotiations with ISAGEN initially focused on curbing both the appropriation of the wetlands by large landowners and their interference in community-based management plans.

Conflicts over rules and rights, indeed, are crucial in the Sogamoso basin and reconfigure the hydrosocial network. These conflicts play out in the arena of official versus customary rulemaking frameworks but are equally important when local communities face the rules of intervening companies. The company uses its power to divide and rule, allowing some local practices while forbidding others. For example, small-scale miners working under customary rules were driven from their work areas (dry areas that are part of the riverbed) over which ISAGEN has gained formal rights. Similarly, subsistence agriculture is displaced by declaring the project's zone of influence a "public domain." This means that farmers' traditional activities are declared illegal, creating a de facto enclosure of the commons.

In the end, the practice of rulemaking and enforcement follows the laws of power in the basin. For instance, although construction of the mega-project pollutes the water and negatively impacts native fish species, the environmental license and management plans are ultimately only formalities.[6] This shows how Sogamoso's hydropower rulemaking practice increasingly aligns local, regional, and national government bodies, to the detriment of local people and the rules and rights that used to structure their livelihood practices.

Who Holds Legitimate Authority

The construction of dams such as Hidrosogamoso is an exercise in the power that dominant national and global actors hold over others, using nature as an instrument (see also McCully 2001). Here, an elite controls water and reorganizes the territory in terms of their own interests, restricting and conditioning other social groups' access. Clearly, the Sogamoso River no longer flows freely but is expropriated through a multi-scalar alliance with privileged authority. The newly introduced water governance concepts relate to formal state authority, the financial-economic power of transnationally operating companies, and scientific expert knowledge; positivistic and universalized laws are used to validate and unify the diversity of water management forms.

Over the last two decades, a powerful cluster of actors has formed to not only build the project but also make and rule the territory. This network did not replace formal government but gradually embedded national and local government in its hydrosocial network, increasingly weakening the power of diverse, local, and customary authorities. From 1973 to 1976, ISAGEN engaged the Hidroestudios-Harza engineering firm to conduct the feasibility study. Several foreign companies were involved, fostered by the investor confidence model promoted by recent governments, including Siemens from Germany which is renting machinery, Impregilo from Italy which is operating the project, and the Banco Santander from Spain which is lending to purchase machinery.

Much of the project area belonged to powerful landlords connected to para-militarism. These stakeholders negotiated directly with ISAGEN over their land use and became important network allies. Council members from local municipalities have worked to persuade others with legal land ownership to end their resistance and join in negotiations. At the same time, regional politicians have taken advantage of the company's development plans, including them as achievements of their government projects. Similarly, candidates for municipalities have negotiated their campaign funding in exchange for incorporating the development model offered by ISAGEN in their campaign platforms.

So, in most cases, the communities learn about the project directly through ISAGEN. Therefore, the Regional Government and municipalities get out of the way, no longer serving as government authorities defending their constituencies' interests but rather becoming facilitators of the intervention. Among many illustrations is the role played by public officials responsible for employment and consensus-building. When affected families and workers mobilized against the company's plans and working practices, in both cases, regional authorities assumed apparent neutrality regarding the conflict while, in fact, sustaining the Company's territorial re-patterning proposals (rather than enforcing the rights of the affected people). The alliance among political and economic powers makes social and political action by local communities difficult. In Sogamoso, this new "hydrocracy" holds powerful authority as a network of interests linking politicians, building companies, landowners, and development banks. This hydrosocial re-patterning of authority takes place within a neoliberal policy environment in which the government has stopped playing its role in supplying public services while letting the private sector manage water in the region.

Struggle over and among Discourses

> In Santander, there has never been any project of the magnitude of the Sogamoso River hydroelectric construction, nor will there ever be any. A long-cherished aspiration of Santandereans for decades.[7]

The global energy crisis, generated both by the high costs of petroleum and by the decrease in reserves and increased energy consumption worldwide, drives expanded construction of hydroelectric mega-dams. In Colombia, discourses of energy security, competitiveness, productivity, development, and environmental sustainability further reinforce the promotion and acceptance of these projects (Roa-Avendaño and Duarte-Abadía 2012, 2013). Consequently, Colombia neatly follows the current international discourse that frames hydropower as a key "clean development mechanism," claiming among other benefits that reservoirs would reduce greenhouse gas emissions from fossil-fuel-fired powerplants (e.g. Jasanoff 2010; McCully 2001).

Control over nature is discursively framed as progress and civilization. It is no coincidence that ISAGEN christened the dam "Tora," a Yariguie word that means "The place where man controls the river." Luis Fernando Rico-Pinzón, ISAGEN's manager, explained, "What we did was cut off the Sogamoso River, to force it through some tunnels 800 m long, to leave an 800 m stretch of river dry, to build the dam" (Gamarra and Suárez 2011). This illustrates how the construction of dams like Hidrosogamoso is a form of conquest, an act of taming nature for the benefit of mankind. As Kaika (2006) expresses, such projects reconfigure the relationships between nature and urban spaces to fulfil the Promethean endeavor of modernization. They act as a symbol of modernity and bring foreign investment accompanied by advanced water engineering knowledge, establishing or strengthening the status quo in geopolitical relations (Boelens and Post Uiterweer 2013). Also in Colombia, mega-hydraulic dams are seen as an infrastructure of progress, reinforcing discourses of (Western-oriented and racialized) nationhood.

The media, politicians, public institutions, and many academicians joined in presenting a view of the Hidrosogamoso project as bringing progress to an undeveloped region, where government action always had been deficient. In other words, the project theoretically addresses this past negligence through a modern, public-private collaboration, installing efficient rules and authority to order the public domain. Paradoxically, this same discourse of transforming backwardness serves to exclude local people and expropriate the assets of those who cannot negotiate in the name of development. Local communities are dispossessed of their customary rights, while Hidrosogamoso is constructed under a discourse of social welfare.

At the same time, the company positions itself in the territory as a development alternative that will bring improvements through jobs, socioeconomic projects, roads, upgraded housing, and public services such as sewers and potable water supply. Discourses of inclusion, participation, and recognition of farmers and fishers are strategically deployed to stifle opposition by local communities. ISAGEN and government agents seek legitimacy for the territorial re-patterning project through a process of social organization and including people in work commissions. So, communities' formal participation commits them to staying in the negotiation game to accept and identify with the project. However, their mandates do not allow for critical questioning of the hydropower territorial transformation itself. They can talk about the mitigation of effects and suggest adaptations that are in line with the territorial re-patterning process but cannot deviate from its basic design. The Hidrosogamoso's hydrosocial network establishes subtle mechanisms of alignment and inclusion.

The role of NGOs and local government programs is critical for legitimizing the discourses of participation and inclusion. In the Sogamoso project, ISAGEN hired an environmental NGO to mediate relations with communities regarding socioenvironmental impacts generated by the dam. The NGO, through environmental education programs, emphasizes local residents' inadequate environmental practices. Another key role is played by the Mid-Magdalena Peace and Development Program (PPDMM), funded mainly by international cooperation and Colombian companies such as Ecopetrol, ISA, and ISAGEN. The program argues, "All conflicts can be peacefully settled politically, with all parties involved, without exclusion, working for development" (Saavedra 2010:3). References to peaceful solutions in a conflict-ridden region are discursively powerful; indeed, for decades the program has facilitated dialogues among the different stakeholders living in the area. In the Sogamoso basin, agreements follow the conditioning factors of power and are facilitated by poverty and marginalization (see also Escobar 2011). This situation leads to both paternalistic development discourses and subtle discursive forces aimed at aligning local villagers. Asymmetrical negotiations result, where the rules of play are set beforehand by the powerful players and the local population has to accept them.

Social Response of People Affected

The historical context and current sociopolitical dynamics of the zone, involving powerful geopolitical interests, armed conflict, demographic growth, and nomadic communities fleeing from the war, provide a feeble standing for the affected people to negotiate their interests and defend their livelihoods (Roa-Avendaño and Duarte-Abadía 2012). In this region, abundant in natural bounties, the local residents have lived under harsh social conditions and inequitable distribution of resources. This situation produces feelings of "abandonment that can produce both powerlessness and rebelliousness" (Archila 2006:474); both factors have molded their political action in negotiations.

The people affected are small farmers, fishers, fish sellers, migrants, and small-scale miners who extract and gather gravel and sand from the river in dump trucks to sell. They are part of the population that is never recognized by the Colombian state because they have no papers, land title, or registered capital. These communities have found a place to settle on the river because of the very freedom of resources that the river makes available for them to survive. The fact that many are communities that have disintegrated during the last thirty years due to the war, together with the recent peopling of the middle basin, tends to weaken the negotiation power of the heterogeneous groups living within the territory. It requires time to achieve social cohesion and construct new collective, territorial identities in order to respond to proposed transformations. Nevertheless, in 2008 the Social Movement for Defense of the Sogamoso River[8] was formed by environmentalists, NGOs, union leaders, workers, some community leaders, and residents in the dam's impact area. The movement seeks to integrate and unify the people affected in the watershed in order to oppose the project. However, their organizational process began after the project's construction and environmental licensing was a done deal; as of 2009, much of the information was unavailable to the affected residents. This inequality in negotiations and absence of genuine consultation regarding the project has led to polarization between communities that resist the project and do not want to negotiate with the company and those who seek a supposed benefit from the project.

Through intensive dissemination, debate, and capacity-building, the Movement seeks to expand knowledge about the project's dimensions and its possible implications for local residents' territory and livelihoods. It aims to overcome the lack of information about the project and fight for recognition of the rights of affected people. Citizen participation mechanisms, recognized in the Constitution, are strategically used to call for public environmental hearings and to spread information about the project. This intensifies the zone's struggle for recognition of rights. The Movement brings together the diverse expressions of local residents' discontent and organizes marches and protests in the zone and mobilizations toward Bucaramanga, demanding responses from the departmental government.

So far, those negotiations have made little headway on the agreed issues. ISAGEN continues reinforcing its strategy of social reorganization through meetings, work groups, and the allocation of funds to design small, alternative development projects. The discourse and strategies of ISAGEN have successfully co-opted a number of social leaders, who complement and consolidate the dominant hydro-territorial alliance formed among the company, regional authorities, private firms, and the mass media. This situation conceals and stigmatizes the opposition to the dam, so the voices of the resistance movement have a hard time blocking the project or achieving recognition of the rights of the affected people.

Conclusions

This article demonstrates how hydropower development in the Sogamoso River Basin affects territorial resource bases, water control practices, and the broader livelihood strategies of marginalized, affected groups. It offers insights into the material and discursive practices that concretize and legitimize large-scale river water diversion and damming and analyzes the conflicts and responses that emerge from these socionatural transformation transformations.

Paradoxically, while current frameworks for integrated water governance are increasingly widespread and promote stakeholder consultation and participation around the globe, the Hidrosogamoso case illustrates how in hydropower development it is common for these same approaches to provide greater social legitimacy for large-scale water diversions and reallocations, while disregarding the underlying power dynamics that underpin marginalization. The interests, perceptions, and values held by local communities, with alternative, territory-grounded ideas on water rights, ecological dynamics, environmental problems, and in particular, locally embedded cultural understandings and meanings attached to nature and livelihood construction, are often sidelined.

Modernist policies—including Integrated Water Resources Management policies applied in concrete contexts—continue to see the environment and human societies as two separate domains of policy and action. The Sogamoso basin evidence shows, however, how in hydropower development, the production of material nature, strategic representations of nature, and forms of governance over nature, strategically and directly interrelate. Material and discursive hydropower development practices also align water resources, water technology, water users, and water governors within particular hydro-political network hierarchies.

Because of their profound impact, these large-scale water developments necessarily involve political contestation, negotiation, and struggle. Examining Sogamoso Basin interventions, we demonstrate how these water struggles happen around the water resources themselves but also how they are about the rules, norms, and laws that form the basis of water distribution and flow regulation processes, as well as about who has (or should have) the political authority and legitimacy to decide these questions. Further, contestations also occur over the discourses and knowledge used to frame or legitimize water policies and hydropower development.

This use of particular, powerful narratives that legitimize "structural violence" (Galtung 1990) by means of "symbolic violence" (Zizek 2009), means that attention to conflicts—in forms of overt and covert encounters—gets replaced by a consensual discourse in which there is little allowance for political debates about the distribution of burdens and benefits or about winners and losers. They carefully align a diversity of public and private actors at local, national, and global scales in a new Sogamoso hydrosocial network. Hidrosogamoso's cultural politics carefully direct the flows of money, people, and information in the network and secure particular regimes of representation and flows of water (cf. Zwarteveen and Boelens 2014; Rodriguez-de-Francisco and Boelens 2014). Consequently, negotiations among the company, the government, and residents regarding construction of the Sogamoso Hydroelectric Plant began and continue under profoundly asymmetrical conditions.

The hydropower development discourses that are officially deployed, of development, sustainability, and public utility, end up declaring traditional subsistence activities (small-scale mining, fishing, agriculture) illegal. They underpin the strategies of official inclusion and recognition, which ultimately deny the locally existing body of rights and rules. Such official recognition and inclusion simultaneously illegalizes local normative and production systems that do not suit the interests and views of the new dominant hydrosocial constellation. Social participation discourse and strategies promoted by the company sought to legitimize deviating the river and damming its water, rather than generating mechanisms to construct agreements and rights to access for different stakeholders. Development projects and economic power are used to co-opt public officials, politicians, media, and social leaders, while breaking down existing social relationships. Under such conditions, as the Hidrosogamoso case makes clear, getting into the game of negotiations becomes a trap that ends up polarizing the affected communities and weakening their political efforts to defend their territory and livelihoods. Further, negotiations tend to be skewed toward just economic values: excluding ecological, social, and cultural values while undervaluing responsible human interaction with nature.

Rather than confirming and conforming to the current neutralizing, depoliticizing, and naturalizing hydropower development approaches, solutions should address underlying structures of inclusion and exclusion, water deviation, unequal access, and appropriation. Given the current state of affairs, several key issues need to be resolved through transparent and multi-actor policy decision making and concrete action that responds to the voices, needs, and opportunities of the affected communities. First, how should the socioenvironmental harm and abuses towards the local dwellers' lives and livelihoods be compensated? Second, how can the benefits and burdens of Sogamoso hydropower be equitably shared between Sogamoso Basin's families, on the one hand, and on the other, the institutions, cities, and countries that gain from diverting the river flow? And, third, given the co-optation-prone neoliberal setting and its public-private power plays, how can we guarantee and concretize the state's duties and responsibilities regarding the protection of public interests and affected people's environmental and humanitarian rights? Currently, the constitutional court has transferred the resolution of investment conflicts to international judges, entirely without discussing the corresponding hydropower environmental (in)justice issues. Therefore, in everyday reality, Sogamoso communities require effective judicial and practice-based mechanisms to defend their territorial rights. They know that they will have to mobilize a network entwining a diversity of societal actors, operating at local, national, and international scales, to challenge the economic, political, and discursive powers of the dominant hydrosocial territory network in the Sogamoso Basin.

Notes

1 URL:<www.youtube.com/watch?v=PF6av7EbCJg&feature=youtu.be> (June 15, 2014).

2 This research is conducted in coordination with the Justicia Hidrica/Water Justice international research alliance. It is based on primary and secondary information collected throughout 2011–2013. The methods included literature research, local and national archival investigation (also including newspapers, mass media, and Internet), semi-structured interviews, and group discussions with the various stakeholders affecting and being affected by changing control over the Sogamoso River's water.

3 At present, other infrastructure projects in the area include: the Ruta del Sol (highway Bogota-Caribbean Coast), the Multimodal Port on the Magdalena River, the Train of Carare, expansion of the Refinery in Barrancabermeja, expansion of the petroleum frontier, mining extraction (coal and gold) in the Yariguies Mountains, and agroindustrial complexes, among others.

4 In 2011, for instance, while the dam was being built, heavy rains suddenly increased the water levels inundating the alluvial plains, causing an emergency situation. Villagers had to be evacuated from their homes and riparian subsistence agriculture was destroyed. On other occasions, because of sudden dam closures, ecological flows dried out and the fish population died (see El Espectador 2015).

5 During three months, ISAGEN offered jobs to women, and they received a salary of $400 per month.

6 In March 2013, residents denounced fifteen spills of polluted water into the watershed, causing massive die-offs of fish. In June 2014, a socioenvironmental drama took place because of reservoir mismanagement, profoundly impacting the flow regime and community livelihoods.

7 Horacio Serpa, Governor of Santander, public hearing in 2009.

References

Archila, Mauricio. (2006). Las identidades en el Magdalena Medio. *In* Conflictos, poderes e identidades en el Magdalena Medio 1990–2001. M. Mauricio Archila, Ingrid J. Bolívar, Alvaro Delgado, Martha C. Gonzales, Fernan E. Gonzales, Patricia Madariaga, Esmeralda Prada, and Teófilo Vásquez, eds. Pp. 505–467. Bogotá, Colombia: CINEP and COLCIENCIAS.

Bakker, Karen. (2010). Privatizing Water: Governance Failure and the World's Urban Water Crisis. New York: Cornell University Press.

Baleta, Estefan. (2005). Los emberas katios: Un pueblo desgarrado de Colombia. Ecología Política 30', Icaria Editorial, diciembre de 2005 (30):25–32.

Baud, Michiel, Fabio de Castro, and Barbara Hogenboom. (2011). Environmental Governance in Latin America: Towards an Integrative Research Agenda. European Review of Latin American and Caribbean Studies 90:78–88.

Boelens, Rutgerd. (2009). The Politics of Disciplining Water Rights. Development and Change 40(2):307–331.

(2014) Cultural Politics and the Hydrosocial Cycle: Water, Power, and Identity in the Andean Highlands. Geoforum 57:234–247.

Boelens, Rutgerd, Jaime Hoogesteger, Erik Swyngedouw, Jeroen Vos, and Philippus Wester. (n.d.) Hydrosocial Territories and Water Governance Systems: An Introduction. Water International (Special Issue). In press.

Boelens, Rutgerd, and Nynke C. Post Uiterweer. (2013). Hydraulic Heroes: The Ironies of Utopian Hydraulism and Its Politics of Autonomy in the Guadalhorce Valley, Spain. Journal of Historical Geography 44:44–58.

Budds, Jessica. (2009). Contested H2O: Science, Policy, and Politics in Water Resources Management in Chile. Geoforum 40(3):418–430.

Cernea, Michael., ed. (1999). The Economics of Involuntary Resettlement: Questions and Challenges. Washington, D.C.: World Bank.

Departamento Nacional de Planeación (DNP). (2007). Agenda intema para la productividad y la competitividad. Bogotá, Colombia: Documento Regional: Santander.

El Espectador. (2015). Otra visión sobre Hidrosogamoso. Habitantes de La Playa protestan. URL:<www.elespectador.com/noticias/economia/otra-vision-sobre-hidrosogamoso-articulo-538137> (January 16, 2015).

Escobar, Arturo. (2011). Ecología política de la Globalidad y la Diferencia. *In* La Naturaleza colonizada. Ecología Política y minería en América Latina. Héctor Alimonda, ed. Pp. 61–92. Buenos Aires, Argentina: Clacso and CICCSUS.

Fals Borda, Orlando. (2002). Historia doble de la Costa: Resistencia en el San Jorge. Bogotá, Colombia: El Áncora Editores.

Foucault, Michel. (1982). The Subject and Power. *In* Michel Foucault: Beyond Structuralism and Hermeneutics. Hubert Dreyfus and Paul Rabinow, eds. Pp. 208–226. Chicago: University of Chicago Press.

(2007) Security, Territory, Population: Lectures at the Collège de France 1977–1978. New York: Picador.

Galtung, Johan. (1990). Cultural Violence. Journal of Peace Research 27(3):291–305.

Gamarra, Tercero, and Mario Suárez. (2011). Temen afectaciones por desvío del río Sogamoso. URL:<http://www.vanguardia.com/historico/90276-temen-afectaciones-por-desvio-del-rio-sogamoso> (July 20, 2012).

Harvey, David. (2003). The New Imperialism. Oxford, United Kingdom: Oxford University Press.

Hoogesteger, Jaime, Rutgerd Boelens, and Michiel Baud. (n.d.) Territorial Pluralism and the Consolidation of a Water Users Movement in the Ecuadorian Highlands. Water International. In press.

ISAGEN. (2013). Proyecto Hidroeléctrico Sogamoso. URL:<www.isagen.com.co/comunicados/CartillaSogamoso_2013.pdf> (September 16, 2013).

Jasanoff, Sheila. (2010). A New Climate for Society. Theory, Culture, and Society 27(2–3):233–253.

Kaika, Maria. (2006). Dams as Symbols of Modernization: The Urbanization of Nature between Geographical Imagination and Materiality. Annals of the Association of American Geographers 96(2):276–301.

Latour, Bruno. (1993). We Have Never Been Modern. Cambridge, MA: Harvard University Press.

Martínez-Alier, Joan. (2002). The Environmentalism of the Poor, Edward Elgar, Cheltenham, UK and Northampton, MA: Edward Elgar.

Mançano, Bernardo. (2009). Territorio, teoría y política. *In* Las configuraciones de territorios rurales en el siglo XXL Fabio Lozano and Juan Guillermo Ferro, eds. Pp. 35–66. Bogotá, Colombia: Pontifica Universidad Javeriana.

McCarthy, James, and Scott Prudham. (2004). Neoliberal Nature and the Nature of Neoliberalism. Geoforum 35(3):327–341.

McCully, Patrick. (2001). Silent Rivers: The Ecology and Politics of Large Dams. London: Zed Books.

Molle, François, and Philippe Floch. (2008). Megaprojects and Social and Environmental Changes: The Case of the Thai "Water Grid." Ambio 37(3): 199–204.

Molle, François, Peter Mollinga, and Philippus Wester. (2009). Hydraulic Bureaucracies and the Hydraulic Mission: Flows of Water, Flows of Power. Water Alternatives 3(2):328–349.

Moore, Debora, John Dore, and Dipak Gyawali. (2010). The World Commission on Dams + 10: Revisiting the Large Dam Controversy. Water Alternatives 3(2):3–13.

Mosse, David. (2008). Epilogue: The Cultural Politics of Water—A Comparative Perspective. Journal of Southern African Studies 34(4):939–948.

Novoa, Diana D. Pilar, Carlos Alberto Pardo, and Angie L. Rico. (2011). Estudio histórico sobre los territorios de San Vicente de Chucuri y Betulia inundados por la hidroeléctrica sobre el rio Sogamoso. Bucaramanga, Colombia: Universidad Industrial de Santander.

Oslender, Ulrich. (2008). Another History of Violence: The Production of "Geographies of Terror" in Colombia's Pacific Coast Region. Latin American Perspectives 35(5):77–102.

Pécaut, Daniel. (2000). Configurations of Space, Time, and Subjectivity in a Context of Terror: The Colombian Example. International Journal of Politics, Culture, and Society 14(1): 129–150.

Roa-Avendaño, Tatiana. (2010). Crisis alimentaria y la respuesta de los mundos locales, el caso de una organización de pescadores, campesinos e indígenas. Quito, Ecuador: Universidad Andina Simón Bolívar.

Roa-Avendaño, Tatiana, and Bibiana Duarte-Abadía. (2012). Aguas Represadas. El caso del proyecto Hidrosogamoso en Colombia. Bogotá: Censat agua viva-Amigos de la Tierra Colombia.

—(2013) Desarrollo hidroeléctrico, despojo y transformación territorial. El caso de Hidrosogamoso, Colombia. *In* Aguas Robadas. Despojo hídrico y movilización social. Aline Arroyo and Rutgerd Boelens, eds. Pp. 313–338. Quito, Ecuador: Abya Yala.

Robbins, Paul. (2004). Political Ecology: A Critical Introduction. Oxford: Blackwell.

Rodriguez-de-Francisco, Jean Carlo, and Rutgerd Boelens. (2014). Payment for Environmental Services and Power in the Chamachán Watershed, Ecuador. Human Organization 73(4):351–362.

Rodríguez-Garavito, César, and Natalia Orduz-Salinas. (2012). Adiós al Río. La disputa por la tierra, el agua y los derechos indígenas en tomo a la represa de Urra. Bogotá, Colombia: Centro de Estudios de Derecho y Sociedad, Dejusticia.

Rosero, Evelio. (2007). Los Ejercitos. Barcelona, Spain: Tusquets.

Saavedra, María del Rosario. (2010). El Programa de Desarrollo y Paz del Magdalena Medio y la red Prodepaz. Ciencias Sociales (l):239–260.

Saldías, Cecilia, Rutgerd Boelens, Kai Wegerich, and Stijn Speelman. (2012). Losing the Watershed Focus: A Look at Complex Community-managed Irrigation Systems in Bolivia. Water International 37(7):744–759.

Seemann, Miriam. (n.d.) Inclusive Recognition Politics and the Struggle over "Hydrosocial Territories" in Two Bolivian Highland Communities. Water International. In press.

Sneddon, Chris, and Coleen Fox. (2008). Struggles over Dams as Struggles for Justice: The World Commission on Dams and Anti-dam Campaigns in Thailand and Mozambique. Society and Natural Resources 21(7):625–640.

Steiner, Achim. (2010). Preface. Water Alternatives 3(2): 1–2.

Svampa, Maritsella. (2011). Modelos de desarrollo, cuestión ambiental y giro eco-territorial. *In* La Naturaleza Colonizada. Hector Alimonda, ed. Pp. 181–218. Buenos Aires, Argentina: Consejo Latinoamericano de Ciencias Sociales—Clacso and Ediciones CICCSUS Centro de Integración Comunicación Cultura y Sociedad.

Swyngedouw, Erik. (2007). Technonatural Revolutions: The Scalar Politics of Francos Hydro-social Dream for Spain, 1939–1975. Transactions of the Institute of British Geographers 32(1):9–28.

—(2014) "Not A Drop of Water ...": State, Modernity, and the Production of Nature in Spain, 1898–2010. Environment and History 20(1):67–92.

Vélez-Torres, Irene. (2012). Water Grabbing in the Cauca Basin: The Capitalist Exploitation of Water and Dispossession of Afro-descendant Communities. Water Alternatives 5(2):431–449.

Vos, Hugo de, Rutgerd Boelens, and Rocio Bustamante. (2006). Formal Law and Local Water Control in the Andean Region: A Fiercely Contested Field. International Journal of Water Resources Development 22(1):37–48.

Whatmore, Sarah. (2002). Hybrid Geographies: Natures, Cultures, Spaces. London: Sage.

White, Richard. (1995). The Organic Machine: The Remaking of the Columbia River. New York: Hill and Wang.

World Commission on Dams (WCD). (2000). Dams and Development: A New Framework for Decision-making. London: Earthscan.

Zizek, Slavoj. (2009). Violence. London: Profile Books.

Zwarteveen, Margreet, and Rutgerd Boelens. (2014). Defining, Researching, and Struggling for Water Justice: Some Conceptual Building Blocks for Research and Action. Water International 39(2): 143–158.

Bibiana Duarte-Abadía is a researcher with the Alexander von Humboldt Institute, Biological Resources, Bogotá, Colombia; associated with the Water Resources Management Group, Wageningen University, The Netherlands; and a Ph.D. researcher with CEDLA, University of Amsterdam. Rutgerd Boelens is a Professor of the Political Ecology of Water in Latin America, CEDLA, and the Department of Geography, Planning, and International Development Studies, University of Amsterdam; Senior Researcher with the Department of Environmental Sciences, Wageningen University, The Netherlands; and Visiting Professor, Department of Social Sciences, Catholic University Peru. Tatiana Roa-Avendaño is the Managing Coordinator and Researcher with Censat-Agua Viva, Bogotá, Colombia. The research forms part of the activities of the international research alliance Justicia Hidrica/Water Justice (www.justiciahidrica.org).

How to Finance Our Sustainable Development Goals (SDGs)

Socioecological Quantitative Easing (QE) as a Parallel Currency to Make the World a Better Place

Stefan Brunnhuber

Abstract

This paper tries to find an answer to the question of how to finance the Sustainable Development Goals (SDGs) that the world has just decided to implement. I argue that besides the existing wealth of proposals, mainly along the lines of better governance and co-financing strategies, we need a complementary approach: parallel Quantitative Easing (QE) for SDGs only. Reverse pricing effects, drying out shadow economies and the impact of such a QE-SDG on the current liquidity trap and the debt trap are explained.

1. Introduction

In September 2015, the world agreed upon a map for mankind's future up to 2030. The Sustainable Development Goals (SDGs) formulated in this map with 17 targets will replace the Millennium Goals.* This consensus was reached through the UN's largest consultation and review process in history. Hundreds of surveys, expert groups, panels and hearings took place, and millions of citizens were engaged in population-based questionnaires contributing to this agenda. With the SDGs, the world has provided itself with a map charting its course for the next

*UN, Global Sustainable Development Report, 2015 edition

Stefan Brunnhuber, "How to Finance our Sustainable Development Goals (SDGs): Socioecological Quantitative Easing (QE) as a Parallel Currency to Make the World a Better Place," *Cadmus*, vol. 2, no. 5, pp. 112-118.

COPYRIGHTED MATERIAL — DO NOT DUPLICATE, DISTRIBUTE, OR POST

few years with the aim of living in a more just, more sustainable, more wealthy and more stable world. However, this commitment does not come cheap. For example, an additional 30 billion USD annually is required to finance the climate pathway over the next 15 years.* The transition towards a more cyclical economy would cost Europe some 100 billion USD over the same period. The overall costs of the SDGs are estimated at around 4–5 trillion USD per year in public spending, investments and direct aid. According to the United Nations Conference on Trade and Development (UNCTAD), there is an annual investment gap of at least 2.5 to 4 trillion USD.† Despite this global UN consensus, there is less clarity on how to finance this agenda towards greater "dignity, prosperity, justice, partnership, planet and people" (Ban Ki-moon 2015). However, if we fail to discuss where the money will come from, the SDGs are basically dead at birth. In short: where will the money come from to make this huge global shift?

2. The Fiscal and Monetary Dilemma

From a fiscal and monetary perspective, the world faces a multi-layer dilemma in coping with these challenges. First, increasing public debt is reducing states' and governments' willingness to further finance social and ecological issues.‡ Second, the liquidity trap prevents central banks from further stimulating the economy through Quantitative Easing (QE). At an interest rate close to or below zero the Central Banks empirically failed to provide and increase credits to the private sector.§ Third, a shadow economy equaling the official world GDP in volume is in fact stabilising world economy. But, crime, human trafficking, drugs, guns, illegal financial transactions—all part of the shadow economy—are pulling the society in the opposite direction to the SDGs.[1] Fourth, an increase in income and wealth disparity¶ is preventing the world economy from generating a massive demand stimulus and keeping global savings above investments. The higher the income gap, the lower the middle class and therefore the lower the mass demand.**

* Ellen Mac Arthur Foundation, Growth within: A Circular Economy Vision for a Competitive Europe, 2015

† UNCTAD, 2014, Developing countries face $2.5 trillion annual investment gap in key sustainable development sectors, UNCTAD report estimates, 24 June 2014

‡ Global debt has increased by one third since 2008, totalling over 250 trillion USD, compared to world GDP; Geneva report 2014, Leveraging? What Leveraging, 16, ICMBS

§ In fact, empirically the amount of QE increased by factor 4–5 with regard to the year of financial crisis 2008; the credit to private sector however stayed the same. Richard Koo, The Escape from Balance Sheet Recession and the QE Trap. John Wiley & Sons, 2014

¶ Cf. Stiglitz, Josef (2012); Thomas Piketty (2014); Sir Anthony Atkinson (2015)

** E.g.: Summers, Larry (2013): Speech at the IMF fourteenth annual research conference in honor of Stanley Fischer

> *"What is required is additional liquidity at a high scale, at full speed, and soundly targeted towards SDGs in a smart way that is different from what has been done in the past."*

Conventional strategies for financing the SDGs consist of a host of proposals, including regulatory agendas (offshore and off-sheet), different taxation schemes (progressive income tax; inheritance tax; financial stability contribution), and co-financing protocols (e.g. Global Marshall Plan Initiative), all designed to improve global governance.* None of the proposals is wrong. Yet, despite the intellectual scrutiny and practical heterogeneity, they all have one aspect in common: they all imply that the required liquidity will be created through the standard protocol of Quantitative Easing (QE) stewarded by central banks (CBs), where the commercial banking system eventually creates 95% of the credits loaned to the real economy.† Meaning, all the proposals consider a monetary monoculture to solve real problems. If we consider the most optimistic scenario in which the world is growing at the rate of 2% per annum over the next few years and we dedicate 1% of world GDP to SDGs, we end up with roughly 750 billion USD a year.‡ Following the UN statement, financing the SDGs however require an investment and aid strategy almost 6 to 8 times higher and we have to achieve these goals much faster than assumed.§ Apparently, the conventional approach is one scale too small and one gear too low. However, withdrawing 6–7% (4–5 trillion USD) of world GDP (70 trillion USD) every year—even if done in a smooth and subtle way—from the market economy and steering it towards the SDGs would create the largest economic recession the world has seen in modern times.

We have to think of a different mechanism, both in terms of scale and speed. Clearly we are not only running out of time, we are also running out of capital to finance our common future. What is required is additional liquidity at a high scale, at full speed, and soundly targeted towards SDGs in a smart way that is different from what has been done in the past.

---

* Radermacher, Franz J. (2011)

† IMF (2012) Jaromir Benes and Michael Kumhof, The Chicago Plan Revisited (IMF Working paper 12/202 (August 2012); Werner, Richard A., 2014 "Can banks individually create money out of nothing?—The theories and the empirical evidence." International Review of Financial Analysis 36 (2014) 1–19

‡ Agenda 21 cost around 600 billion USD annually worldwide, and the industrialised countries were supposed to contribute 100 billion USD annually, which is equivalent to 0.7% of the GDP of the rich countries at that time. The idea was to extract this amount of money from the "Peace Dividend" of disarmament after the end of the Cold War and redirect it into ecological and social projects. In actuality, most of those dividends went into tax reductions within the rich countries. See: United Nations. 1992. Agenda 21 available at: https://sustainabledevelopment.un.org/content/documents/Agenda21.pdf

§ Cf.: https://www.ecb.europa.eu/press/pr/date/2015/html/pr150122_1.en.html

3. A Different View: Complementary Quantitative Easing

We could look at the matter from a different angle. Currently we are demanding economic growth in the first place in order to redistribute parts of it to co-finance SDGs, which take the second place. This is not wrong, but is relatively inefficient. If we take the 4–5 trillion USD as the rough figure required to "make the world a better place", we have to do it differently: if the major monetary players and regulators (IMF, WB, CBs, UN, governments)[*] launch an annual 4–5 trillion USD QE that is linked directly to the SDGs,[†] the whole situation changes. Let us call it a complementary QE (QE^{COM}) or a QE^{SDG}[‡], created solely to reach the SDG targets the world has just signed up for. However, a different design and purpose than the conventional mechanism (QE^{CON}) is required. This comprises at least 5 features (see graph below) and runs *in parallel* to the QE^{CON}:

1. QE^{SDG} is 100% electronic. There will be no cash available. This makes it trackable and recordable and limits access to the shadow economy for money laundering and tax fraud. Governments decide to accept this form of liquidity to pay taxes.
2. The QE^{SDG} has a "demurrage fee" in place. This means essentially that its negative interest rate encourages users to invest in SDGs. With a demurrage fee, there will be no hoarding, but investing.[§]
3. The QE^{SDG} is bounded: in contrast to the QE^{CON} mechanism, the purpose of the QE^{COM} is investments in SDGs only. This restriction of the investment portfolio avoids the liquidity trap. Bounded liquidity is injected into the real economy directly and consequently steers society towards greater sustainability.
4. A "banned list" guarantees that the money is only spent on issues that are healthy, fair and sustainable. While it is difficult to identify a list of positives, it is much easier to come to a consensus on a negative list. This would, for example, exclude drugs, guns, prostitution, human trafficking and so on from expenditure.

---

[*] If governments are allowed to issue these "notes", the design would be similar to that of the Chicago Plan (see IMF 2012). It is important to understand that the only real power and leverage that governments have in the monetary domain is the capacity to specify the kind of currency or currencies they accept in payment of fees and taxes.

[†] This amount of money reflects roughly the M0 quantity that central banks are issuing worldwide in order to stimulate the conventional economic sector. The same amount of liquidity, within the different design described above, is necessary to provide sustainable wealth for 80% of the world population.

[‡] Werner, Richard A. (2012): How to end the European crisis—at no further cost and without the need for political changes. Southampton, GB, University of Southampton, 12pp. (Centre for Banking, Finance and Sustainable Development Policy Discussion Paper, 2–12).

[§] However, a negative interest rate has two impacts: first, it can encourage inefficient and hazardous investments that would have never been made under a positive interest rate. Second, it can stimulate long-term socioeconomic investments. The question is: bad or long term? Taking a design in which the QE^{CON} has a long-lasting perspective and is targeted towards SDGs, any investment in this field will do good or better, even if efficiency is partly reduced.

5 The QE^{SDG} has a limited convertibility with the conventional money system of, for example, a 10–15% exchange rate. This will encourage clients, companies and states to reinvest into the SDGs or to convert money with a loss.

"We are psychologically trapped by the idea that there can be just one monetary system, providing a single, specific form of liquidity for all purposes, pretending that the power of allocative distribution is most efficient."

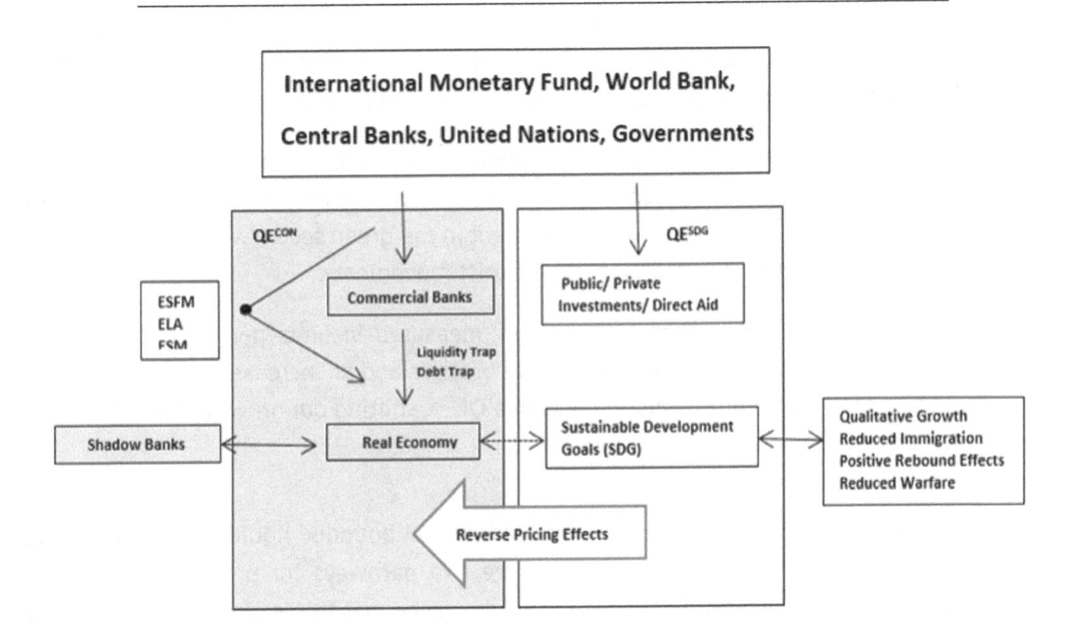

Figure 12.1 To meet the SDGs, the world requires a parallel, complementary QE (QE^{SDG}); QE^{con}: Conventional Quantitative Easing; enhanced qualitative growth, reduced entropic sector through "inverse pricing" and consecutively drying out the shadow economy

4. Consequences and Challenges

> *"A parallel currency system would make our world more resilient."*

We are psychologically trapped by the idea that there can be just one monetary system, providing a single, specific form of liquidity for all purposes, pretending that the power of allocative distribution is most efficient. Historically, this is an exception, not the rule.* The challenges the world is facing and the SDGs humankind has imposed itself on require a

*There is historical evidence that multiple and parallel currencies have worked throughout the centuries, providing local and regional liquidity on one side and currencies for international trade on the other. See Margit Kennedy & Bernard Lietaer. (2005)

different view: a parallel currency system. Such a complementary, parallel liquidity boost would have at least the following impact:

1. *Ending the liquidity trap:* In a globally deflationary situation of 4–5 trillion USD, a QE^{SDG} offers additional liquidity in an intelligent design. Instead of providing liquidity through the standard protocol, which failed to provide credits to the private sector, bounded direct investments* in green and social projects (including a demurrage fee) can ensure that the liquidity hits the real market.

2. *Reducing the debt trap:* Most countries are overindebted with little or no leverage funding additional ecological or social projects. The additional liquidity ensuing from QE^{SDG} will trigger green and social investments most countries are short of.

3. *Drying out shadow-economy activities:* There is less need for people to make an income through drugs, crime, and human trafficking. Regional wars on resources and forced immigration will be reduced and employment in the 'green sector' would reduce attractiveness of unemployed youth joining terrorist movements.

4. *Growth:* Our conventional growth process, measured in units per GDP, will change. Long-term investments in socio-ecological projects and an increase in labour intensity are two of the most prominent impacts of a QE^{SDG}, shifting our growth paths towards a more green, balanced and healthy planet.†

There are indeed two further challenges. First, additional bounded liquidity will reduce the efficiency of any economic transaction, as there are two pathways for processing economic activities instead of one. Systems theory has shown, however, that forms of parallel processing will render systems more resilient, shock-proof, greener, safer, fairer and richer, despite the loss of efficiency.[2] This is known in engineering (power grid), air plane safety measures, agriculture (monocultures versus higher diversity) as well as in the human immune system. This is true for the monetary system, too. In short: there is a net gain to be derived from a parallel system to stabilize the overall system. Taking into account the number of debt (186), state banking (96) and currency crises (180) since 1975,[3] a parallel currency system would make our world more resilient.

Second, we have the hazard of inflation, and indeed, a 4–5 trillion USD additional stimulus will create an inflationary pressure on price levels. However, any dollar spent through this "green"

*With the Emergency Liquidity Assistance (ELA)-Mechanism, the ECB has several years' experience in injecting additional liquidity into the market (https://www.ecb.europa.eu/press/pr/date/2015/html/pr150628.en.html). ECB would indeed become, in collaboration with UN, IMF and WB a green investment bank.

†A positive "rebound effect" will accelerate the SDGs, moving the world in the right direction.

mechanism will reduce costs in the conventional economy in the so-called entropic sector.* This "reverse pricing" effect will reduce the price level in sectors nobody really wants: crime, forced immigration, human trafficking, ecological disaster management, unemployment, poverty are just some examples, as human activities are getting invested in a greener and more socially just world.

5. Final Remarks

If we start looking at the world from an SDG perspective, we can see that it is vastly deflationary, meaning there is by far not enough available liquidity to finance these unmet needs. In numbers, about 4–5 trillion USD is lacking every year to make the world a better place. However, the conventional way of creating that liquidity is restricted due to the liquidity trap and the debt trap, providing little to no future additional leverage. An additional but different design of liquidity is required, running in parallel to cope with the SDGs.

The advantage of a QE^{SDG} is that it would work on different scales: locally or regionally as well as globally. The stimulus thus created could be adjusted and scaled up according to the investment plan and unmet needs. We could start with local and regional projects identified as SDGs and scale up.

With a QE^{SDG}, we can begin to rethink the relationship between society and the money system. Money will eventually serve people and not the other way round.

Author Contact Information
Email: brunnhuber.cor@gmxpro.de

Notes

1 F. Schneider and C. Williams, *The Shadow Economy* (London: Institute of Economic Affairs, 2013).

2 Bernard Lietaer, Christian Arnsperger, Sally Goerner & Stefan Brunnhuber, *Money and Sustainability: The Missing Link. A Report from the Club of Rome–EU Chapter* (Triarchy Press, 2012).

3 Hans Werner Sinn, *The Euro Trap. On Bursting Bubbles, Budgets, and Beliefs* (Oxford University Press, 2014).

*The entropic sector includes investments we are forced to be engaged in, but nobody really wants: Crime protection, end of pipe technologies avoiding global warming instead of green technology to begin with, unemployment fees instead of having a real job, costs for cure due to the exposure to unhealthy environment etc. See Nefiodow. A. Leo: Der sechste Kondratieff. Wege zur Produktivität und Vollbeschäftigung im Zeitalter der Information. Sankt Augustin, 2006

Bibliography

Anthony Atkinson (2015), Inequality, What can be done, Harvard University Press.

IMF (2012) Jaromir Benes and Michael Kumhof *The Chicago Plan Revisited* (IMF Working paper 12/202 (August 2012).

Global Financial Integrity Report 2014: 'Illicit Financial Flows from the Developing World 2003–2012'. www.gfintegrity.org/reports/

Kennedy, Margrit & Lietaer Bernard, A. (2005): Regionalwährungen. Neue Wege zu nachhaltigstem Wohlstand. München: Riemann.

Kjell Hausken, Mthuli Ncube, Quantitative Easing and Its Impact in the US, Japan, the UK and Europe, Springer Science & Business Media, 2013.

Nefiodow. A. Leo: Der sechste Kondratieff. Wege zur Produktivität und Vollbeschäftigung im Zeitalter der Information. Sankt Augustin, 2006

Radermacher, Franz J. (2011) Welt mit Zukunft: Die ökosoziale Perspektive. Hamburg: Murmann-Verlag

Summers, Larry. (2013): Rede an der IMF fourteenth annual research conference in honor of Stanley Fischer.

UNCTAD, 2014, Developing countries face $2.5 trillion annual investment gap in key sustainable development sectors, UNCTAD report estimates, 24.6.2014

UN General Assembly, 15-8-2014, Report of the Intergovernmental Committee of Experts on Sustainable Development Financing

Stiglitz, Joseph E. (2012): The Price of Inequality: How Today's Divided Society Endangers Our Future. New York City: W. W. Norton.

Piketty, Th. (2014): Das Kapital im 21. Jahrhundert (übersetzt von Ilse Utz und Stefan Lorenzer). München: Beck

Report of the UN Conference on Environment and Development, Rio de Janeiro, 3–14. June, 1992;

Werner, Richard A., 2014 Can banks individually create money out of nothing?—The theories and the empirical evidence; International Review of Financial Analysis 36 (2014) 1–19

Werner, Richard A. (2012): How to end the European crisis—at no further cost and without the need for political changes. Southampton, GB, University of Southampton, 12pp. (Centre for Banking, Finance and Sustainable Development Policy Discussion Paper, 2–12).

Werner, Richard A. (2014) Enhanced Debt Management: solving the eurozone crisis by linking debt management with fiscal and monetary policy. *Journal of International Money and Finance*, 1–27. (doi:10.1016/j.jimonfin.2014.06.007).

READING 13

Children's Environmental Health Indicators as Tools to Measure Progress Toward Sustainability

Rebecca Rehr, Gregory Miller, and Brenda Foos

Improving children's environmental health is integral to achieving sustainability. Sustainability is often presented as the balance among three interdependent components—environment, economy, and social dynamics—the goal of which is to improve life for future generations. Traditionally rooted in resource conservation and management, sustainability efforts have focused on environmental and economic elements, at times neglecting human health as an important aspect of the social component. Improving quality of life for future generations requires protecting the environmental health and well-being of today's children and women of childbearing age. During early stages of physiological development, from critical prenatal windows of development through infancy and childhood, people may be particularly sensitive to environmental hazards. Children also have higher exposure to certain factors, per unit of body mass, than adults. Consequently, environmental insults during development may increase the risks for adverse health outcomes at birth, during childhood, or later in life. Protecting children's environmental health has overlapping environmental, economic, and social benefits. This research analyzes the intersections between children's environmental health and sustainability and explores children's environmental health indicators as quantitative metrics to evaluate existing sustainability initiatives in the United States.

KEYWORDS: public health, pollution effects, children, environmental indicators, developmental stages

Introduction

The modern concept of sustainability originated in physical resource use and was conceived to design strategies to ensure that, for example, a harvested catch of fish did not threaten extinction of the overall population (Dixon & Fallon, 1989; Bartlett, 1998; Bell & Morse, 2008). Broadly interpreted, the term now encompasses the idea of living without jeopardizing the needs of future generations (WCED, 1987; Institute of Medicine, 2013). Research has linked physical resources and health; for instance, dominant patterns of planning in the United States and concepts such as urban sprawl have been correlated with health outcomes including obesity, diabetes, and depression (Frumkin et al. 2004). Initiatives like the Safe Routes to Schools National Partnership (2014) and its local counterparts strive to design the built environment to encourage children to walk and bike to school. Goals of the Partnership and similar programs include reducing obesity, improving air quality, and enhancing cardiovascular fitness (Rosenberg et al. 2006; Davison et al. 2008; Watson & Dannenberg, 2008; Wendel et al. 2008). Much guidance on evaluating these initiatives focuses on reductions of vehicle emissions, increases in the number of miles walked or biked to schools, and changes in attitudes toward physical activity (Boarnet et al. 2005; NCSRS, 2012). These are important metrics in addressing the environmental component of sustainability, but they do not allow evaluation of children's environmental health.

The benefits of improving children's health are sizeable and should not be overlooked. Trasande & Liu (2011) estimated direct and indirect costs of children's diseases with an environmental origin including lead poisoning, methylmercury toxicity, and asthma, at US$76.6 billion in 2008. While the link between asthma and air pollution is often made in introductions to and justifications for Safe Routes to Schools programs, asthma reductions are not included in the evaluation metrics. Further, these programs do not address how improving present-day children's environmental health will continue to improve health for future generations. More holistic integration of children's environmental health and sustainability is needed, particularly efforts to quantify improvements in children's environmental health as it relates to sustainability goals. When sustainability is measured in terms of children's environmental health—not just general health or adult health—we can more efficiently measure the health of current and future generations.

Sustainability

A common illustration of sustainability includes three pillars: economic, environmental, and social (Hecht et al. 2011; 2012; National Research Council, 2011; USEPA. 2012a). Sustainability can be achieved when equal weight is given to all three pillars in decision-making processes across sectors. These ideas are also found in the National Environmental Policy Act of 1969, which states that the federal government in the United States will "create and maintain conditions under which man and nature can exist in productive harmony, and fulfill the social, economic, and other requirements of present and future generations of Americans" (NEPA, 1969).

Sustainability continues to be pursued at different geopolitical scales. On the federal level in the United States, President Obama's Executive Order 13514 focuses on reducing energy use and greenhouse-gas (GHG) emissions across agencies (Obama, 2009). This effort is laudable in its goals to reduce the federal government's environmental footprint while saving taxpayers' money, but it neglects the social component. Including children's environmental health goals would help address this gap. For example, the United States government has changed its purchasing decisions to only include EnergyStar certified appliances. This same approach may also change purchasing decisions to include only furniture without chemical-flame retardants, since some of these ingredients have been implicated in childhood disease when exposed in utero (Boekelheide et al. 2012).

To help achieve sustainability, many cities in the United States have also developed plans to reduce their GHG emissions. For instance, New York City has targeted a 30% reduction below 2006 levels by 2017 (City of New York. 2013), Los Angeles a 35% reduction below 1990 levels by 2030 (EnvironmentLA. 2011), and Washington, DC a 30% reduction below 2006 levels by 2020 (DDOE, 2010). In contrast to these ambitious targets, sustainability plans have overlooked how improving children's health can contribute. Most city and state agencies have not integrated their sustainability initiatives with ongoing children's environmental health efforts to reduce risk and to enhance well-being. These cities have concurrent but separate efforts to improve children's environmental health by reducing blood-lead levels (BLLs) and asthma hospitalizations. For example. New York's city sustainability plan, PlaNYC (2011), focuses on housing and neighborhoods, but does not mention childhood-lead poisoning, even though New York City' had 1.316 new cases of children with BLLs equal to or greater than 10 micrograms per deciliter (pg/dL) in 2008 (NYSDH, 2008). The Centers for Disease Control and Prevention (CDC) recommend 5 pg/dL as the reference level for taking public health action (CDC. 2013). PlaNYC does include information linking ozone and asthma and acknowledges the economic burden of asthma on the individual and the state. However, this plan does not include reducing asthma as a goal with respect to achieving sustainability, exemplifying the neglect of sustainability's social pillar and of the holistic goal of finding the intersection of the three pillars. Improving children's environmental health represents this intersection; improving environmental, economic, and social conditions improves children's health and a healthy child is more likely to grow into a healthy adult. Although the New York City report includes indicators and milestones for each of the proposed initiatives, its plans do not include health (PlaNYC. 2011). The plans developed for Washington. DC and Los Angeles are similar in their consideration of health, with the Washington plan referring to health as an ancillary benefit with no metrics, and the Los Angeles plan simply acknowledging that GHG emissions harm human health without further detail. As examples of why such plans should include health, this article will expand upon BLLs and ozone exceedances as case studies of indicators to measure progress toward sustainability while improving children's environmental health.

Children's Environmental Health

Two key concepts must be addressed to fully explain how children's environmental health can contribute to evaluating progress toward sustainability. First, the concept and biology of developmental life stages are important (USEPA. 2014). Although they may seem like smaller versions of us, children are not simply miniature adults. Their experiences, exposures, and physical characteristics do not mirror those of adults. Any exposures through inhalation will be different in children because a child's lungs are small and still developing through age 18, and their mean breathing rate through age 12 is about twice as rapid as that of adults (Miller et al. 2002). Therefore, assessment of environmental exposures and effects must consider the sequence of physiological life stages, from conception through maternal/fetal development, infancy, toddlerhood, childhood, and adolescence. The contemporary physiological life-stage concept moves beyond the historical classification of children as a "susceptible subpopulation' and fully captures their unique health and developmental stages (USEPA, 2014).

In addition to biological differences, children exhibit unique behaviors at each life stage. For example, infants spend much of their time lying, sitting, or crawling on the ground. Further, increased hand-to-mouth activity during this stage can augment exposure to environmental contaminants (Cohen Hubal et al. 2000). Children's susceptibilities can lead to acute symptoms, and a growing body of research indicates that early exposure, including prenatal environmental exposure, can also have chronic health effects. The same environmental exposure at one life stage may have a dramatically different effect than at another stage. Among several later-life diseases associated with early exposure, researchers have identified associations between exposure to chemicals like polybrominated diphenyl ethers—used as flame retardants in couch cushions and clothing—and children's development and are studying these chemicals as potential carcinogens (Boekelheide et al. 2012). The physiological life-stage approach is particularly important to consider within the framework of sustainability.

The second key concept is the novel one of approaching children's environmental health as a product of the three pillars of sustainability. Figure 9.1 illustrates these pillars, with examples of indicators in each pillar, and in every combination. Children's environmental health is at the center, demonstrating overlap among all three pillars and the importance of using children's environmental health indicators to measure progress toward sustainability.

Opportunities for Integration of Children's Environmental Health in Sustainability: Children's Health Indicators

A sustainability indicator is "a measurable aspect of environmental, economic, or social systems that is useful for monitoring changes in system characteristics relevant to the continuation of human and environmental well-being" (Fiksel et al. 2012). Common examples include GHGs

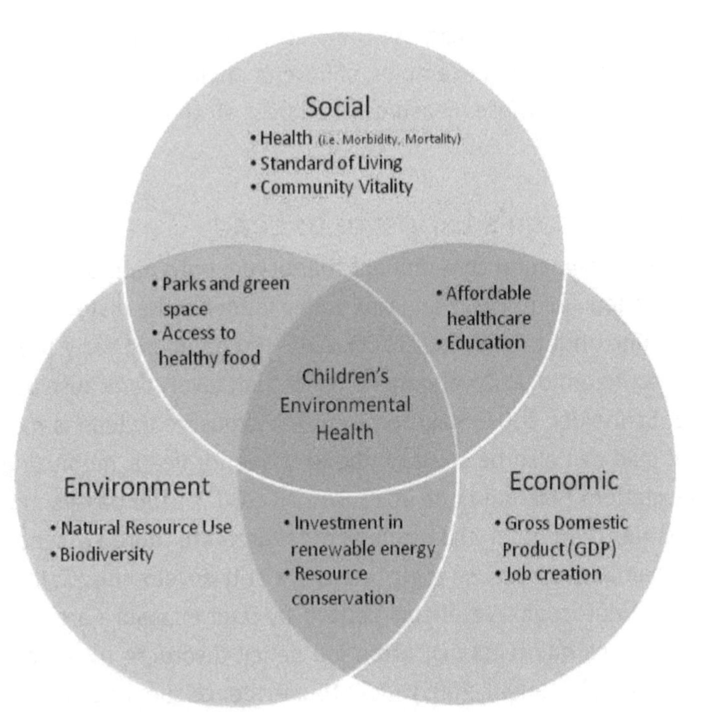

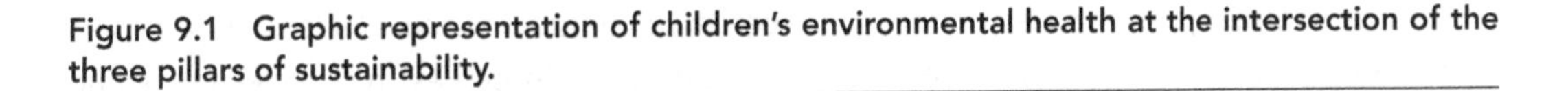
Figure 9.1 Graphic representation of children's environmental health at the intersection of the three pillars of sustainability.

as measured by grams of carbon dioxide (CO_2) emitted per gallon of gasoline and resource consumption as measured by energy use per household in kilowatt hours. An environmental health indicator is a summary statistic that synthesizes available data to represent a topic such as environmental condition, human-body burden of a particular chemical or substance, or health outcomes due to environmental stressors (Axelrad et al. 2013). Examples include mercury emissions from power plants, the number of asthma hospitalizations, and additional cases of lung cancer caused by environmental tobacco smoke. Both sustainability and environmental health indicators are chosen to measure trends over time and are limited by the strength of the collected data.

In an October 2012 report, the United States Environmental Protection Agency (USEPA) recommended several indicators appropriate for national scale sustainability reporting. The report concludes that existing definitions of sustainability are difficult to operationalize using indicators and therefore defines sustainability as "the continued protection of human health and the environment while fostering economic prosperity and societal well-being" (Fiksel et al. 2012). Based on this definition, children's environmental health indicators, such as BLLs and air-quality exceedances, can serve as strong measures of sustainability, as they often address all three pillars—economic, environmental, and social (Bell & Morse, 2008; USEPA. 2012c; 2013a). The report, *America's Children and the Environment* (ACE), is one source for children's environmental health indicators that policy makers can use to measure holistic progress toward sustainability (Axelrad et al. 2013). The following examples, children's environmental health indicators found in ACE, illustrate the ability of these measures to address all three pillars of sustainability.

Case Study #1: Children's Exposure to Lead

Lead is a pervasive environmental contaminant that occurs both naturally and as a result of human activities. Lead exposure remains an issue today following its historical use as an additive in paint and in gasoline until the 1970s (ATSDR, 2010). Prenatal and early-life exposure, even at low levels, can impact neurologic development, while high levels can cause abdominal pain and seizures (Lidsky & Schneider, 2003; Makri et al. 2004). Exposure to lead is measured through a blood sample, but lead can also be stored in bone tissue for years, mobilizing later in life (for instance, during lactation) (Axelrad et al. 2013; ATSDR, 2007). Lead passes more easily through the blood-brain barrier than other chemicals and children are more susceptible to the effects of lead exposure than adults because their brains are still developing (Goldstein, 1990; Lidsky & Schneider, 2003). Neurocognitive effects caused by lead exposure are irreversible and can lead to lower intelligence quotients (IQ), attention deficit disorders, hyperactivity, and criminal behavior (Wright et al. 2008; Gould, 2009). Mounting evidence suggests there is no safe level of lead exposure (Jones et al. 2009); accordingly, the CDC does not identify a safe level, but rather a reference BLL of 5 µg/dL—based on the 97.5th percentile of the National Health and Nutrition Examination Survey's (NHANES) blood-lead distribution in children—as the trigger for public health action (CDC, 2012).* The USEPA continues to research sources of lead exposure and ways to reduce risk of lead poisoning in children.

In the United States, USEPA (2008) regulates lead through several statutes, including the Clean Air Act, the Safe Drinking Water Act (1986), and the Toxic Substances and Control Act (1976), which have greatly reduced or eliminated many sources of exposure in the United States.† Lead was unregulated in drinking-water pipes and soldering until congressional passage of the Safe Drinking Water Act Amendments in 1986. However, exposure continues today mainly via deteriorating paint in houses built before 1978, dust from demolition projects, and contaminated soil and water (ATSDR, 2010). The United States Department of Housing and Urban Development is striving to eliminate lead exposure as a major threat to children's environmental health by providing grants and technical assistance to states and local governments addressing unsafe housing (USHUD, 2009).

---

*The CDC website explains that "Experts now use a reference level of 5 micrograms per deciliter to identify children with blood lead levels that are much higher than most children's levels. This new level is based on the U.S. population of children ages 1–5 years who are in the highest 2.5% of children when tested for lead in their blood." See http://www.cdc.gov/nceh/lead/acclpp/blood_lead_levels.htm.

† Safe Drinking Water Act of 1986, CFR 141.43—Prohibition on use of lead pipes, solder, and flux. Toxic Substances Control Act of 1976, 40 CFR 745—Lead-based paint poisoning prevention in certain residential structures.

Adverse health effects resulting from lead exposure may differ by life stages. In addition to increased risk of a lower IQ, an early-life exposure of a female child may jeopardize neurodevelopment in her offspring through the remobilization of lead stored in bone tissue (Lanphear, 2014). During pregnancy, lead in the mother's bones may mobilize, resulting in fetal exposure. In a number of animal studies, up to 39% of the maternal lead burden transferred to the fetus during pregnancy came from the maternal skeleton, with the remainder from current external environmental exposures (Kirrane et al. 2013). Domestic regulations now ban lead in most commercial uses, but its historical use continues to affect current and future generations (USHUD, 2009). Limiting the lead exposure of today's children simultaneously decreases the risk of current and lifelong neurocognitive deficits and the risk to the next generation via *in utero* exposure to lead, thus working toward sustainability.

Data on lead in the blood of children can be used to measure sustainability (Axelrad et al. 2013). Not only is lead present in several media (environmental), but lead exposure affects neurocognitive development (social), which can be costly to treat and can limit an individual's earning potential throughout his or her lifetime (economic) (Needleman et al. 1990; Gould, 2009; Jones et al. 2009). Table 9.1 summarizes some of these effects, but is not an exhaustive list.

Indirect costs of lead poisoning include potential loss in lifetime earnings, loss of tax revenue for the state from reduced earning potential, increase in special education costs for lead-poisoned children, and the cost of crime. Neurocognitive effects have been well documented for decades and more recent studies have associated prenatal and early childhood elevated BLLs with a greater likelihood of arrest and criminal behavior. Adults who had been exposed to lead in early-life stages are less likely to achieve their full academic and social potential (Wright et al. 2008), exemplifying potential health and economic impacts in different life stages. Furthermore, lead's health impacts have both short- and long-term costs which constitute a marked economic impact for the individual and society. Direct medical costs for testing and treatment can be several thousand dollars per child with very high BLLs (>70 μg/dL), and abatement can cost up to US$7,000 per housing unit, hugely burdensome amounts for residents of low-income communities where older housing and lead exposure are more common (Gould, 2009). Landrigan

Table 9.1 Sustainability Issues related to Blood Lead Levels[+]

ENVIRONMENT	SOCIAL	ECONOMIC
• Naturally occurring metal • Additive in paint & gasoline until the 1970s - Chipping paint in old residential structures is a main source of exposure • Used in drinking water pipes & soldering until 1936	• Prenatal and early life exposure can impact neurologic development • Children are more susceptible to the effects of lead exposure than adults • Neurocognitive effects associated with lead exposure can be irreversible	• Total cost of pediatric lead poisoning could be $43.4 billion annually • Net lifetime earnings loss could be between $165–233 billion

+*The* citations used for this figure can be found in the text.

& Garg (2002) estimate the total cost of pediatric lead poisoning in the United States to be US$43.4 billion annually, while Gould (2009) estimates that for a 2006 cohort of children aged 6 and under with BLLs between 2–10 μg/dL, the net lifetime earnings loss would be between US$165 and US$233 billion. Based on 2004 and 2006 data, this same study estimates that the total number of crimes that could have been averted if a there were a 1 μg/dL reduction in the average preschool BLL (including 116,541 fewer burglaries, 2,499 fewer robberies, 53,905 fewer aggravated assaults, 4.186 fewer rapes, and 717 fewer murders) would result in savings of a total of US$1.8 billion in direct costs.

Case Study #2: Children's Exposure to Ozone

Tropospheric, or ground-level, ozone is harmful to human health, aggravating existing respiratory conditions such as asthma and increasing susceptibility to respiratory infections (USEPA, 2012a). Ground-level ozone is formed through chemical interactions among nitrogen oxides, sulfur oxides, and volatile organic compounds that can come from anthropogenic emissions or other sources, such as wildfires. In the United States, ozone is primarily regulated via the National Ambient Air Quality Standards (NAAQS) provision of the Clean Air Act, which has currently set the eight hour (8-hr) standard for ground-level ozone at 75 parts per billion (ppb) (USEPA, 2012b). States can be more stringent; California set its 8-hr standard for ozone at 70 ppb in 2005 based on a study mandated by the state's Children's Environmental Health Protection Act (Ozone and Ambient Air Quality Standards, 2008).

Ozone is an environmental contaminant that also touches all three pillars of sustainability. In 2009, 12% of American children lived in counties that exceeded the 8-hr standard for at least four days in the calendar year (Axelrad et al. 2013). Children are more likely to have asthma than adults, and they may be exposed to higher levels of ozone because they are more likely to be outside at peak ozone times (i.e., at recess during school or just after school) (Hall et al. 2008). Ozone can initiate and exacerbate asthma symptoms in children who already suffer from the disease (Brown et al. 2013), and long-term exposure can also cause asthma in healthy children (McConnell et al. 2002). Exposure to ozone and resulting respiratory distress (social) can lead to missed days of school and work for children and their caretakers respectively (economic), and is the product of interactions among environmental chemicals (environment). Table 9.2 summarizes some of these effects, but is not an exhaustive list.

Hall et al. (2008) estimate that implementing more stringent ozone standards saved California between US$156–334 million annually in prevented school absences during the 1990s just in the state's South Coast Air Basin (vicinity of Los Angeles), when considering direct medical costs as well as lost revenue from caretakers' missed work days (Hall et al. 2008). On average, counties in this region exceeded USEPA's ozone NAAQS 30 days per year from 2005–2007. Annual ozone-related incidences during this period included approximately 1.1 million school absence days (ages 5–17), 120,970 asthma attacks (all ages), and 825 respiratory hospital admissions (all ages), costing US$105.97 million, US$6,514 million, and US$33 million, respectively (Brajer et al. 2011).

Table 9.2 Sustainability Issues related to Elevated Ozone+

ENVIRONMENT	SOCIAL	ECONOMIC
• Tropospheric ozone is the main component of smog; may be elevated on hot, sunny days in urban environments • Ozone is formed by chemical reactions between NO_x & volatile organic compounds • Ozone is regulated by the Clean Air Act, which currently sets the 8-hr standard at 75 parts per billion	• Children may be exposed to higher levels of ozone than adults because they are more likely to be outside at peak ozone times • Children are more likely to have asthma than adults • Children's lungs are still developing • In 2009, 12% of children lived in counties that exceeded the 8-hr standard at least 4 days	• CA saved between $156–334 million annually in prevented school absences during the 1990s after more stringent ozone standards

+*The* citations used for this figure can be found in the text.

Recommendations

Based on the research presented in this article, we offer several concrete recommendations. Rather than creating new indicators that would require time and funding, we recommend synthesizing work across sectors to develop a comprehensive suite of indicators measuring sustainability.

First, include human health explicitly in the definition of sustainability. A recent Institute of Medicine (2013) publication states that health has not been fully incorporated into work on sustainability in the United States and health practitioners have yet to take an active role in this work (National Research Council, 2013). The USEPA (2012a) definition of sustainability as "the continued protection of human health and the environment while fostering economic prosperity and societal wellbeing" should be more widely adopted to better incorporate health considerations into policy decisions. This definition not only reflects USEPA's mission to protect human health and the environment, but it is also responsive to National Research Council (2011) recommendations and advice from USEPA's Children's Health Protection Advisory Committee (CHPAC) (2011),* which recently stated, "Protecting health during early life stages is fundamental to the concept of sustainability." While the USEPA definition and CHPAC's recommendation are targeted to USEPA (Fiksel et al. 2012), sustainability initiatives in general would benefit from a broader incorporation of health needs. For example, within the scope of smart growth, local planning boards could consult children's environmental health and public health practitioners to provide input on land-use decisions. These would address certain children's unique exposures to chemicals in the environment associated with adverse health outcomes like delayed neurocognitive development, respiratory disease, and increased susceptibility to later life and intergenerational disease.

*See http://www2.epa.gov/sites/production/files/2014-05/documents/chpac_ord_letter_3.pdf.

Second, no matter the level of governance (state or federal), it is important to clearly define sustainability goals prior to the initiation of a project or action. Recent recommendations from the National Research Council (2013) outline a structured decision framework to aid decision makers in their sustainability planning. Plans need to be explicit about how improving health outcomes contribute to sustainability. Setting children's environmental health-related sustainability goals solidifies a commitment to the health of future generations. This strategy also enables organizations to identify what indicators they will measure to define successful implementation of their goals, by setting benchmarks that quantify their sustainability initiatives during program evaluation.

Third, use children's environmental health indicators as measurement tools to fully assess progress toward sustainability initiatives. To operationalize health within a sustainability framework, it is imperative to include indicators and benchmarks with specific health targets and to shift from a framework of reducing risk to one that maximizes benefits (Goldstein, 2011). Rather than creating artificial silos, officials should be working to achieve sustainability by improving children's environmental health and well-being.

Finally, integrate children's environmental-health indicators with sustainability indicators to enable consideration of resource quality alongside quantity. This approach is applicable to regulatory agencies, as well as state and local governments, planning commissions, and others addressing smart growth to provide measures on the progress of sustainability initiatives. The smart growth and sustainable community movements are beginning to address health—through, for example, efforts to promote asthma reduction—as part of a healthy homes program, but there is still a need for a three-pillar approach on a large scale (Yee et al. 2012). Identifying elevated BLLs in children can stimulate action to prevent exposure and/or alleviate adverse health outcomes caused by lead exposure. Sustainability plans should therefore include goals to lower BLLs in children, which saves money, improves physical and mental health, and reduces toxins in the environment. Government, urban planning, and business sustainability planning should include the reduction of ozone exceedances, which improves children's health and education outcomes, saves money, and improves the environmental outlook. One way to facilitate this change is to systematically include indicators of children's environmental health as sustainability goals in strategic plans.

Conclusion

Former USEPA Administrator Lisa Jackson recently stated, "A child born in America today will grow up exposed to more chemicals than a child from any other generation in our history."* Rather than focus exclusively on conserving resources and maintaining healthy ecosystems,

*See http://yosemite.epa.gov/opa/admpress.nsi78d49f7ad4bbcf4ef852573590040b7f6/913b9a5dd8ea6507852579c-60054dele!Open Document.

sustainability must also make sure people are healthy enough to utilize those resources. One way to maximize benefits in terms of sustainability is to improve the environmental health of today's children (Landrigan & Garg, 2002), a concept thus far lacking in the sustainability literature. Using children's environmental health as a guiding principle behind sustainability strategies can address many gaps that currently hinder a balance among environmental, economic, and social goals. The recommendations made in this article are feasible—many children's environmental health and sustainability indicators already exist, but they need to be integrated. Children's environmental health is not just one more benefit *from* sustainability and sustainable development, but should be an integral part of any truly sustainable initiative from the outset.

Authors' Note

The views expressed in this article are those of the authors and do not necessarily represent those of the United States Environmental Protection Agency or the Association of Schools and Programs of Public Health.

Acknowledgements

We thank the staff of the USEPA Office of Children's Health Protection. We also appreciate the assistance of the following individuals from USEPA for their invaluable help: Joseph Fiksel, James Quackenboss, Sally Darney, John Thomas, Elizabeth Zgoda, and Doreen Cantor. Finally, we gratefully acknowledge the following ASPPH (Association of Schools and Programs of Public Health) Fellows: Gaelle Gourmelon, Lindsay McCormick, and Alyson Lorenz.

References

Agency for Toxic Substances and Disease Registry (ATSDR). 2007. *Toxicological Profile for Lead.* Atlanta: ATSDR.

Agency for Toxic Substances and Disease Registry (ATSDR). 2010. *Case Studies in Environmental Medicine (CSEM) Lead Toxicity.* Atlanta: ATSDR.

Axelrad, D., Adams, K., Chowdhury, F., D'Amico, L., Douglass, E., Hudson, G., Koustas, E., Lam, J., Lorenz, A., Miller, G., Newhouse, K., Nweke, O., Cantor Paster, D., Sturza, J., & Weber, K. 2013. *America's Children and the Environment,* 3rd Edition. EPA 240-R-13-001. Washington, DC: USEPA.

Bartlett, A. 1998. Reflections on sustainability, population growth, and the environment: revisited. *Renewable Resources Journal* 15(4):6–23.

Bell, S. & Morse, S. 2008. *Sustainability Indicators: Measuring the Immeasurable?* 2nd Edition. London: Earthscan.

Boamet, M., Anderson, C., Day, K., McMillan, T., & Alfonzo, M. 2005. Evaluation of the California Safe Routes to School legislation: urban form changes and children's active transportation to school. *American Journal of Preventive Medicine* 28(2): 134–40.

Boekelheide, K., Blumberg, B., Chapin, R., Cote, I., Graziano, J., Janesick, A., Lane, R., Lillycrop, K., Myatt, L., States, J., Thayer, K., Waalkes, M., & Rogers, J. 2012. Predicting later-life outcomes of early-life exposures. *Environmental Health Perspectives* 120(10): 1353–1361.

Brajer, V., Hall, J., & Lurmann, F. 2011. Valuing health effects: the case of ozone and fine particles in Southern California. *Contemporary Economic Policy* 29(4):524–535.

Brown, J., Bowman, C., Buckley, B., Cao, Y., Clark, M., Dubois, J. J., Dutton, S., Fiore, A., Gillespie, K., Gordon, T., Henderson, B., Herrick, J., Hines, E., Ito, K., Johns, D., Kotchmar, D., Lassiter, M., Liu, L., Long, T., Luben, T., Mickley, L., Novak, K., Oesterling Owens, E., Patel, M., Peel, J., Pinto, J., Postlethwait, E., Rice, J., Sacks, J., Thurston, G., Vinikoor-Imler, L., & Wiese, C. 2013. *Integrated Science Assessment for Ozone and Related Photochemical Oxidants*. EPA 600/R-10/076F. Research Triangle Park, NC: USEPA.

California Environmental Protection Agency. 2008. Ozone and Ambient Air Quality Standards, http://www.arb.ca.gov/research/aaqs/caaqs/ozone/ozone.htm. May 22, 2013.

Centers for Disease Control and Prevention (CDC). 2012. Lead: What Do Parents Need to Know to Protect Their Children? http://www.cdc.gov/nceh/lead/ACCLPP/blood_lead_levels.htm. Mayó, 2014.

Centers for Disease Control and Prevention (CDC). 2013. Lead. http://www.cdc.gov/nceh/lead/. September 16, 2013.

Children's Health Protection Advisory Committee (CHPAC). 2011. *Letter to the Administrator: ORD Research Strategies Supporting Sustainability.* Washington, DC: USEPA.

City of New York. 2013. Energy Efficiency & GHG Reduction (30x17). http://www.nyc.gov/html/dem/html/conservation/conservation.shtml. June 17, 2013.

Cohen Hubal, E., Sheldon, L., Burke, J., McCurdy, T., Berry, M., Rigas, M., Zartarian, V., & Freeman, N. 2000. Children's exposure assessment: a review of factors influencing children's exposure, and the data available to characterize and assess that exposure. *Environmental Health Perspectives* 108 (6):475–486.

Davison, K., Werder, J., & Lawson, C. 2008. Children's active commuting to school: current knowledge and future directions. *Preventing Chronic Disease: Public Health Research, Practice, and Policy* 5(3):A100.

District Department of the Environment (DDOE). 2010. *Climate of Opportunity: A Draft Climate Action Plan for the District of Columbia*. Washington, DC: DDOE.

Dixon, J. & Fallon, L. 1989. The concept of sustainability: origins, extensions, and uselulness for policy. *Society and Natural Resources* 2(1):73–84.

EnvironmentLA. 2011. Climate Change: Overview. http://www.environmentla.org/ead_climatechange.htm. November 12, 2013.

Fiksel, J., Eason, T., & Frederickson, H. 2012. *A Framework for Sustainability Indicators atEPA*. Washington, DC: USEPA.

Frumkin, H., Frank, L., & Jackson, R. 2004. *Urban Sprawl and Public Health: Designing, Planning, and Building for Healthy Communities*. Washington, DC: Island Press.

Goldstein, B. 201E EPA at 40: reflections on the office of research and development. *Duke Environmental Law and Policy Forum* 21(2):295–308.

Goldstein, G. 1990. Lead poisoning and brain cell lunction. *Environmental Health Perspectives* 89:91–94.

Gould, E. 2009. Childhood lead poisoning: conservative estimates of the social and economic benefits of lead hazard control. *Environmental Health Perspectives* 117(7): 1162–1167.

Hall, J., Brajer, V., & Lurmann, F. 2008. Economic valuation of ozone-related school absences in the south coast air basin of California. *Contemporary Economic Policy* 21(4):207–217.

Hecht, A., Fiksel, J., & Anderson, M. 2011. Sustainability and the U.S. Environmental Protection Agency. http://www.eoearth.org/article/Sustainability_and_the_U.S._Environmental_Prot ectionAgency. January 24, 2013.

Hecht A., Fiksel J., Fulton S., Yosie T., Hawkins N., Leuenberger H., Golden J., & Lovejoy T. 2012. Creating the future we want. *Sustainability: Science, Practice, & Policy* 8(2):62–75.

Institute of Medicine. 2013. *Public Health Linkages with Sustainability: Workshop Summary.* Washington, DC: National Academies Press.

Jackson, R. 2012b. *Designing Healthy Communities.* Hoboken, NJ: Wiley.

Jones, R., Homa, D., Meyer, P., Brody, D., Caldwell, K., Pirkle, J., & Brown, M. 2009. Trends in blood lead levels and blood lead testing among US children aged 1 to 5 years, 1988–2004. *Pediatrics* 123(3):e376-e385.

Kirrane, E., Blain, R., Brown, J., Bushnell, P., Davis, A., Diamond, G., Dietert, R., Dubois, J., Fairbrother, A., Gandy, J., Gonick, H., Graham, M., Greaver, T., Hines, E., Kotchmar, D., Lassiter, M., McDow, S., Meng, Q., Mendez, B., Mielke, H., Moudgal, C., Oesterling Owens, E., Palmquist, K., Pinto, J., Richmond-Bryant, J., Rothenberg, S., Selgrade, M., Stanek, L., Svendsgaard, D., Vinikoor-Imler, L., Weaver, V., Weisskopf, M., Pierce Wise, Sr., J., Wright, R., & Wright, R. 2013. *Integrated Science Assessment for Lead.* EPA/600/R-10/075F. Research Triangle Park, NC: USEPA.

Landrigan, P. & Garg, A. 2002. Chronic effects of toxic environmental exposures on children's health. *Clinical Toxicology* 40(4):449–456.

Lanphear, B. 2014. Lead. In P. Landrigan & R. Etzel (Eds.), *Textbook of Children's Environmental Health,* pp. 262–272. New York: Oxford University Press.

Lidsky, T. & Schneider, J. 2003. Lead neurotoxicity in children: basic mechanisms and clinical correlates. *Brain* 126(1):5–19.

Makri, A., Goveia, M., Balbus, J., & Parkin, R. 2004. Children's susceptibility to chemicals: a review by developmental stage. *Journal of Toxicology and Environmental Health Part B* 7(6):417–35.

McConnell, R., Berhane, K., Gilliland, F., London, S., Islam, T., Gauderman, W., Avol, E.. Margolis, H., & Peters, J. 2002. Asthma in exercising children exposed to ozone: a cohort study. *The Lancet* 359(9304):386–391.

Miller, M., Marty, M., Arcus, A., Brown, J., Morry, D., & Sandy, M. 2002. Differences between children and adults: implications for risk assessment at California EPA. *International Journal of Toxicology* 21 (5):403–418.

National Center for Safe Routes to School (NCSRS). 2012. *Methods for Estimating the Environmental Health Impacts of SRTS Programs.* Madison, WI: State Smart Transportation Initiative.

National Environmental Policy Act of 1969 (NEPA). 42 U.S.C. 4321–4347.

National Research Council. 2011. *Sustainability and the U.S. EPA* Washington, DC: National Academies Press.

National Research Council. 2013. *Sustainability for the Nation: Resource Connection and Governance Linkages.* Washington, DC: National Academies Press.

Needleman, H., Schell, A., Bellinger, D., Leviton, A., & Allred, E. 1990. The long-term effects of exposure to low doses of lead in childhood. *New England Journal of Medicine* 322(2):83–88.

New York State Department of Health (NYSDH). 2008. *Reducing Lead Exposure in Children: Lead Testing and Lead Poisoning Among New York State Children.* New York: NYSDH.

Obama, B. 2009. Executive Order 13514: Federal Leadership in Environmental, Energy, and Economic Performance. http://www.whitehouse.gov/administration/eop/ceq/sustainability. October 5, 2012.

Rosenberg, D., Sallis, J., Conway, T., Cain, K., & McKenzie, T. 2006. Active transportation to school over 2 years in relation to weight status and physical activity. *Obesity* 14(10): 1771–1776.

Safe Routes to School National Partnership. 2014. About Us. http://saferoutespartnership.org/about. April 2014.

Trasande, L. & Liu, Y. 2011. Reducing the staggering costs of environmental disease in children, estimated at $76.6 billion in 2008. *Health Affairs* 30(5):863–870.

United States Department of Housing and Urban Development (USHUD). 2009. *Leading Our Nation to Healthier Homes: The Healthy Homes Strategic Plan*. Washington, DC: USHUD.

United States Environmental Protection Agency (USEPA). 2012a. Ground-level Ozone: Health Effects., http://www.epa.gov/glo/health.html. April 11, 2013.

United States Environmental Protection Agency (USEPA). 2012b. National Ambient Air Quality Standards (NAAQS). http://www.epa.gov/air/criteria.html. March 17, 2014.

United States Environmental Protection Agency (USEPA). 2012c Administrator Lisa P. Jackson, Remarks at Congressman John Lewis' Breaking the Glass Ceiling Event, As Prepared. http://yosemite.epa.gov/opa/admpress.nsf/8d49f7ad4bbcf4ef852573590040b7f6/913b9a5dd8ea6507852579c60054dele!OpenDocument. September 16, 2013.

United States Environmental Protection Agency (USEPA). 2014. Early Life Stages, http://www2.epa.gov/children/early-life-stages. August 13, 2014.

Watson, M. & Dannenberg, A. 2008. Investment in safe routes to school projects: public health benefits for the larger community. *Preventing Chronic Disease: Public Health Research, Practice, and Policy* 5(3):A90.

Wendel, A., Dannenberg, A., & Frumkin, H. 2008. Designing and building healthy places for children. *International Journal of Environment andHealth* 2(3 4):338 355.

World Commission on Environment and Development (WCED). 1987. *Our Common Future*. New York: Oxford University Press.

Wright, J., Dietrich, K., Ris, M., Homing, R., Wessel, S., Lanphear, B., Ho, M., & Rae, M. 2008. Association of prenatal and childhood blood lead concentrations with criminal arrests in early adulthood. *PLoS Medicine* 5(5):732—740.

Yee, S., Bradley, P., Fisher, W., Perreault, S., Quackenboss, J., Johnson, E., Bousquin, J., & Murphy, P. 2012. Integrating human health and environmental health into the DPSIR framework: a tool to identify research opportunities for sustainable and healthy communities. *EcoHealth* 9(4):411–426.

Fostering Dignity and Achieving Sustainability

Any service to the common good attends to the comprehensive problem and is a portal to our greatest opportunity.

Illuminating Sustainability

In the early 1800s French physicist and civil engineer Augustin-Jean Fresnel (1788–1827) invented a light system that was first deployed (ca. 1823) in the Cordouan lighthouse on the Gironde Estuary at the mouth of Garonne River and access to the Port of Bordeaux (Wikipedia, 2019). The "Fresnel lens" is an intricate system of dozens of precisely arranged and inextricably connected crystals or facets, each of equal importance to the functioning of the system. Due to its unique design the Fresnel lens can project the light from a relatively small source many miles across open water. If you are wondering what the invention and deployment of a lighthouse lens has to do with sustainability in general and human dignity in particular, bear with me.

Figure C.1 Fresnel Lens

Prior to Fresnel's invention countless ships were sinking as sailors attempted to make port. The Gironde Estuary with its narrow channel and characteristically strong tidal currents was among the most dangerous of port passages (Wikipedia, 2017). With each sinking ship many lives were lost and tons of cargo were sent to the bottom of the sea. Sailors killed in shipwrecks left widows, children without fathers, and families without any means of support, and cargo from Europe and round the world, for example grain, fish, whale oil, fabric, and dairy products, was not only lost from commerce but contaminated near shore waters. Those waters were also home to the most productive fisheries. With every shipwreck more trees had to be cut to make more ships, accelerating deforestation and consequent environmental damage elsewhere. Damage to human ecology, commerce, fisheries, and water quality likely seemed inevitable and unending.

Recognizing the humanitarian crisis being wrought by shipwrecks and understanding that what sailors often needed most to make safe passage was light, Fresnel employed his knowledge of physics and engineering to develop a system that would light their way, and do so with greater efficiency and at a fraction of the cost, energy, and materials of any lighthouse system of the time. By developing the lens, Fresnel addressed many factors that were eroding human dignity; for example, families would not as often be broken by tragedy at sea and could remain intact with the support that they needed, availability of food and material goods was improved, commerce was bolstered thus improving the economy, and environmental damage—a factor impacting quality of life and an aspect of dignity—was curtailed.

The story of Augustin-Jean Fresnel and the Fresnel lens illustrates the inextricable nature of all facets of sustainability, as well as the centrality of human dignity in any effort to achieve sustainability. Just as the loss of one facet diminishes the strength of the system, so too will the loss of an individual's dignity weaken our human ecology. By extension the loss of multiple facets threatens the system's existence, as the loss of dignity by many endangers our chances for achieving sustainability. We can take heart, however, as just as in nature the reverse of this relationship is also true; the restoration and protection of human dignity improves our chances of achieving sustainability.

Sustainability is every problem combined; therefore, it is the comprehensive problem. Thus, what originally might seem an isolated problem, for example the need for light to guide ships safely to port, actually becomes an opportunity, the greatest opportunity, to foster human dignity and achieve sustainability.

An Anecdote and a Few Examples

In 2000 I co-founded Conversation Initiative for the Asian Elephant (CIFAE) with Dr. Amirthraj "Christy" Williams. A few years after forming CIFAE Christy called me from the sight of gruesome poaching incident where eight great Asian one-horned rhinos had been slaughtered. The poachers were captured, which resulted in many arrests and the breaking of a large poaching ring. What made this incident particularly perplexing was that it occurred in one of the most closely protected national parks in India, and that the perpetrators were among those who received the greatest economic benefit from keeping rhinos alive.

As I listened to Christy describe the scene it occurred to me that if we were to be successful at protecting the Asian elephant we must first come to understand factors affecting the human condition (I would later refer to this collectively as human dignity). We changed CIFAE's conservation approach from a more conventional one to a human-centered approach that first sought to understand issues negatively affecting human dignity and to resolve these issues while also addressing factors impacting elephant well-being in socioculturally continuous ways. We have successfully worked in elephant habitat with several tribal and indigenous groups, in concert with NGOs, and have helped them develop greater safety and security, while earning their trust and support for elephant conservation. We entered the comprehensive problem through the lens of Asian elephant conservation and discovered our greatest opportunity for achieving sustainability.

I encourage you to watch the following TEDx presentations to learn more about how others' efforts to improve human dignity have also resulted in the advancement of sustainability. As you watch these presentations keep the seven tenets of the psychology of sustainability in mind.

Seven Tenets of the Psychology of Sustainability

Any solution to a sustainability problem that does not first address factors negatively affecting human dignity will ultimately not be sustainable.

Every sustainability problem is first a social problem and therefore a psychological problem.

Thinking creates emotion; emotion creates behavior.

The future is nothing more or less than a decision today.

The effective agent for sustainability is first her or his own fear master.

At the heart of all human behavior (the worst, the best, and all points between) is the unconscious or conscious experience of personal mortality.

Any service to the common good attends to the comprehensive problem and is a portal to our greatest opportunity.

TEDx Talks

Dapo Oyewole on Development as Dignity
https://www.youtube.com/watch?v=X3aJnP4nwNo

John Carey on Creating Dignity through Architecture
https://www.ted.com/talks/john_cary_how_architecture_can_create_dignity_for_all

Ray Anderson on Resource Sustainability and Dignity
https://www.ted.com/talks/ray_anderson_on_the_business_logic_of_sustainability

Alberto Cairo: Finding Dignity in the Midst of War
https://www.ted.com/talks/alberto_cairo_there_are_no_scraps_of_men

Alicia Ely Yamin: Dignity Matters: Applying Human Rights Frameworks to Health
https://www.youtube.com/watch?v=ezeA2UfCHTw

Donna Hicks on the Essentiality of Dignity in Conflict Resolution
https://www.youtube.com/watch?v=GPF7QspiLqM&t=21s

Parenthetical Citations

Wikipedia. (2019, April 23). *Augustin-Jean Fresnel*. Retrieved from https://en.wikipedia.org/wiki/Fresnel_lens

Wikipedia. (2017, December 20). Gironde estuary. Retrieved from https://en.wikipedia.org/w/index.php?title=Gironde_estuary&oldid=816311314

Figure Credit

Fig. C.1: Copyright © Frank Schulenburg (CC BY-SA 3.0) at https://commons.wikimedia.org/wiki/File:Fresnel_Lens_at_Point_Arena_Lighthouse_Museum.jpg.

ABOUT THE EDITOR

Sustainability Psychologist, Environmental Scientist

Dr. Ron Chandler is currently a lecturer in the Department of Psychology at the University of Florida (UF). He graduated from Stephen F. Austin State University with a BS in aquatic biology and wildlife science in 1979, Texas State University with an MS in limnology and aquatic chemistry in 1984, and in 2009 returned to school to earn a PhD in educational psychology from Walden University in 2014. He currently teaches several classes at UF, including Psychology of Sustainability, Social Psychology, and Positive Psychology.

His principal area of interest is understanding and describing the role of dignity in education in general, and education and action for social change and sustainability in particular. Central to this work is the placement of psychology at the center of research for and development of approaches for resolving factors negatively affecting human dignity. He believes that to the extent we can resolve factors negatively affecting individual and societal experience of dignity it is to that extent that we can create and maintain a sustainable human ecology. To that end, he continues the development of *sustainability psychology*, the application of psychology in context for development and implementation of approaches to education and program design for social change and sustainability. He considers his most important work to date to be the development of I am the paradigm shift theory (IPST). IPST describes undergraduates' cultivation of the six essential characteristics of the effective prosocial/sustainability agent.

In addition to his work with University of Florida, Ron is also president of Conservation Initiative for the Asian Elephant (CIFAE) a 501 (c)3 organization that he cofounded with Dr. Amirthraj Williams in 2000. CIFAE's mission is to "identify issues of critical importance to the sustainability of the Asian elephant and the peoples sharing its habitat." One example of this is his ongoing work in northeast India through CIFAE where he and his colleagues seek to understand and explain Indigenous Peoples' experience of landscape and wildlife in context of their culture, and through their perspective develop resilient solutions to factors threatening sustainability. CIFAE, along with Meghalayan Department of Forests, and a number of specialists from India and around the world, are working to establish a dual status (cultural and environmental) UNESCO World Heritage site in the Garo Hills region of Meghalaya, India. This campaign is now in its fourth year and will likely be reviewed for inscription in 2020.

Ron lives in Gainesville, Florida, with his partner Dr. Maureen Conroy and their one dog and two cats.

COPYRIGHTED MATERIAL — DO NOT DUPLICATE, DISTRIBUTE, OR POST

COPYRIGHTED MATERIAL — DO NOT DUPLICATE, DISTRIBUTE, OR POST

COPYRIGHTED MATERIAL — DO NOT DUPLICATE, DISTRIBUTE, OR POST

COPYRIGHTED MATERIAL — DO NOT DUPLICATE, DISTRIBUTE, OR POST

COPYRIGHTED MATERIAL — DO NOT DUPLICATE, DISTRIBUTE, OR POST

COPYRIGHTED MATERIAL — DO NOT DUPLICATE, DISTRIBUTE, OR POST